CHAMBERS
& PARTNERS

A Guide to the Legal Profession

Student Edition
1999

Jo Stafford
Editor

Chambers & Partners Publishing
Saville House, 23 Long Lane, London EC1A 9HL
Tel: (0171) 606 1300

Published by Chambers & Partners Publishing
(a division of Orbach & Chambers Ltd)
Saville House, 23 Long Lane, London EC1A 9HL
Tel: (0171) 606 1300 Fax: (0171) 600 3191

Chambers & Partners Legal Recruitment: (0171) 606 8844

Copyright © Michael Chambers and Orbach & Chambers Ltd 1998
ISBN: 0 85514-301-0

Publisher: *Michael Chambers*
Managing Editor: *Reena SenGupta*

Editor: *Jo Stafford*

Deputy Editor: *Caroline Walker*

Editorial Assistant: *Jackie Tilston*

Researchers: *Richard Freeland, Gordon McBain, Chris Hallatt Wells,
            Baron Armah-Kwantreng*

Production Manager: *Kerry Hall*
Production Editor: *John Crookes*
Production Assistant: *Ralph Davies*

Business Development Manager: *Benedict Seymour*
Business Development Team: *Mark Lomeli, Karol-Ann Roberts*

Database Manager: *Derek Wright*

Printed in England by: *The Burlington Press*

Acknowledgements:
*Our thanks to the Chambers & Partners' Directory team 1998-1999 for the use of their
research; to the Chambers & Partners' Recruitment consultants for their knowledge of the
profession; and to the students, trainees and lawyers who assisted our journalists and
researchers.*

COMPILING THE STUDENT EDITION

The main purpose of this student edition of Chambers' Directory is to help students find a suitable firm or set of chambers in which to train. It also provides an introduction to the principal areas of law and the firms and sets which specialise in them.

The book draws on three sources:

1. the rankings of law firms and barristers' chambers contained in the original directory;

2. fresh research by a team of journalists and lawyers who spoke to students, trainees, and the firms and sets themselves;

3. information provided by consultants from the Chambers legal recruitment agency.

The stars awarded to firms and sets in the 'Specialist Practice Areas' follow the rankings given in the main directory. These in turn are based on research by a team of 11 full-time researchers – all of them lawyers – over a period of six months. In total, more than 4,000 telephone interviews were conducted with individual practitioners and clients, each one lasting an average of 30 minutes. The results are generally recognised to be the most reliable currently available.

Looking for a legal training contract?

www.lawstudent.demon.co.u

CONTENTS

TRAINING AS A SOLICITOR

Introduction

Applying

The Firms

After Training

Specialist Practice Areas

A-Z of Law Firms

TRAINING AS A BARRISTER

Introduction

Specialist Practice Areas

A-Z of Barristers' Chambers

Training as a Solicitor

Introduction
- Applying
- The Firms
- After Training

Applying

- *Timetable for 1999 - 2001*
- *The Law Society's guide to recruiting trainees*
- *Writing a CV*
- *Interview technique*
- *Vacation schemes*
- *The selection process*
- *Candidate profile*
- *Preferred universities*

TIMETABLE FOR 1999 – 2001

LAW STUDENTS

Penultimate Year

October 1998 - February 1999: Compile information about law firms. Obtain firm brochures. Attend presentations and law fairs on campus.

January - February 1999: Apply for open days and vacation schemes.

June - August 1999: Attend vacation schemes. Apply to law firms for training contracts for 2001. Apply for a place on the LPC.

Final Year

September 1999 - December 1999: Attend interviews for training contracts for 2001.

Post Graduation

September 2000: Commence LPC.

July 2001: Finish LPC.

September 2001: Commence training contract (first intake).

March 2002: Commence training contract (second intake).

September 2003: Qualify as a solicitor (first intake).

March 2004: Qualify as a solicitor (second intake).

TIMETABLE FOR 1999 – 2001

NON-LAW STUDENTS

Penultimate Year

October 1998 - February 1999: Compile information about law firms. Obtain firm brochures. Attend presentations and law fairs on campus.

January - February 1999: Apply for open days and vacation schemes.

June - August 1999: Attend vacation schemes.

Final Year

October 1999 - February 2000: Compile information about law firms. Obtain firm brochures. Attend presentations.

November 1999: Apply for a place on the CPE course.

January - June 2000: Apply for open days and vacation schemes. Apply to law firms for training contracts for 2002.

February - June 2000: Attend interviews for training contracts for 2002.

Post Graduation

June - August 2000: Attend vacation schemes and interviews for training contracts for 2002. Apply for a place on the LPC if your CPE institution does not guarantee you a place.

September 2000: Commence CPE.

June 2001: Finish CPE.

September 2001: Commence LPC.

July 2002: Finish LPC.

September 2002: Commence training contract (first intake).

March 2003: Commence training contract (second intake).

September 2004: Qualify as a solicitor (first intake).

March 2005: Qualify as a solicitor (second intake).

THE LAW SOCIETY'S GUIDE TO RECRUITING TRAINEES

The Law Society's guide is summarised below. Any breaches of this guide should be notified to the Law Society in Redditch.

Employers

Employers will not interview for trainee posts before 1 September in the student's final year. Students shall not be required to apply earlier than 31 July at the end of their penultimate year. No offer to any student who has done a summer placement will be made before 1 September in the student's final year.

Students will be told at interview if there are further selection stages to go through. They will also be told the likely date by which an offer of employment will be made. An offer of employment will not be withdrawn before the time for acceptance has expired.

The employer will write to interviewees within two weeks telling them the outcome of the interview.

Time limits for accepting an offer of a training contract must not expire before 1 November in the student's final year (or in the CPE year). In any case, the time period for accepting must never be less than three weeks from the date the offer is sent. If the training contract is not due to start within a year, it is not good practice to set a time limit on the offer.

Employers will consider sympathetically a request to extend the time limit, provided a good reason is given.

Employers will not discriminate directly or indirectly on the grounds of race, religion, or sex.

Employers providing financial assistance to trainees in relation to undergraduate or post-graduate studies will explain in writing the terms on which such assistance is offered at the time the offer of a training contract is made. The above rules governing time limits for accepting an offer of a training contract apply equally to an offer of financial assistance.

Students

Students will respond to offers promptly, and not later than three weeks after receipt of the offer (unless the offer is for a contract beginning more than a year later, in which case there is no fixed time limit).

Students will not accumulate offers. Two is the maximum number to be held at any one time. Others (old or new) must be rejected.

An acceptance must be in writing. All other outstanding offers and invitations to interview must be rejected, and no further interviews accepted. ∎

WRITING A CV

A lot of nonsense is written about preparing CVs. Keep to one page, for instance. Make it two or three pages. Set it in chronological order. Set it in reverse chronological order. And so on.

Rather than lay down assorted rules, let's look at essential principles.

1. Firstly, a good CV is clear and readable. All the information is organised logically and in a way that the reader can follow. Try it on your friends. If they stumble over anything, accept that the fault lies in your CV, not in their ability to read. Watch their face as they read it. The hint of a frown, a brief pause while they go back a sentence or two, should tell you that there's a lack of clarity.

It helps the reader if the way you've organised your CV is self-evident. If it's chronological, let this show clearly, and stick to it. If it's on any other basis, show clearly – at a glance – what the structure is.

Some people design their CVs. They add borders, patterns, wonderful typographical innovations with bold headlines or italicised subheads running vertically up the left-hand margin. These CVs are a marvel to behold, but they can be difficult to read and therefore defeat their very purpose.

2. Secondly, a good CV focuses on those things which are relevant, those things which will interest the employer. The most relevant ones should come first, or at least towards the top. Be careful not to see yourself through your own eyes, stating the things you're most proud of. Bunjee jumping may be your first love, and winning the Blackpool bunjee competition may have been a supreme moment in your life, but is it relevant, and will the employer be impressed?

Discuss this with friends and advisers. What will prospective employers want to know? Study them, read their literature, see what they value. Ring them up. It's amazing how much people will tell you when asked.

3. Lastly, a good CV is honest. Naturally, it will be tailored to conform to the style expected by the employer, but it will give a true picture of you. It then serves its purpose. It gets you interviews with employers who will appreciate you. The CV will not appeal to everyone, but that's its advantage. You won't waste time seeing employers who are impressed by your CV but who are less impressed when they meet you face to face.

There is an advantage, therefore, in preparing a CV yourself rather than getting a bureau to do it. Your own personality will come through. You won't be reduced to the standard impersonal word-processed form.

Enough of these general principles. We do in fact have a preference for a particular style. We prefer the CV which starts with the subject's name, address and date of birth, and sets out the educational and career details in simple chronological order, ending with general information, such as other interests, gap year activities, or special accomplishments and achievements. Everything has its place in a clear ordered structure that anyone can follow without difficulty.

Remember, though, that anything you mention as an interest or activity may be seized on by the interviewer. You must be able to talk about it with knowledge and enthusiasm. ∎

INTERVIEW TECHNIQUE

No interview will be what you expect, however much you've prepared for it. But preparation is still useful. It just has to be realistic.

Let's start with you yourself. All the obvious points are really common sense. Dress appropriately, turn up on time, don't go if you're suffering from a bad cold. Also obvious is the need to be confident about the information you've provided in your CV. If you've mentioned Thomas Hardy as a favourite author, be sure you know *The Trumpet Major* and *Under the Greenwood Tree,* as well as *Tess of the D'Urbervilles* and *Far from the Madding Crowd.*

Before attending the interview, think in detail about your achievements and strengths, about your activities, your social life, your ambitions. Making lists can help, as long as you don't take them with you.

Knowing about the firm is important. Get their brochures and publications. Talk to contacts at the firm, or people who know it well. Read directories. Get an all-round perspective on where the firm is placed in the profession, and where it is trying to go.

But don't feel you need to know too much. Detailed knowledge of their latest transactions will not be expected. You can risk becoming too knowing, too clever, slightly threatening, as if you've learned more about them than they would like you to know. And an ostentatious display of your knowledge is likely to alienate them.

Preparing answers to specific questions can be counter-productive. Even if you get the questions you hope for, your response may appear too pat. What does make sense, though, is to think about subjects which the interviewer is likely to raise. Don't prepare answers, but give the matter some thought. Your ambitions, for instance, what you most enjoy doing, your strong points, your weaknesses, how you see the firm, and so on. Talk these matters over with family and friends. There'll always be someone prepared to listen, even if it's your mother.

Once you're into the interview itself, you'll just have to be yourself. Advice which urges you to be somebody else – to be confident if in fact you're naturally timid – is not going to help. But whoever you are, with whatever nature, there are one or two golden rules.

The first is to be enthusiastic about what you want to do. Enthusiasm is the best quality in any candidate being interviewed, just as a world-weary superiority is the worst. While waiting to be seen, think about the things you like doing, and why you like them. Think about the opportunities the firm you're seeing will give you. If you feel positive, you will come across well.

The other golden rule is to show interest in the interviewer's business, the actual work undertaken. All candidates will ask about the firm, and about their prospects within it. They all want to know what's in it for them. But candidates who are genuinely interested in what the interviewer does will be remembered favourably. Politicians learnt this years ago, when they first started smiling at babies in prams. They knew the babies wouldn't vote for them, but they hoped the mothers would. ∎

VACATION SCHEMES

Once upon a time, the director of an important corporate client of a top City firm called the senior partner. His son was thinking about doing law at university. Could he come in for a couple of weeks to 'shadow' one of the partners? The senior partner of course obliged. The 17-year-old hung around for a week, got taken out to lunch on the marketing budget, was of no help whatsoever and wrote a very nice thank-you letter afterwards.

Of course it still happens, occasionally. But these days firms run their vacation schemes like well-oiled machines, feeding in bright, keen undergraduates in the hope that by the time they emerge at the other end they will be bright, keen recruits for training contracts.

Law Society guidelines (see page 12) do not allow interviews for training contracts to take place before 1 September in the student's final year at university. However, more than one trainee who had done a vacation scheme commented that at the end of their placement they were given an unofficial interview and were led to understand that a job offer had been made. One trainee at a large prestigious City firm noted that the interview for her training contract was surprisingly easy. "It was the interview for the summer placement which was the killer - a lot of questions to put you on the spot." In other words, the subsequent interview was a formality; decisions had already been made on the basis of the student's performance on the vacation scheme.

Although no firm would admit to using the vacation schemes to get round Law Society restrictions, they make it clear that the experience can certainly help you to get a training contract. At Burges Salmon most training contracts are given to students who attend open days and summer placements with the firm. "When it comes to interview, we have more of a feeling for them and can talk about the work they've done with us." Many London firms shared this view.

Most schemes are one to three weeks in length and many are well-paid; as much as £200 per week in the largest firms. Often students sit at the desks of fee-earners who are on holiday at the time, so they may be in a room with anyone from a senior partner to a first seat trainee. Trainees will generally be assigned to look after them and find 'do-able' jobs for them. Many firms find accommodation for summer students by emailing fee-earners asking if they have rooms to let for a couple of weeks at a low rent.

One interviewee at Allen & Overy commented that all her friends viewed her as very lucky to get a place on the A&O scheme, which is "one of the best." She spent a week in property and a week in corporate, both with junior assistants. She was given research to do, dating of final completion documents, and took notes of meetings she attended. She also took part in negotiation exercises with the other vacation students.

On the social side there were drinks parties with trainees and partners, theatre trips, a meal out and sports activities. "The whole thing was very well-organised. We weren't made to feel like spare parts." Another trainee at a smaller media firm, spent two weeks working on a libel trial – helping with research, meeting barristers, attending court and looking after witnesses. "It was the best experience of my legal career," he says, "and nothing since has been as exciting."

Of course not all schemes are so well-organised. One trainee remembers spending a day touring London while an assistant explained the derivation of various street names. Other trainees sensed they were "filling in time"; being shown endless presentations which just repeated what they'd already read in the firm brochure. Such experiences are unlikely to encourage good candidates. In other instances, students get a real "warts and all" view of the firm. A trainee who attended several vacation schemes rejected one trendy media firm because "the trainees worked so hard. They were always exhausted and they had no lives."

All trainees who had experienced vacation schemes strongly recommended them as the best means of finding out whether a particular firm is for you. The overwhelming reason given by trainees as to why they had chosen their firm was chemistry. They liked the atmosphere, they felt they fitted in. Spending more time at the firm than the length of an interview can only be beneficial. It may also help you decide which area of practice is for you.

However, students should be warned against clocking up one scheme after another. "Far better to do a couple of well-chosen schemes in different types of firms and then go off to Nepal or learn a foreign language - you'll have a lot more to talk about," commented one City recruitment partner. Alternatively, gaining work experience in industry can give you a valuable insight into the commercial world, as well as showing you've used your initiative.

Vacation Scheme information at a glance

Firm Name	Places for 1999	Duration	Remuneration	Closing date
Addleshaw Booth & Co	24	2 wks	£125 p.w.	28 Feb 1999
Allen & Overy	70	3 wks	£200 p.w.	18 Feb 1999
Ashurst Morris Crisp	45-50	3 wks	£200 p.w.	28 Feb 1999
Baker & McKenzie*	30	2–3 wks	£200 p.w.	12 Feb 1999
Barlow Lyde & Gilbert*	30	2–3 wks	–	31 Dec/28 Feb
Berrymans Lace Mawer[†]	–	2 wks	depends on office	31 Mar 1999
Berwin Leighton	50	1 wk	£160 p.w.	31 July 1998
Bevan Ashford	30	1 wk	–	31 Mar 1998
Bond Pearce	60	1 wk	£150 p.w.	end Mar 1999
Burges Salmon	24	2 wks	£100 p.w.	5 Mar 1999
Cameron McKenna	55	2 wks	£200 p.w.	12 Feb 1999
Clifford Chance*	80	2 wks	£200 p.w.	26 Feb 1999
Davies Arnold Cooper	35	3 wks	under review	31 Jan 1999
Dibb Lupton Alsop	100	2 wks	£125–£175 p.w.	28 Feb 1999
Edge Ellison	80	1 wk	£100 p.w.	15 Feb 1999
Eversheds	120	2 wks	regional variations	28 Feb 1999
Freshfields	100	2 wks	£200 p.w.	14 Feb 1999
Garretts	70	2 wks	£100-£175 p.w.	n/a
Hammond Suddards	30	4 wks	£150–£200 p.w.	26 Feb 1999

The table represents the vacation scheme information for the top 50 firms nationwide in alphabetical order. Some information has been summarised, so for further details and information on smaller firms, see the A-Z section. Firms marked with an asterisk run Summer and Easter schemes. Firms marked with a † indicates availability for 2000 only. Where there are gaps, full information has not been supplied.

Vacation Scheme information at a glance (cont.)

Firm Name	Places for 1999	Duration	Remuneration	Closing date
Herbert Smith*	80	1–3 wks	£200 p.w.	Mid-Feb
Irwin Mitchell	30	2 wks	£50 p.w.	1 Mar 1999
Lawrence Graham†	20	2 wks	£160 p.w.	28 Feb 1999
Linklaters*	85	2–4 wks	£200 p.w.	–
Lovell White Durrant*	70	2-3 wks	£200 p.w.	19 Feb/Nov 99
Macfarlanes	40	2 wks	£180 p.w.	Feb 1999
Masons	40	2 wks	£125–£175 p.w.	12 Feb 1999
Mills & Reeve	20	2 wks	£80 p.w.	1 Mar 1999
Nabarro Nathanson	60	3 wks	£150-£200 p.w.	28 Feb 1999
Norton Rose*	60	2–3 wks	£185 p.w.	26 Feb/5 Nov 99
Osborne Clarke	12	1 wk	£80 p.w.	26 Feb 1999
Pinsent Curtis	100	1 wk	£85 p.w.	28 Feb 1999
Richards Butler	30	2 wks	£200 p.w.	13 Mar 1999
Rowe & Maw	25	2 wks	£200 p.w.	26 Feb 1999
S J Berwin & Co†	60	3 wks	£200 p.w.	14 Feb 1999
Shoosmiths & Harrison	20	2 wks	£100 p.w.	31 Mar 1999
Simmons & Simmons	40	4 wks	£200 p.w.	26 Feb 1999
Slaughter and May	60	2 wks	£200 p.w.	26 Feb 1999
Stephenson Harwood	21	2 wks	£175 p.w.	26 Feb 1999
Taylor Joynson Garrett	30	2 wks	£180 p.w.	26 Feb 1999
Theodore Goddard	20	2 wks	£200 p.w.	Feb 1999
Titmuss Sainer Dechert	80	2 wks	£190 p.w.	26 Feb 1999
Travers Smith Braithwaite	45	3 wks	£200 p.w.	End Mar 1999
Wansbroughs Willey Hargrave	8	8 wks	£100 p.w.	1 Mar 1998
Wilde Sapte	75	1 wk	£160 p.w.	28 Feb 1998
Wragge & Co	40	2 wks	£125 p.w.	12 Feb 1999

THE SELECTION PROCESS

Eight years ago a third year student at Birmingham University did a summer placement with a top five City firm. She liked the firm and they liked her. Without a single interview or assessment they offered her a job. In 1990, this was not particularly unusual.

Now, however, it's a different story. Students applying for training contracts are likely to face an assault course of group exercises, written tests and day-long assessments before they secure a job.

A typical assessment day consists of a couple of written tests, a number of group exercises, a couple of interviews and perhaps a presentation to a group. One student told us of her "nightmarish" experience at a large City firm. She and three others were given a group exercise where they had to imagine they were stranded in the desert. They were given fifteen items to rank in order of importance to their survival. The exercise lasted half an hour and a recruitment officer closely observed the whole process. What she found particularly difficult was the awkward behaviour of everyone in the group. Nobody seemed to know what was expected of them and the individuals ranged from being over-assertive to quiet and difficult.

A very different group exercise at another City firm involved a more business-like situation. Twelve candidates were divided into two groups and asked to advise on the purchase of two factories. One had union problems, but solid financial backing, the other had a different set of problems. Again the group was observed and again, our student found the experience quite "tense". She must have performed well though because she was offered a job. When asked why she thought she was successful at one firm and not at the other, she said it had a lot to do with the nature of the group. She felt more comfortable with the second set of people and also with the task. So, it was partly down to chance. However, she also felt more prepared second time round and realised it was better just to be herself. What can a candidate in their first selection round learn from this?

The most obvious answer is to be yourself and you will find the right firm for you. Bob Llewellin, training director with Burges Salmon, says: "It's important not to be a pushover - say something, but it doesn't help to be bombastic." If your arguments aren't accepted by the group don't worry - you might have been asked to argue an unwinnable case. Firms are looking for how good a team player you are - do you listen, can you compromise, do you keep an eye on the time and on details such as budget? You should also remember that firms are looking for all kinds of people - the more measured, thoughtful type as well as the outgoing team leader.

Away from the group exercises, there will often be written tests. These vary from advising on a contract, to rewriting a complex document in simple English to answering multiple choice personality questions. Firms place varying emphasis on the different exercises; for some the interview is crucial while for others, the group exercises are of primary importance. If it is possible to find out in advance (from current trainees perhaps) then this might be advantageous.

The selection and recruitment process is, in many firms a polished, highly professional procedure and the City firms, in particular, waste no time in letting successful and unsuccessful applicants know. In many cases, candidates hear the next day. With the benefit of hindsight, most of our interviewees said they enjoyed their assessments and "the day will almost certainly end with a drinks party" - but don't relax too much - you're probably being assessed there too! ▶

Selection information at a glance

Firm Name	Method of application	Selection Procedure	Required degree
Addleshaw Booth & Co	Application form	Interview, assessment day	2:1
Allen & Overy	Application form	Assessment centre	2:1
Ashurst Morris Crisp	Letter and CV	Interview with 2 partners	n/a
Baker & McKenzie	Letter and application form	Short presentation, interview with 2 partners, meeting with trainee	2:1
Barlow Lyde & Gilbert	Application form	Interview with 2 partners	–
Berrymans Lace Mawer	CV with covering letter	First interview, assessment day, second interview	2:1
Berwin Leighton	Application form and covering letter	Open day, assessment centres, interview with 2 partners	2:1
Bevan Ashford	Application form	Open day, tests and interview	2:1
Bond Pearce	Application form, handwritten letter, CV and photograph	Interviews and selection day	2:1
Burges Salmon	Application form	Open day, work experience + interview or interview, psychometric test and written exercise	2:1 or higher
Cameron McKenna	Application form	Initial interview followed by assessment centre.	2:1
Charles Russell	Handwritten letter and application form	Assessment days to include: interview, fact finding exercise and group exercises	2:1
Clifford Chance	Application form	Interview with partner and senior assistant, followed by assessment day and interview	2:1
Clyde & Co	Application form and covering letter	Individual interview with recruitment officer, followed by interview with two partners	2:1
Davies Arnold Cooper	Application form	Open days and individual interviews	2:1 capability
Denton Hall	Application form and handwritten letter	Interview with 1 or 2 partner(s) and/or a member of personnel	2:1
Dibb Lupton Alsop	Application form	First interview, assessment afternoon, second interview with 2 partners	2:1
Edge Ellison	Application form	Selection day, including group exercises and interview	2:1
Eversheds	Application form and handwritten letter to London address	Selection days include group and written exercises, plus interview	2:1
Field Fisher Waterhouse	CV and handwritten letter and application form	Interview	2:1

The table represents the selection process for the top 50 firms nationwide in alphabetical order. Further information on smaller firms can be found in the A-Z section. Where there are gaps, full information has not been supplied.

Selection information at a glance (cont.)

Firm Name	Method of application	Selection Procedure	Required degree
Freshfields	Application form	1 interview with 2 partners	2:1
Garretts	Application form or covering letter and CV	1 hour interview in London, second interview held in regional office of choice	2:1
Hammond Suddards	CV and covering letter	Interview	2:1
Herbert Smith	Application form	Interview	2:2
Irwin Mitchell	Application form	Assessment centre, second interview with 2 partners	n/a
Lawrence Graham	Application form	Interview and written exercise	2:1
Linklaters	Application form	2 Interviews (same day)	2:1
Lovell White Durrant	Application form	Assessment day: interview, group exercise, critical reasoning test	2:1 or better
Macfarlanes	Application form and letter	Interview and practical assessment	2:1
Masons	Firm's own application form	Assessment day followed by an interview	2:1
Mills & Reeve	Application form	Application form, assessment day	2:1
Nabarro Nathanson	Application form	Interview and assessment day	2:1
Norton Rose	Application form	Interview and group exercise	2:1
Osborne Clarke	Application form	Individual interviews and group exercises	2:1
Pinsent Curtis	Application form	Interview	2:1
Richards Butler	Application form	1 interview	n/a
Rowe & Maw	Application form	Selection workshops including an interview and a business exercise	2:1
S J Berwin & Co	Handwritten letter and CV	Interview	2:1
Shoosmiths & Harrison	Application form	Assessment centre–one day	2:1
Simmons & Simmons	Application form, CV and covering letter	Assessment day: document exercise, interview and group session	2:1
Slaughter and May	Covering letter and CV	Interview	Good 2:1
Stephenson Harwood	Application form	Interview with 2 partners	2:1
Taylor Joynson Garrett	Firm's application form, CV and covering letter	2 interviews, 1 with a partner	2:1
Theodore Goddard	Application form	Initial interview, followed by short assessment or second interview	2:1+
Titmuss Sainer Dechert	Letter and application form	1 interview with at least 2 partners	2:1 capability
Travers Smith Braithwaite	Handwritten letter and CV	Interviews	2:1
Wansbroughs Willey Hargrave	Application form	Initial interview: written test, verbal reasoning, numerical analysis. Second interview: personality test	–

Selection information at a glance (cont.)

Firm Name	Method of application	Selection Procedure	Required degree
Wilde Sapte	CV with covering letter (including breakdown of university examination results)	Initial interview and test with personnel department, followed by interview with partner	2:1
Wragge & Co	Application form	Assessment day and interview	2:1 (preferred)

The table represents the selection process for the top 50 firms nationwide in alphabetical order. Further information on smaller firms can be found in the A-Z section. Where there are gaps, full information has not been supplied.

CANDIDATE PROFILE

What do firms look for in prospective trainees? We asked over two hundred firms for their ideal trainee profile. Together with the predictable replies (strong academic background, confident, enthusiastic, team player etc), we had some interesting responses. Many firms look for candidates who have taken time off to travel or to gain general commercial experience. Baker & McKenzie "encourage their trainees to take time out whether just to travel or undertake further studies." Osborne Clarke say "time spent travelling is viewed positively", Tarlo Lyons believe "a well spent gap year or commercial experience can be an advantage" and Shadbolt & Co say "travel is viewed favourably."

Extra-curricular activities and non-academic achievements are also important to both City and provincial firms. They look for "interesting" and "lively" personalities, with a "good sense of humour", a "resourceful nature", "ambition" and "resilience", as well as more specific skills such as IT proficiency.

It emerged that some firms will still take only law graduates, although most now appreciate students with a variety of degree subjects. Science and language degrees are particularly sought after. Clyde & Co look for "those with modern languages or science degrees", while shipping firm Holman Fenwick & Willan say "good foreign languages or a scientific or maritime background are an advantage." Other firms are more specific about their language requirements. Pritchard Englefield state: "Normally only high academic achievers with a second language (especially German and French) are considered." Withers look for "a genuine international outlook and foreign languages, particularly Italian", while Wilde Sapte look for "French, Spanish, German, Russian, Japanese or Mandarin."

Many firms emphasised individuality as an important quality. Hempsons are "not searching for one particular type of personality as they recognise the importance of a varied team." Hill Dickinson "recruits people who

vary greatly in terms of personality", and Lovell White Durrant want "individualists not clones".

Regional firms are keen that recruits have a connection with the area, and local candidates will stand a better chance than general applicants. Pannone & Partners look for "a connection with the north west", Donne Mileham & Haddock state "local connections are of value" and Foot & Bowden look for "a well-reasoned wish to develop a career in the south west."

Firms invest considerable sums in their trainees and, as Titmuss Sainer Dechert concludes, "We want people who will remain with us on qualifying and make their careers with us." Fishburn Boxer state: "Commitment is essential as the firm expects to have a first option to employ its trainees for at least a further two years." Radcliffes "aim to recruit trainees who have a real prospect of becoming partners in due course", while Rowe & Maw say they "want trainees to become future partners" and add "the current senior partner trained with the firm." Even in these times of frequent job moves, it is clear that firms want dedication and long-term commitment from the outset.

Above all, firms want the right person for them. This will be partly a matter of luck and will depend on how well you fit into and complement the existing team. As Biddle comment "Our aim is to build a team of varied yet complementary personalities where, for example, the more bookish are balanced by the charismatic." Dibb Lupton Alsop want people with "different backgrounds and skills" and Davenport Lyons are looking for the "extra piece in the jigsaw."

In addition to luck, your own focus at the outset will go a long way to ensuring you get a job with the right firm for you. Read the criteria carefully and apply only to those firms where you fit the bill. If an employer is looking for an interest in shipping and you fake a passion for boats, you will only end up wasting everyone's time. ∎

PREFERRED UNIVERSITIES

Firms ranging widely in size and location were asked which universities they prefer to recruit their trainees from. Of the 152 responses, 62 firms said they would consider applicants from any university as long as individual performance was high. These firms made comments such as "We recruit individuals not badges", "Candidate ability and personality are more important", "We have an open mind", "Selection depends on the applicant's skills and qualifications and how he/she presents him/herself" and "We select based on the individual's application and then on performance at interview/assessment."

Fifteen firms expressed preferences such as "established universities rather than former polytechnics", "any 'old' university" and "red-brick universities".

Seventy five firms provided lists of the universities they prefer to recruit from. There were some interesting regional preferences. Firms based in the south often mentioned only a couple of southern universities such as Southampton, Bristol, Bath or Exeter. One south west firm specifed Exeter only, and one Welsh firm listed only the University of Glamorgan. Similarly northern firms preferred universities such as Manchester and Liverpool, while one north east firm specified only York, Leeds, Hull and Sheffield. Establishments in the midlands such as Nottingham, Birmingham and Warwick were favoured by firms from the north and south alike. Predictably, Oxford and Cambridge received the most mentions.

The table alongside ranks the specified universities by the number of times each one was listed.

Cambridge	55
Oxford	55
Bristol	51
Nottingham	48
Durham	42
Kings College	34
UCL	34
Exeter	33
Manchester	33
LSE	27
Warwick	25
Birmingham	24
Sheffield	22
Leeds	19
Southampton	18
Liverpool	15
Leicester	9
Newcastle	9
York	5
Cardiff	4
Hull	4
University of West of England	4
Liverpool John Moores	2
Northumbria	2
Reading	2
Aberdeen	1
Aberystwyth	1
Bath	1
Bournemouth	1
Brunel	1
Derby	1
East Anglia	1
Glamorgan	1
Imperial College	1
Kent	1
Lancaster	1
Manchester Metropolitan	1
Nottingham Trent	1
Sussex	1

Completed
the CPE or LPC
– what now?

If you haven't been successful in securing a training contract, this may be what you are asking yourself. Paralegal work could be a sensible alternative as it may lead to exemptions from part of your training or to a full training contract.

Chambers & Partners have specialised in the recruitment of lawyers for over 20 years and are currently looking for promising candidates with legal qualifications.

We are instructed by the top law firms and blue chip companies throughout the UK who are looking for suitable candidates for the following types of vacancies:

- **Paralegals for private practice**
- **Legal Assistants for industry**
- **Junior Company Secretarial**
- **<u>Occasional</u> Trainee Solicitors**

If you are immediately or shortly available and would like to register with us please send, fax or e-mail your CV to Samantha Smith. Please state in your covering letter your preferred geographical areas and whether you are looking for long or short term work.

CHAMBERS
PROFESSIONAL RECRUITMENT

Saville House, 23 Long Lane, London EC1A 9HL
Fax: 0171 600 1793
e-mail: samsmith@chambersrecruitment.co.uk

The Firms

- *Leading firms – the true picture*
- *Firms ranked by training contracts per year*
- *Training with American firms*
- *Trainees abroad*
- *Trainee salaries*
- *Table of perks offered*

LEADING FIRMS – THE TRUE PICTURE

These days it is not enough for a student simply to bang off applications to hundreds of law firms and hope for the best. It is important to think seriously about the kind of training you want. If you're not interested in working for corporate clients, then there's no point applying to the top City firms just because all your friends are doing so. Similarly, if you're desperate to go abroad, you should do your homework. At the 70 largest firms there are only some 450 foreign seats available in total per year. If you have commitments in a particular city, perhaps you should steer clear of multi-branch firms which require trainees to move to different towns for different seats. You want to be a solicitor; here's where you start honing your research and decision-making skills. The aim of this section of the book is to give you a unique insight into the largest firms which take on the most trainees.

In preparing this section we interviewed trainees about the structure and quality of their training. We asked the 70 largest firms to provide us with lists of their trainees and newly-qualified staff. We then chose names at random from those lists, aiming to speak to five from each firm; those five representing a cross-section of experience from first seat trainees to newly qualifieds. Several firms declined to provide names for interviewing and those firms are notable by their absence from the section, leaving us with 50 firms out of the possible 70.

Some points are made by trainees across the board. Client contact and responsibility varies depending upon which department the trainee is sitting in. Almost all trainees who sat in a property seat appreciated the positive experience of handling 40 or so small files virtually alone. Many trainees choose to do this seat for this reason even if they have no intention of qualifying into it. On the other hand, the quality of a seat such as litigation may vary. Trainees may experience many small cases and progress them through discovery, witness taking and court appearances. Or they may be stuck for months on discovery in a giant piece of litigation.

The longest hours are mainly experienced in corporate departments and the shortest hours can be found outside London, although this certainly does not reflect the experience of all trainees in the large regional firms.

The majority of the firms surveyed provide a traditionally-structured training consisting of four seats of six months each. The trainee will rotate around departments and share a room with a partner or senior assistant for whom they will do the majority of their work. The most common structure is to do property, litigation and company/commercial seats as compulsories. Obviously within the larger firms choices are broader and very specialist seats may be undertaken (such as intellectual property, EU/competition and environment).

Some firms vary the number of seats to five (eg Richards Butler), six (eg Linklaters) or even more (occasionally available at Allen & Overy).

A number of firms surveyed have radically different training programmes. At Ince & Co and Gouldens, for example, trainees do not move from department to department, but take on work from all areas of the firm and continue to progress that work throughout their training contract rather than handing it over at the end of six months.

At other firms (such as Clyde & Co) trainees may spend a year in the department of their choice, while some practices send trainees out on secondment for six months or so.

In general, our interviewees seemed happy with their chosen firms. At the end of the day, most attributed their choice to the "right feeling" when they visited the firm. So your decision will probably be based on chemistry as much as anything else. This guide aims to help applicants narrow down their choice of firms. But only by attending open days, vacation schemes and interviews will a potential trainee get a 'true picture' of where he or she will fit in.

ALLEN & OVERY

A large City firm with strong international connections and a renowned finance practice. There is flexibility to split the training programme into four, five or six seats. In minority focus groups such as private client, environment or planning it is standard to do only three months. Trainees interviewed approved of this system; "it gives you a lot of flexibility. You can even do just three months in litigation if you're not interested in it." Finance is a key strength of the firm so in theory, nine months of the training contract must be in finance ie. banking or ICM (International Capital Markets). Trainees were "not sure how rigidly that is adhered to." There are some client secondments available and overseas seats to offices such as Moscow and New York are taken in the final seat.

'Off-the-job' training has three strands: basic PSC training which is run in-house; a training programme run within each department (some of which is for trainees only); and seminars run for the whole firm. A popular way of learning is to help run negotiations and workshops for vacation students. Incidentally, the vacation scheme at this large City practice is viewed as one of the best; "it was much better organised than others that I went on and I didn't feel like a spare part."

There were mixed reviews about levels of responsibility. In a firm of this size it can be very dependent on the work that happens to be in a department at the time. One trainee in his projects seat was sent out to Croatia several times. Although he was sometimes doing very basic things, he was given a lot of independence. "I had enough rope to have some fun but never enough to hang myself. When I was proactive people were very responsive."

Said one trainee "The worst thing about being at A&O is the inflexibility of the hours." Another said his weekly average was between 40 and 50 hours; "it would certainly look unusual to leave the office at 5.30."

The firm's 'University of Finance' training programme won the award for 'Best use of training by a Law Firm' at the 1997 Lawyer/HIFAL awards and this has had an effect on the atmosphere; "everyone's on a buzz at the moment."

BAKER & MCKENZIE

Viewed as a truly international firm, having 57 offices worldwide. It may therefore come as a surprise to know that overseas secondments for trainees are only just being introduced. Recent starters are the first to be offered half-seats overseas from September 1999. However the firm offers 20 international clerkships worldwide per year, open to students who have completed two years of a UK law degree. One interviewee had spent six weeks in a southern hemisphere office and six weeks in London. This was a mixed experience as seasonal differences meant she was the only 'summer' clerk in the overseas office and was a bit isolated, with no organised social activities laid on for her. Her time in London was more rewarding; "it was very friendly and very organised with good, if basic, work to do. The time in London made my mind up."

Of the four seats, one must be in corporate and one in litigation. For its size it is less broad-based than other firms and is often described as a "niche practice firm," known, for example, for its employment and IT practices. One trainee recommended it as a good choice for people interested in technology, or with a science background, or for people keen to work with EU or emergent markets. "Ensure that the firm covers your particular interest area of law before applying."

Supervisors were generally praised as "approachable", although sometimes too busy to volunteer help. In the majority of cases, "it is drummed in to you to ask."

An effective trainee liaison committee campaigned for unpaid leave after qualification and successfully obtained it. New qualifiers can now take six weeks off before starting work as an assistant; two as holiday and four unpaid.

The firm is seen as personality-driven. "People are very different and interesting, many people come from different backgrounds. You do not have to conform to a stereotype."

BARLOW LYDE & GILBERT

Best known for its insurance and reinsurance litigation practice. Training will inevitably be heavily weighted towards contentious work, although everyone must do one non-contentious seat to fulfil Law Society requirements. However the firm is developing its corporate division and has recently taken on six new qualifiers in this division.

The insurance work varies from defendant personal injury to professional indemnity work and defending police forces against civil claims. This involves working very closely with force solicitors and attending numerous trials and interlocutory applications. In the reinsurance seat there is a lot of contact with brokers and underwriters due to "a policy that you attend meetings and cons with counsel." Input is encouraged – "your boss wants you to add value by putting in what you know." The most hands-on seat is in the personal injury department which provides trainees with lots of advocacy experience in county courts. "You are out of the office two or three days a week." In other departments learning is more "by osmosis from observing your partner."

Open-plan working is being introduced in some departments, although specific supervisors are still assigned. Partner mentors are allocated from the beginning and take their trainee out to lunch every few months to discuss career progress. They are usually very senior partners who "help you to network and to find out how the internal structures of the firm work." The success or otherwise of the mentor relationship is felt to be very much personality-dependant.

In the past trainees were sent on secondment to clients and to the Hong Kong office. At the time of going to press this was not the case, but both options are under review by the training department. Trainee involvement in client-marketing is heavy. "Lots of clients in accountancy firms or small IT companies are our contemporaries and social contact is encouraged." Trainees are also encouraged to be involved in the Pro Bono Unit at the Royal Courts of Justice advice centre. In summary, the firm is "relatively large with a relatively small intake of trainees. We get good training with lots of hands-on experience."

BERWIN LEIGHTON

Trainees see Berwin Leighton as "young, dynamic and entrepreneurial; this atmosphere permeates throughout the firm." Berwin's self-image as a business impacts straight away on trainees. "We are actively encouraged to get involved in marketing events, write articles, take clients out, and really get stuck in." One of the trainees in the commercial department saw and took an opportunity to organise a marketing seminar with "one of the senior partners who I saw as a real go-getter."

New trainees who start their first seat in property are presented with forty files from their predecessor. "I was thrown in at the deep end. I didn't expect it to be easy, but the team were so supportive". One felt it would help to 'shadow' the work before assuming full responsibility. Life in the corporate department is rather different. "You are much more in a team with hard work and long hours, but it is sexy seeing your deal in the newspaper." In contrast, the commercial department is appreciated for its "nine to seven routine." Trainees are expected to draft "bespoke" agreements which are checked by their supervisor.

It is possible to do a secondment in the Brussels office or in the legal department of a client such as a commercial property firm. "You gain good commercial experience and really understand what the client expects." One trainee gave this advice to potential applicants; "Although we have an office in Brussels, Berwin Leighton is probably not the firm for trainees who want major international corporate-type work. We are very much a new City/UK firm."

BEVAN ASHFORD

Training at this large regional firm is organised between two independent profit centres; London/Bristol/Cardiff and the 'West Country' branch offices. Although there is a precedent for West Country trainees swapping over to the other branches, trainees generally stay within one or the other. Once a year the trainees from the different offices get together for a weekend, a training day and team-building sessions.

Cardiff trainees are 'encouraged' to do six months in Bristol, and Bristol trainees have the opportunity to go to the London or Cardiff office for 6 months. At the time of interviewing, the first London trainee had just started. The seat is general litigation and involves agency work for other offices, although medical negligence and employment are also practised there. Trainees interviewed thought that the package in the London office would only appeal to someone who had contacts in the City since no accommodation is provided. They do pay a London salary and help with agency fees though. "They may need to make it slightly more attractive before people will want to do it" said one trainee, although the London office was praised as being "very laid-back, very small and friendly."

In Cardiff the only compulsory seat is litigation. One Bristol trainee who did a seat there was impressed by the amount of advocacy available to trainees, both in the County Court and before a Master in Chambers.

The firm majors in defendant medical negligence. Trainees pointed out that over the last six months to a year the med neg department has grown significantly and other seats have decreased, meaning the majority of trainees are now asked to do two med neg seats. The firm also does a lot of public sector work including procurement issues for public bodies and PFI schemes.

The perception amongst trainees interviewed was that the firm is very committed to training

people and to disseminating information. It is also seen as one of the leaders in IT provision amongst law firms. "You're trained in everything. If you do some research and you haven't looked at the Internet, then that's not very impressive." Complaints were about "overinterventionist personnel" and the practice of trainees spending one week in every four opening post in the Bristol office.

BIRD & BIRD

One interviewee who had done several summer placements praised Bird & Bird as "a lot more friendly – everyone would always take time out to explain stuff to you and you were involved in what everyone else was doing as well."

One of the four training seats must be in commercial and one in litigation, which may be either general litigation or intellectual property litigation. It is for its IP work that the firm is best known. Some secondments to large corporate clients are available.

Trainees do their PSC course in a two-week block before starting. Although interviewees thought it "useful to get it out of the way" it was "quite dull...sitting in a classroom for five days." After a three to four day induction into the firm trainees start in their seats.

There is a firm-wide seminar programme; several a week taken by internal and external speakers, and trainees are encouraged to go to as many as possible. Attendance is also encouraged at external lectures.

The firm is piloting a system of open plan working for all fee-earners other than partners, who sit in their own offices. Interviewees enjoyed the firm's "very good social life. There are partners drinks every six months. We are renowned for our bad behaviour." There is no pressure to work late hours, the firm is generally thought of as friendly and "it is small enough to get to know pretty much everyone."

BOND PEARCE

A West Country commercial law firm which this year expanded from its Plymouth and

Exeter origins, through a merger with Southampton-based Hepherd Winstanley & Pugh and a new office in Bristol. Trainees state their location preference at interview. Plymouth is known for family, employment and probate; Exeter for corporate finance; Southampton for shipping and general commercial, and the Bristol office for insurance. There is currently only one trainee at the Bristol office. "I am the guinea-pig, although there is one newly-qualified and emails are a god-send."

External training is cross-office, and though no longer through the Norton Rose M5 Group, will continue with Burges Salmon and Wragge & Co until the year 2000. "It is cheaper and is a good way for trainees to meet other groups." This training was very highly rated in general, especially the week-long advocacy course at Warwick University.

There are no compulsory seats. There is a mid-seat appraisal where trainees are asked to set personal goals, and an end of seat review, "I wanted more client contact in my personal injury seat and a better understanding of the litigation process, which I got over the next three months." The appraisals are reviewed with "our mum" – the trainees' personal training supervisor. Trainees have asked for a vacation scheme to be established, but so far the firm has declined this request. Plymouth and Exeter socialise together, but Southampton is largely autonomous. Fee-earners contribute monthly payments to a sports and social club. Events such as go-karting, pony-trekking, quiz nights and even shopping trips to other cities are subsidised by the firm. Bond Pearce is felt to attract "people who are dedicated to their work but have a sense of humour and know how to enjoy themselves as well."

BROWNE JACOBSON

"At Browne Jacobson you are not just a small cog in the big machine, you actually feel part of things," was a typical view of trainees at this Nottingham-based firm.

The first week at the firm is taken up with an induction course consisting of the PSC

together with a programme to familiarise trainees with the logistics of the firm and computer training. The first seat is preordained and thereafter trainees are able to express a preference at the regular training appraisals that take place with the supervising partner in each seat. There are opportunities to go to the London office, and if a trainee has a particular yearning to go abroad the firm's association with ELSA (European Lawyers of Land, Sea and Air) means that short-term placements in European law firms may be possible.

Trainees are actively encouraged to take responsibility, but the friendly atmosphere means they do not feel they have to say yes to work if they feel overloaded. The second year of training sees most trainees having increasingly autonomous client contact. As with all new jobs the first seat is always the hardest in terms of anxiety but "partners are available for advice if a trainee is prepared to be proactive in seeking assistance." There is an informal mentoring system in that all the trainees know each other, and those in their second year advise their less seasoned colleagues.

BURGES SALMON

Training is divided into six four-month seats. Practice areas range from commercial work to private client, matrimonial and agriculture – "there is an enormous spread of work available." There are compulsory seats in property, property litigation, commercial litigation and company/commercial. The fifth seat is optional and for the sixth trainees return to the seat into which they want to qualify.

Generally the six-seat system was popular in that it provides a greater range of experience while allowing escape from less enjoyable seats. Experience of different seats varies widely. There is some relief that private client is no longer compulsory since it was found to be fairly boring – "probate work is given to trainees because any monkey could do it." In litigation seats trainees do a lot of advocacy because the firm does agency work for large regional firms. There can also be "heavy client exposure" in litigation. "The firm is good at spotting when you want responsibility and good at backing you up when you are out of your depth."

There is a firmwide programme of lectures for fee-earners and a number of talks and workshops for trainees. Over the course of their training contract, trainees must give two presentations to other trainees and supervisors; one law-related, one on a general topic of interest. This is part of presentation skills training and feedback is given afterwards.

The training department is perceived as taking trainees' opinions into account. There are 'between the seats' meetings where "trainees get a chance to whinge to training managers." A tongue-in-cheek training video showing a nightmare boss was recently produced by trainees for principals. It is used for 'training the trainers.'

Trainees spoken to seemed happy with their lot. "If you want a life outside the firm this is a good place" said one interviewee "you get to leave the office at 5.30 or 6pm most days."

CAMERON MCKENNA

The Cameron McKenna merger is considered a great success in the market-place. It certainly appears to have benefited trainees. Current trainees had been recruited to either McKenna & Co or Cameron Markby Hewitt before the merger on 1 May 1997. Because it was an "unsettling" time for trainees post-merger, there were a lot of meetings between personnel and trainees. The perception is that organisation of seat-rotation is now much improved. There is also a broader base for training with much more choice available. Initial confusion arose because Cameron Markby trainees were in the middle of six four-month seats and the new firm has the traditional four six-month seats. However, once those trainees qualify, this will cease to be an issue. There is now a policy of compulsory property and corporate or banking seats in addition to a contentious seat. There are some secondments available in England and France to corporate clients, as well as a secondment to a German associate office and overseas seats including Hong Kong and Warsaw.

The firm has a smaller office in Bristol. One interviewee waxed lyrical about his time there, praising the extra responsibility, saying he was able to run his files like a newly qualified. A "far more relaxed atmosphere" leaves the last person in the office to lock up behind them. Trainees are all seconded from the City office and are provided with a house in Clifton to share. It is a downhill stroll into work every morning.

The London office is harder work but supervisors are seen as "very amenable. You can always discuss your problems," although you have to be proactive in seeking feedback. The Trainee Representative Committee reports to personnel how supervisors perform and this has resulted in a training programme for them. "They take steps to ensure your supervisor has the right attitude." The personnel department produces a guide to practice areas in which trainees write about their experiences within the groups.

"At some of the more intense firms it's not easy to separate office from social life. Above all at Camerons people forget about their work at the end of the day." There is also room for personalities, not just clones. Said one trainee "I don't have to be a stereotype. I can be loud and northern. I can be me."

CLARKE WILLMOTT & CLARKE

Clarke Willmott & Clarke is one of the largest West Country firms with a wide range of departments and offices in Bristol, Taunton, Yeovil and Blackbrook. Trainees are allocated to one office for their training, but can be transferred to others. Bristol is the most popular office. Trainees in Yeovil are generally happy about their training and find the open plan office a "positive" thing. The office is felt to favour candidates with a local connection. Trainees at the high street Blackbrook office find themselves dealing with wills and legal aid work from clients off the street.

The firm has recently changed from running an unusual mix of four month, eight month and year long seats to the standard six month seats. Trainees felt the training department "will accurately assess you and plan your work accordingly." In the planning department, trainees "are involved in high-level work including sitting in on inquiries, 60% research and some drafting." The commercial property department is seen as "intellectually stimulating." In criminal, there was a high level of satisfaction, "in seeing the value of my input and in the very varied work." The agricultural department have just established a secondment to a major union client's legal department in London.

The firm was recently supportive to a trainee who wanted to be seconded to work with death row cases in the United States for three months, "I was really surprised when they said yes and even more surprised when they said 'Do you want to be paid for it?'"

Trainees feel that the firm has a progressive recruitment policy. "They have this unofficial policy of taking on people with a bit of a past. There is a stress on trainees being able to cope in a professional environment and deal with people." All trainees were positive about the value of their training; "I have as much independence as I want, whereas some of my friends at City firms have less autonomy."

CLIFFORD CHANCE

Trainees at Clifford Chance realise that being at one of the largest UK law firms is "a fantastic opportunity and great to have on the CV." Some are attracted to working at a large firm. "I came down to London without any connections and wanted the opportunity to play in team sports and have a large social network," said one. The firm is acknowledged to be "a very slick, professional operation with great facilities." New trainees are sent a folder with an introduction to the firm and comments on each department by current trainees.

Although Clifford Chance is a large firm trainees get the benefit of working in smallish teams. "In the corporate department we work in teams of between 30-40 with six trainees and a number of supervisors. This allows trainees to learn from each other as well as from more qualified staff." Trainees denied the

commonly-held perception that they spend their time photocopying. "We actually have a dedicated photocopying department and would only ever spend half an hour photocopying." They acknowledge that work such as proof-reading can be routine.

For those trainees seeking the experience of an international seat, Clifford Chance offers considerable opportunites with 82 overseas seats available a year. "I joined because I wanted to work in an international environment, hearing the buzz of foreign languages in the office. I was surprised that so many people didn't want to go abroad which was why I was able to go to Paris." This interviewee has now been offered a secondment to Brazil as a newly qualified lawyer. Competition for the more popular seats like New York is intense. Spanish or Portugese language skills are an advantage.

Trainees are expected to learn on the job. One trainee, however, felt this could be more effectively supplemented; "I'd quite like to see a bit more education." Others feel there are many opportunities to attend lectures on a wide range of topics; "I recently saw a video conference lecture on American securities from our New York office, which interested me because I hope to go to there on secondment."

Trainees accepted and understood that they sometimes did not get the responsibility of trainees in smaller firms. "We work on very, very big transactions, so you are never going to play a large role or hold your own files on deals of this size. You do get great satisfaction though, when you see something you have done written up in the *Financial Times* the next day".

CLYDE & CO

This firm, which has London, Guildford and Cardiff offices, is known for its shipping and insurance practices. Although nothing is compulsory "you would be hard pushed not to do some shipping or insurance" during training. Traditionally a strong litigation firm, it is now growing the non-contentious side, particularly in Guildford. There is some interchange between London and Guildford trainees and some training is shared via a video link. Although no trainees are taken on in Cardiff, when the need arises someone is sent across to "fill in."

Training is not formally structured but very flexible with trainees expected to be proactive to get what they want. "Sometimes this flexibility is not necessarily an advantage. You are expected to chop and change at short notice." It is a four-seat system, although 12-month seats are not unknown. Law Society requirements are the only limitations on freedom to choose seats. There was some confusion about ongoing checks and assessments. Career Development Reviews should take place at the end of seats although practice "varies from partner to partner." However, as one trainee pointed out, "if they weren't happy you'd know about it!"

In the London office each trainee is assigned to a group of two or three partners who "share" them. On day one they "come and throw files at you"and the partner in charge "tells you to get on with it." Shrinking violets should not apply. Responsibility is piled on early, as is client contact. "We are not presented as trainees on our business cards. Within the first two months we are expected to chat to clients at corporate 'do's." This approach means a smooth transition between second year training and qualification.

Languages are important in a firm with such an international workload. It has a thriving South American litigation department which takes on Spanish/Portuguese-speaking trainees. Those with exotic languages such as Russian, Japanese or Mandarin may be given one-to-one language training. The firm seems to attract people who are not run of the mill. "There are quite a lot of eccentrics. It breeds very self-confident people. One thing that stands out is they are not at all impressed by snootiness."

D J FREEMAN

A medium-sized firm set up in multi-disciplinary teams based around market sectors such as media and communications, property services and insurance. "Far from being limiting" says one trainee "the firm is playing to its strengths. It says, 'Let's be really good in what

we know we can do well.'" There is also a strong commercial litigation department. Specialist litigation seats are available in property, insurance and media. The media litigation seat is particularly popular so cannot accommodate everyone who wants to do it.

A trainee entering each department will have workshops once a week for the first fourteen weeks, some in the form of lectures, some interactive. There are also departmental lectures which "come before everything bar a real crisis." A "quite formal" trainee committee meets every six to eight weeks with the recruitment partner and trainee representatives. In general, the training is "quite broad with a lot of client contact and responsibility." This can have its downsides. Said one interviewee "it is sometimes a bit sink or swim because there are not that many trainees so you have to get on and do it." However trainees are not made to feel they need to stay late if there's no urgent work to do.

The firm prides itself on having more women partners than any other City law firm, a factor which influenced some female interviewees to train with the firm. In practice, however, this did not appear to make a noticeable difference to daily life.

DENTON HALL

The firm is particularly known for its media, telecomms and entertainment practice, the glamour of which is particularly attractive to some. The relatively new training scheme includes weekly lunchtime lectures for trainees, as well as Tuesday and Thursday evening lectures for all fee earners. At first trainees will attend an outside course of some description most weeks, with the frequency of these tailing off somewhat after the first seat.

Hours of work are generally felt to be reasonable with no undue pressure to stay late into the evening. "Of course when the work load or type demands it there will be late nights but the firm generally recognises that after a period of intense work a less pressured period is a necessity." The training partners were widely praised for their accessibility and the efficient

Freshfields has acquired a reputation in the market place for its incredibly long working hours. "They seem to do horrendous hours and some people get absolutely stuffed" was the opinion of several trainees at other firms who had friends at Freshfields. However hours vary from person to person, from department to department and from deal to deal, and may be no worse than in other City firms.

More than any other law firm Freshfields also has a reputation for recruiting "the beautiful people" – blond, blue-eyed Oxbridge clones who take themselves seriously and have an 'attitude' that would not be tolerated at more down-to-earth firms. Interviewees at the firm denied this; "the firm is friendly and light-hearted. There is a very nice team environment across the whole spectrum."

GARRETTS

As a member of the Andersen Legal international network of law firms, Garretts is closely associated with accountants, Arthur Andersen. It has branches in London, Birmingham, Cambridge, Leeds, Manchester and Reading. Each office is based in the same building as Arthur Andersen and computer systems and technology are shared.

Last year saw the first ever intake of trainees to the firm. Trainees interviewed did not see this as a disadvantage; "we're still a novelty and they treat us very well." The four seats are taken in property, company/commercial, litigation or technology. However one interviewee stressed that the firm is "very accommodating. If you're enjoying something and you're thinking about qualifying into it, they're willing to give you another taste of it."

The training scheme is run with Andersens. There is a one week induction before the start of the training contract and a further week every six months. This week is a residential course at Milton Keynes and consists of three days of team-building and two days of department-specific training.

All enjoyed the informal atmosphere of this young partnership, free from the expected hierarchies. The office is open-plan and most people sit near, rather than with, a supervisor who will be a partner or senior manager.

Many trainees felt the link with Andersens is an advantage and makes them look at things from more of an all-round business perspective. "Having the Andersens people there means that you're going to be exposed to issues apart from the legal ones." Levels of responsibility were also felt to be high. "I find we are encouraged to take initiative and are then rewarded for it."

GOULDENS

The firm is unusual in having a 'no seat' system. On day one trainees are given their own office in which they sit for the duration and from which they take on work from all departments concurrently. "The onus is on you to find work. You are not spoon-fed." The system is something of a "baptism of fire." However, weekly workload reports completed by each trainee and monthly meetings with the training partner, enable the firm to keep tabs on individual workloads and work spread.

Client contact is encouraged and trainees are seen as the first port of call for clients. Says one interviewee "Within my first week I had already been to one client meeting. Within five months I had my first meeting alone with clients." There is also plenty of opportunity to go to court – "perhaps more than some people want."

The firm is broadly divided into three departments; company/commercial, property and litigation, with sub-groups such as tax and planning within each. The system enables trainees to seek work from practice areas in which they have a particular interest, or to develop skills learned earlier in the training contract. Although it can be daunting at first and there is a very steep learning curve "you get more out of it. Compared to friends at other firms I feel like I do a harder day but a shorter day." This intensity is not confined to fee-earning time. "The atmosphere is work hard, play hard." Each trainee is assigned both a junior (second year trainee) mentor to answer day to day queries and a senior (partner) mentor, with whom they have monthly meetings for the first six months.

All trainees interviewed agreed that self-confidence is very important at Gouldens. "You must believe that you can do the task." Perhaps for that reason the percentage of older trainees was thought to be higher than in other firms. There is a high retention rate on qualification. Because of the system the firm "recruits to retain" and there is little outside recruitment. A word of warning to potential candidates; "Do your homework first. You can't blag your way through the interview not really understanding the firm and how its training works."

HALLIWELL LANDAU

A large Manchester commercial firm. Trainees do seats in the main departments of property, litigation and corporate/insolvency. In the fourth seat they may go to the seat they want to qualify into, or to a smaller department such as employment or intellectual property.

In the insolvency department a trainee can expect to go to lots of court hearings but not get much client contact. In the IP department one trainee is "instantly given lots of responsibility and even brought in clients." There is currently one client secondment available, involving "lots of contract-drafting and IP work."

The PSC is now done externally as a crash course. Internally there is a departmental training video every fortnight, as well as regular seminars taken by lecturers from Manchester University. This training is thought to be "very practical, applicable stuff." Every trainee has to prepare talks as part of their presentation skills training. Trainees find the atmosphere at the firm down-to-earth and approachable. The partnership is seen as "young and energetic."

Those doing their training here "can expect to get a good flexible training" as long as they are proactive; "It is a very good firm in Manchester terms, but maintains a friendly atmosphere. It has grown but has not become impersonal."

HAMMOND SUDDARDS

The policy at this major regional firm, introduced in the last 18 months, is for at least one seat to be taken in each of the three offices (Leeds, London, Manchester) and/or in Brussels. The London seat is the most popular because of the excellent package provided; a £40 a week flat in the Barbican only a short walk from the office. There are flats or houses available at the other locations and the firm will help out with travelling expenses and mortgages. There is now also a permanent base at Lloyd's of London to which two trainees are sent.

It is fair to say that when the system of rotating round offices was first introduced it was not popular amongst trainees, who had initially been recruited to one particular base. The system of six four-month seats means that moving from city to city can be disruptive, particularly to those with family ties. However "you get to give three choices for each seat rotation and so can manage when the changes take place."

Interestingly, trainees found the London office far more relaxed than those in the north, with trainees coming in at 9.30 and being given far less responsibility. This is thought to be a result of the lateral hires of partners from big City firms who are accustomed to giving much less responsibility to trainees. The atmosphere in the northern offices is "very aggressive and competitive;" trainees are given much more responsibility and everyone is in the office by 8.30. This high level of responsibility in the northern offices was commented on by all interviewees; "very high, almost too high at times." It is a "sink or swim" environment in which those who take responsibility are given good quality work.

Trainees at Hammonds were very outspoken interviewees and stated freely the pros and cons of training at the firm. This appears to reflect the openness of the firm rather than suggesting they had more to complain about. "There is a very northern, straight-talking feel throughout. The recruitment/training manager is very, very approachable." Trainees are encouraged to submit anonymous comments about their supervisors to the training department. This "does get acted on although other trainees don't get to see it."

HERBERT SMITH

Known as *the* litigation firm. Trainees had applied on the strength of this reputation but stressed that the firm provides a very good general training. "The reputation for litigation is well-deserved but other work should not be overlooked."

Secondments to corporate clients are available, providing "jack of all trades" experience. Trainees can also go to seats in the Far East, Paris and Brussels. Language training is available if requested by trainees. They must demonstrate its business use for the firm. In other words don't hope to brush up on your 'A' level French, but improving your basic Mandarin might be a starter.

Each department provides a two to three day induction course for trainees on arrival. The PSC is spread throughout the training contract. The firm takes part in a number of community action programmes in which trainees are heavily involved.

Trainees advised potential candidates to "consider carefully whether you want to go to a City firm – you must do some corporate work and some long hours." However, having made that decision, trainees chose this firm on the basis of its atmosphere; "It has a reputation for taking on people from different educational backgrounds which makes for a more interesting mix." If you are set on commercial litigation in a big firm, it is obviously a good choice. The size of the firm is also not seen as a problem; within each group/department, it "feels like a mini-firm within a firm."

HILL DICKINSON

A mainly litigation-based shipping firm which has doubled in partner size since 1995. There are offices in Liverpool, Manchester, Blackpool, Chester, Stockport and London. Trainees know at the outset of their contract that they can be sent to any one of the offices although "they won't send you if you don't want to go." The Manchester and Stockport offices are newly-established. Stockport is a tiny three-partner office; the Manchester office is felt to have more of a "go-getting"attitude than the large, established, Liverpool office.

There are currently no opportunities for secondments outside the firm. However it is a member of ELSA (European Lawyers of Land Sea and Air) and there is "talk of secondments to ELSA firms in Europe" although not all interviewees had heard about this.

Although there is a traditional four-seat system, there is some leeway to spend over six months in a department at a time; and occasionally up to a year. Previously one seat was taken in each of the four departments; insurance litigation, mercantile, health and commercial. However the expansion of the firm has opened up specialist seats such as intellectual property. Some of the last seat may be spent in the department in which you will qualify. Trainees stressed that the firm is very flexible.

The firm encourages as varied a training as possible although "lots of Hill Dickinson's work is insurance litigation" said an interviewee "and I don't know one trainee who has not done at least one insurance lit seat." There are monthly meetings with the training committee for trainees to air their views. Six-monthly appraisals take place half-way through each seat. Trainers emphasise that there is no need to stay late at this stage in your career. The usual day for a trainee is 9 to 5.30.

INCE & CO

This firm is one of the few with a radically different approach to training. There are no rigid departments. Instead it is divided into business groups and trainees cannot expect to be allocated to a particular business group until two years PQE. Although trainees do rotate seats every six months, it is between teams of partners. Work is provided by the partners in the team, but files handled in previous seats will be carried with you throughout training and beyond.

Work need not be limited to the specialism of the partner you sit with; it is left to individuals to lobby for preferred work from the relevant partners. Interviewees agreed that initially the tendency is "not to want to say no to anyone" but you quickly learn to manage your own workload. Since trainees know they cannot palm off a case onto somebody else after six months there is a much greater incentive to think about tactics and case-management. The disadvantage with the system is that "if you get a case that is a lemon you have to carry it all the way through." Work handled is very hands on. "You are asked to do work that assistants might do." Trainees are given "less grunt work." There are plenty of paralegals and support staff to do that. Trainees are also viewed as the link between the firm and clients and are often the first point of contact.

Formal training is provided on an ad hoc basis. Introductions to shipping and insurance law are provided initially. From then on, trainees decide between themselves when they want instruction on particular points. If more than four of them want the same training they let the "very approachable" training partner know and a workshop will be provided. In this way training is provided as it becomes relevant. The atmosphere was felt to be supportive and relatively non-competitive.

All work has a bias towards the shipping and insurance industries. "It's fair to say if you aren't sure which law you want to practice this probably isn't the firm to go to to find out. There is not a broad spectrum." Having said that those trainees who leave the firm on qualification never have a problem getting jobs at top firms "because they know that an Ince & Co trainee is used to handling cases alone." A comment by last years' interviewees was that lack of departmental structure and hierarchy resulted in communication problems. Since last year a new structure within business groups has been implemented and this is felt to be an improvement.

IRWIN MITCHELL

The firm has offices in Sheffield, Leeds, Birmingham and London, all of which take trainees. Trainees sign their contract knowing they could be moved to another office, but generally this is only by choice; "they move only people who want to move."

Upon joining there is a full week's induction, with presentations from each department, team-building exercises etc. Trainees are given the opportunity to express a preference as to their first seat and second year trainees "always get the seat they want." However there are strict rules as to how to go about expressing this preference; it is forbidden to lobby or canvass partners for specific seats. Your choice should be indicated at your mid-seat review.

Unusually for a firm which handles large commercial matters, there is a crime seat. A trainee cannot do court work, but police-station interviews, prison visits and crime-scene attendances make it a very client-oriented seat with little desk-work. The firm also has specialisms in insurance litigation and plantiff personal injury and there is plenty of scope to get fully involved in this kind of work. In most seats trainees have their own office near to that of the partner they're working for. Only in the employment seat do you share with a partner.

LAWRENCE GRAHAM

In this firm, known for its strong shipping, property and private client practices, trainees generally work for two partners during each seat. Partners have offices; trainees and assistants sit in an open-plan area nearby. Trainees are expected, in theory, to do one property, one litigation and one company/commercial seat. They can then do a specialist seat such as shipping, or return to their preferred seat for qualification. However there was some feeling that there is flexibility within that structure; for example, property can be avoided.

There are varying levels of responsibility throughout, but "the firm is not afraid of letting trainees deal with clients, and aptitude is rewarded with responsibility." On the downside, "you can be thrown in a bit – they expect you to muck in from the first."

Internal lectures are well-structured – there are trainee lectures fortnightly and specific departmental courses and a written 'trainee guide' for each seat. Working hours are not excessive. "We pull our finger out while we're here" but "it is a culture where if you can't get the work done by 7pm then there's something wrong."

Prospective trainees are advised to look at the core strengths of the firm when deciding whether to apply. "It picks specialties and does them very well." These are essentially property, corporate, shipping, litigation, tax and financial management. Candidates "must be prepared to get stuck in and get on with the work. Any kind of 'attitude' is not welcomed."

LINKLATERS

"Ultimately, lawyers at Linklaters are quite driven people," said one interviewee. Nevertheless, every trainee we spoke to commented on how friendly the firm is. "It's far less hierarchical than I expected. There's an incredibly relaxed atmosphere. I don't know anyone who's really miserable," are typical comments. Trainees at Linklaters seem to be genuinely happy with their choice of firm. Even those who had decided a legal career was not for them said "you can't fault Linklaters as an employer." The firm has recently linked up with four law firms in Belgium, Germany, The Netherlands and Sweden. It now has 28 offices in 16 countries.

The quality of work, levels of responsibility and client contact depend on "luck, your principal and how willing you are to push for what you want." Most trainees had more responsibility than they expected – even in corporate seats. "Discrete parts of the transaction were mine – and not just the data room." Experience with principals, not surprisingly, was mixed. "Some take training seriously, but others, especially the more senior ones, aren't so organised." Principals are, however, now being taught how to teach and "assistants are usually approachable and keen to impart information."

Linklaters has adopted an original approach to training contracts. During the LPC year, future trainees visit the firm and talk to partners and human resources about what they want to do. They then choose a 'seat package.' This consists of a 'home seat' in the department they think they will want to qualify into. Ideally, trainees spend their first year in that seat. In their second year, trainees have three seats which are complementary to their home seat. The seat package is not set in stone. There is an assessment every four months at which time seats can be changed.

LOVELL WHITE DURRANT

This large corporate practice operates the standard four-seat structure, and offers a wide variety of specialist seats. Many client secondments are available as well as overseas seats. Out of a recent intake of 28 people, about three quarters spent time out of the office during their training. A trainee who spent a seat in-house at a major client said: "the seat gave me a huge amount of confidence. I became very involved in the company and its business, whereas usually trainees don't see the other side of the City. I was supervised in-house but always had back-up from the office when I needed it." Seats are allocated with priority to fourth seaters. Everyone seems to get at least one of their first choices, but "you have to be very determined and assertive about what you want to do."

Transactions or cases are often too large to give a trainee much autonomy or client contact and this varies from department to department. Property and property litigation are both seen as excellent learning seats with trainees taking on up to 40 files, attending meetings and having constant client contact. Such experience may be harder to come by in a department such as capital markets.

Overseas seats are generally seen as excellent experience. One trainee who went to Paris had a "fantastic" time. Socially there is a very good trainee network with 20 to 25 trainees from various London firms who send round emails and very quickly get to know one another. Trainees can even make a profit since accommodation is provided, bills are paid and they receive an increment to their London salaries.

On the work side, July and August in Paris are quiet, although our interviewee spent several months working long, hard hours on a huge flotation. Work is general commercial, including intellectual property and capital markets. French to at least 'A' level standard is required.

MACFARLANES

A medium-sized firm which handles both corporate and private client work. There are four seats. Three are in property, litigation, company/commercial/banking and a fourth in tax or financial planning or back in one of the previous seats. Within the company/commercial department there is also an employment seat. "Most partners think it's a good idea to do a tax and financial planning seat because it gives an insight into the whole firm." There are occasional secondments to clients. Post-recruitment, future trainees of the firm are called in before the LPC for a one-week introduction to the firm, which is a mix of work experience and training exercises.

There is "extensive training" at the firm. Seven or eight trainee workshops are spread over the first two to three months of each seat and these are compulsory. Each trainee is assigned a mentor who they see "a couple of times informally/socially" and a supervisor. The end-of-seat review is written by your supervisor but is actually discussed with your mentor and an independent partner.

The firm is open and "very good at listening to trainee concerns". "You are actively encouraged to speak to anyone at all and absolutely everyone, however senior, shares an office." Trainees thought they were getting more responsibility and client contact than their peers at other firms.

Above all there is no emphasis on hours worked. "Pressure is actually put on you to go home and do other things." A trainee social committee called QUACK organises welcome drinks, social events, Christmas parties and summer sports. The firm recruits a "real blend of personalities, but always people who are pretty self-assured and willing to get on with things."

MANCHES & CO

Manches is a commercial firm which also, unusually, has a strong family law practice. It takes trainees in both the London and Oxford offices. Training is conducted in four six-month seats, although one of these may occasionally be split into two three-month seats, giving the trainee experience of six different practice areas. There is also some flexibility if a trainee wishes to propose a secondment to a client for part of a seat, although this is by no means a standard procedure.

Trainees must do seats in company/commercial, litigation and property. The final seat is a choice between family and other niche seats. A recent change of trainee officer has led to a better structure and trainees are now told of their seat allocation well in advance.

The firm has a strong reputation for its family department and trainees there can expect client contact and involvement in very high calibre work.

Training is organised from London. There are Monday lunchtime lectures in the London office which all trainees, including those from Oxford, are encouraged to attend. There is also a series of seminars in London and Oxford for the whole firm and for clients. In some departments, such as corporate, there are internal morning meetings once a week, to discuss know-how matters. As for making suggestions about training, there was a feeling that: "it's easier if you're an Oxford trainee" since the office is "smaller and you can make your voice heard."

MASONS

A leading construction firm which, unsurprisingly, has a strong construction slant to its training programme. The structure of training differs from branch to branch. In the London office a system of six seats of four months each has been introduced "to break up the strong construction element." All trainees do either four or eight months in the construction department.

A limited number of departments in Bristol make for the traditional four seat set-up;

property, property litigation and construction departments provide three; while new public sector/PFI work may soon provide a fourth choice. In the Manchester office trainees usually do twelve months in construction, six in commercial/IT litigation and six in PPE (property, planning and environment).

Seats are available in Brussels (although apparently only for London trainees) and movement between branches can occasionally be accommodated. Trainees are more likely to sit with a senior assistant than a partner.

Marketing contact is encouraged from a very early stage. Trainees are sent on a networking skills course. In the London office all trainees were recently asked to attend an employment seminar and circulate at the reception to make contact with clients. They might also be involved in marketing research.

PSC courses for all trainees are held in the London office. A new training director has brought in an external lecturer to provide training and refreshers in legal research and drafting skills. There has also been a series of eight or nine commercial lectures provided by an in-house consultant. Each first year trainee is assigned a second-year as a 'buddy' to provide informal assistance and information.

MORGAN COLE

At the time of going to press, Morgan Bruce had just merged with Oxford-based Cole & Cole to become Morgan Cole. The training department of Morgan Bruce is not yet sure of the implications for future trainees. At the moment, trainees are split between the Cardiff, Newport, Swansea and London offices. The Swansea office is seen by the other offices as the short straw, "but people always like it after they've been here." Trainees do not seem to interact between the various offices, "I couldn't tell you what happens in the Swansea office" said a Cardiff trainee. The Swansea trainees said they felt isolated from the rest of the firm and would appreciate more firm-wide training seminars which would bring trainees

together. The firm also has some difficulty in finding trainees willing to move between the various offices. "They are trying to get people to move around but it's not working very well. They are so accommodating they won't make you move unless they have to."

Trainees can be seconded to clients for some seats. One trainee who was seconded to a large public sector client for commercial property found the work ethic very different. "I couldn't believe the number of meetings and there wasn't the urgency." Although the secondment was seen as "a great experience" the work soon became repetitive.

The firm appears to be responsive to trainees' criticisms. The level of responsibilty also appears to improve in the second year. "They are giving me more difficult things to do and I am starting to run my own files," said one second year. Some trainees found they were working under pressure. "We have some major clients and you have got to be seen to cope."

NABARRO NATHANSON

A large West End law firm with plans to move to smart new purpose-built 'mid-town' (Holborn) premises in time for the millennium. It has regional branches in Sheffield and Reading as well as offices in Paris and Brussels. Trainees are now being recruited by the smaller Reading office for the first time. The office has a private client and charity group which provides work not available to London trainees. There is occasionally interchange of trainees between Sheffield and London.

New trainees were particularly impressed with the way the firm kept in touch between recruitment and the start of the training contract. Trainees-to-be were invited in for dinner, drinks and a quiz night and assigned a 'buddy' – a current trainee who they could call with any questions.

On arrival, trainees are assigned both a daily supervisor and a partner supervisor. In London and Reading they sit with their daily supervisor who is generally three or four years qualified. In Sheffield they sit in an open-plan office area near their daily supervisor while the partner sits in a private office nearby.

Seats in corporate, property and litigation are compulsory. "They push property within the firm across the board. Even if you really don't want to do it, you can rarely avoid it." As for the non-compulsory seats, personnel are praised as "very good at creating vacancies" in departments where somebody particularly wants to do a seat."

The firm is reputed to have a friendly atmosphere, being a little more relaxed and informal than other firms of a similar size. Most trainees commented on the good mix of people. One trainee in Sheffield commented "They have a good attitude, we feel we're looked after very well. They spend a lot of money on us and we're made to feel useful."

NORTON ROSE

A top ten firm particularly rated for its finance work. The recent dissolution of the Norton Rose M5 Group does not appear to have adversely affected the training or, indeed, any other part of the practice.

The structure of training is unusual in that trainees do four seats of four months each in corporate finance, banking, litigation and one optional seat in a smaller department such as property, tax, company or human resources. These are assigned to you on arrival, although there is leeway to change the fourth. In the final eight months trainees have three options. Eight months in one seat, four in a new seat and four in the qualifying seat, or six months abroad and two in the qualifying department.

There are mixed opinions about this four-month seat system; "if you get into a seat and you get into a big deal it doesn't work, but generally it suited me to try other teams and not become too specialised."

Over half the firm's work is international and this is reflected in the opportunities available to trainees. Overseas seats are available in

Piraeus, Paris, Moscow, Brussels and Bahrain. The Bahrain seat is mainly banking although the current trainee is thought to be doing more litigation – "from a trainee perspective the work is better than in the London office; the deals are smaller so you can do a lot more." Our interviewee pointed out that a seat abroad does not mean 'out of sight out of mind.' "They don't send you abroad unless they want to keep you on."

New arrivals are assigned a "responsible trainee" to look after them and guide them through the early period of their training. There is also a partner mentor system which trainees found very valuable. In the past this did not always work well because "certain partners were too busy or not approachable." Trainees are now asked to give feedback on their mentors and "they are more careful about who they choose."

One of the most popular aspects of training at Norton Rose is the free Monday night bar for all fee-earners, mainly frequented by trainees. "The sort of people they take on at Norton Rose" said one new trainee "know how to work hard, but also want to have a bit of a laugh."

OSBORNE CLARKE

A large Bristol firm with offices in London and Reading which has recently been rebranded to shake off its old traditional image.

The first two seats are given to trainees on arrival and are generally litigation and property. Remaining choices are between corporate, tax and human resources seats. Quite a few people move around the different offices. The Reading office is specialised into employment, corporate and commercial work only. It is small so "a lot more hands-on experience is given and it can get extremely busy. The downside is that they lack a team of support staff." The London office is seen to be developing its IP, IT telecoms and advertising work. Opportunities occasionally arise to go to European offices such as Brussels, Barcelona and Frankfurt.

The trainee officer is "extremely approachable and helpful – if you have a problem it gets sorted out immediately." Flexibility within training is also praised. It is not standard practice to split seats but if trainees really want to they can do five seats. However there is a three-line whip to go to seminars and lectures. "Our principals are very keen to make sure we attend everything properly."

The firm is particularly social. "Senior management are keen to be involved in fun social things." Trainees are busy too: "We run the local Trainee Solicitors Group – all the main social events in Bristol for trainees are organised by us."

RICHARDS BUTLER

The PSC is taught by the fast track method in the first three weeks, which means "it's all out of the way quickly which is very nice." Unusually, there are four five-month seats and one four-month seat. The firm is known for its shipping department although it is also strong in corporate and media.

Richards Butler have a rigorous regime of ongoing training lectures: "You can't avoid them. We have one or two lunchtimes a week of compulsory lectures just for trainees. Then there are firm-wide lectures by external speakers twice a week. You are supposed to go to all of these – we have to sign in. They are all pitched at an introductory level so as a trainee they're very useful."

The firm appears to live up to its statement of accepting "candidates from diverse backgrounds." "I felt they were interested in my previous experience which was the first time that had happened," commented one more mature trainee. The average age of trainee starters is about 25 or 26, which is significantly older than many firms. There's also an apparent trend to recruiting para-legals.

Trainees seem to be happy with the level of responsibility they are getting, although one trainee commented – "I have never had a file of my own." Most feel their working schedule is more relaxed than other big City firms.

ROWE & MAW

One trainee chose Rowe and Maw because of the reception she received on her vacation scheme. "They made a great deal of effort to welcome us," she commented. "You have a trainee who is your mentor, who explains basic things to you and takes you out for lunch." In general, trainees experienced a similar welcome.

Recently, the firm changed the number of seats available to trainees from five to four six-month seats. Trainees who were able to use their fifth seat as a refresher for their qualification subject have mixed views as to whether this is a good idea. "I think the new trainees may resent the lack of choice," said one.

Trainees get an early opportunity to take responsibility. "The supervisors are very fair and if they come across something they think you can do alone, they'll say 'have a bash', and, depending on how you do, you get given more." An interviewee in an employment seat felt the work was "quite exciting – I had a lot of contentious work, four tribunals in four months which was really good."

There are opportunites to do an EU/competition seat in Brussels and an insurance seat at Lloyd's. The seat at Lloyd's is mainly contentious work and involves drafting instructions to counsel and experts, corresponding with witnesses and lots of research. In Brussels, trainees produce a monthly letter on aspects of EU law and run a case-monitoring service for staff in the London office. The work is very much research-based reflecting the raditional use of trainees in a Brussels office.

RUSSELL JONES & WALKER

The firm is a large litigation-based practice with regional branches in the north and Bristol and an office in London. Trainees are expected to handle their fair share of work, "you're expected to take the bull by the horns and make decisions – ask if you get out of your depth – but you're expected to be proactive and pretty much manage files."

The firm allocates all seats when trainees arrive. "Because of the litigation bias, I think this is one of the few firms that has to be quite careful to ensure trainees actually get the required non-contentious experience," commented one trainee. The property seat usually provides this work. The firm appears to be quite flexible with seat allocation, allowing trainees to swap amongst themselves if one has a particular preference.

Criminal is seen as an exciting seat. It involves "fairly hard work, unusual hours and a lot of travelling round the country to take witness statements and go to court." Some of the cases have involved "high profile trials with a lot of media interest." The seat is also viewed as having a good support network. "Wherever I was, I could put a call back to the office and there would be someone at the end of the line to help," said an interviewee.

There are no formal training days or lectures for trainees, although they are invited to attend firm-wide training afternoons and departmental education weekends. Some felt it would be beneficial if there was a programme specifically for them.

S J BERWIN

Trainees found the quality of their training depended largely on their own initiative and confidence at this medium-sized corporate firm. In their first seat they are 'mentored' by a second year trainee, which is good because "they are a bit more in touch and I found I was being given good advice." Trainees work alongside a partner who supervises their work, although it can vary from department to department. "In tax it seems you work for the department as a whole." Although working with partners is seen as the best form of 'hands-on' training, some trainees prefer not to; "for your own development, it can be less nerve wracking to sit with an assistant." First year trainees generally sit together in the dining room for a free lunch in a bit of a "school environment."

In the banking department, there are opportunities to do a two month secondment to a French banking client. Trainees can also do a six month seat in Brussels. A trainee in the corporate department told us that the quality of work depended very much on the economic conditions and could be variable.

Trainees are made aware that S J Berwin is a young firm which is 'hungry for work.' They are encouraged to "keep in contact with friends from university, so that by the time we are applying for partnership they may be directors of companies" and therefore useful contacts. Trainees are informed that there is a marketing budget "if we have any decent ideas or want to host an event."

Although known mainly for its corporate and commercial property practice, S J Berwin also has a human rights department. One final seat trainee found himself travelling to the West Indies to attend a Court of Appeal death row hearing which was "certainly an experience."

SIMMONS & SIMMONS

A top ten City firm, overwhelmingly voted as hardworking but "laid-back and unstuffy." The nice thing is "the people keep a sense of humour about their job." The firm also has a fairly flexible attitude and one trainee who failed one of his LPC exams found them sympathetic. Equally, one had started as a pupil at the Bar and found himself paralegalling at the firm while looking for a third six month pupillage. He ended up entering into a training contract. The firm allowed him to credit his whole year of pupillage in a common law set leaving him only two seats to qualify.

Out of the four seats trainees must do one in corporate and one in litigation. The litigation seat can be taken in a specialist department such as IP, employment or environment. There is a busy programme of lectures (one or two per week), which are compulsory for trainees. On moving into each new department there is an intensive course of one or two weeks of seminars specific to that seat. One trainee observed that the corporate department was much less organised than the commercial department in holding such lectures. Each trainee is assigned a principal; a partner who "looks after trainees and, in theory, checks training records monthly."

There are often opportunities for secondments to both UK and overseas clients. There are also overseas seats available in several countries in the fourth seat. The most popular seats are Hong Kong, New York and Shanghai.

There was much enthusiasm for the voluntary work at Battersea Legal Advice Centre. Groups of five trainees go every Monday evening, accompanied by an assistant, and advise on employment, matrimonial and tenancy issues amongst others. Trainees appreciated the chance to give face-to-face on the spot advice. It was also an opportunity to "meet 'normal' clients and keep your feet on the ground rather than turning into a City automaton."

TAYLOR JOYNSON GARRETT

Taylor Joynson Garrett is a commercial City firm with offices in Brussels and Bucharest and an associate office in Hong Kong. Trainees can do a seat in the Brussels office in EU/competition law and a corporate seat in the Hong Kong office. The first of the four seats is allocated on arrival and the next seats chosen in the last month before changeover. Trainees felt that the training partners and associates made a special effort with them right from the beginning. The size of the intake, about 20 trainees a year, is considered to be about right as it "leads to a close-knit group who support each other and do not aggressively compete with each other." There is also a high proportion of mature students. One trainee for example had practised as a doctor and was contemplating qualifying into the personal injury department.

Supervision appears to reflect the level of experience. "In the first year I did a litigation seat and it was pretty much do something and then get immediate feedback from your supervisor. I am in my second year now and yesterday I went to a meeting where my supervisor just sat back and said nothing while I was making the presentation and negotiating." In the property department by contrast, trainees were less closely supervised from the start. "We were

told: here's a file, tell me what you make of it and let me know when you have a problem."

There are regular seminars which are advertised throughout the firm. These tend to be client-focused and not particularly aimed at trainees. Appraisals with the supervising partner are meant to take place half way through and at the end of each seat; however "that is not always the case in practice."

TITMUSS SAINER DECHERT

This firm has an alliance with US practice, Dechert Price and Rhoads, but trainees will not be much affected by this apart from working on a number of US deals in the corporate department. "I would have expected more opportunities from it," commented one trainee, "personally I would prefer it if we had more of an American dimension." The firm has, however, upgraded its IT system in order to interact more closely with the US.

The system of six four-month seats is popular. "It gives you a lot of variety in the type of work you do and the people you interact with in different areas of the firm." Trainees tend to do property and/or litigation seats in the first year, with a greater choice of seats, including company/commercial, in the second year. The firm runs a 'partner mentor' scheme. Appraisals depend on the partner concerned; "some people have an informal chat and say everything is fine, others are more detailed." One trainee missed an appraisal – "sometimes you have to push to get one."

One interviewee found the litigation department quite quiet when he was there, although "we did a House of Lords case and I did a fair amount of research." In corporate, trainees found they were involved in big demergers and flotations and had a lot more interaction with other parties.

Trainees can do a four month seat in EU/competition law in the small Dechert Price and Rhoads office in Brussels. Research and answering London office enquiries takes up a lot of time, but "I found I had gained a lot of knowledge and when I went back to London I qualified into competition," commented one trainee.

TRAVERS SMITH BRAITHWAITE

One candidate was "very keen to apply" to Travers Smith Brathwaite after attending the three week vacation scheme which gave a "good introduction to different departments of the firm." She said: "I could imagine myself working here." There are four six month seats: litigation, property and corporate and trainees choose their last seat. They are asked their preference before joining and get what they want depending on availability. Work is set by the supervisor who sits with the trainee. "It's fairly hands on and you get involved from day one – you get an opportunity to stand on your own two feet, but the supervisor is never far away – you do feel supported." Trainees felt that this responsibility at an early stage was an important part of their training – "you really feel you are learning." However, it is only in the last few months that "you feel comfortable with the responsibility."

A continuous education programme is run through seminars in the lecture theatre. There are also good information facilities and some departments have their own library. There is a three month assessment which is forwarded to the training principal who oversees each trainee's progress over the two years, and a six month appraisal with the principal. "They do give you an idea of how you're getting on, although it's difficult to know what to judge yourself against."

Property and litigation were felt to offer the most client exposure. "I went to a lot of client meetings in litigation," commented one trainee. Due to the nature of the work the taxation seat offers less client contact. There is the possibility of secondment to outside companies during the banking and taxation seats, but there are no international seats.

TROWERS & HAMLINS

The firm specialises in housing and public law work but also has a strong international commerce department and a private client department. Its location at "the grimier Kings Cross end of Grays Inn Road" is not seen as a selling point. Trainees have the opportunity to be seconded out of the London office either to offices in the Gulf or to the regional offices of Manchester and Exeter, but they need to express an early interest. The seat in the Gulf is a commercial one and trainees must be prepared to "muck in" and work hard. You often get "the opportunity to work on big oil and gas projects." One trainee who decided to stay in Abu Dhabi after qualification thought that being a woman actually helped in dealings with the ministries.

Trainees felt they received better training where they were asked to do more. "Public sector was my best seat because at the time I joined they were slightly understaffed so I had more responsibilty, albeit highly regulated," commented one interviewee.

In Exeter, trainees enjoyed the relaxed and informal atmosphere of a smaller office. "There's not quite the hierarchy of the London office and as a trainee I feel it's useful to do a seat where you are just a fee-earner really. You get your own set of files, your own office and a bit more independence." The seat in Exeter is in housing but the trainee has to be adaptable. "It was certainly a general seat. Mainly housing and property work, but you also get people who come in off the street for wills so I did quite a lot of private client work including a probate."

WALKER MORRIS

Walker Morris is a Leeds-based firm, specialising in commercial litigation and commercial property as well as having a strong building societies practice. There are six four-month seats; three of which are allocated in the first year, with three chosen in the second. Some trainees felt they "never got to grips" with a subject in four months while others appreciated the breadth of choice. Departmental courses were considered "very good" – "half are on video and half are given by external speakers." The major grumble among trainees was the unavailability of computer equipment – they particularly wanted more use of email.

Litigation trainees found that attending agency hearings was invaluable experience. They also had a lot of client contact and were running their own files. The property department has weekly training meetings, but there is "perhaps a lack of breadth to the work" with mortgage and repossession work getting "a bit repetitive." In the corporate seat, there is "a steep learning curve, with a good level of responsibility and quite close supervision." Planning on the other hand is "less hands on."

All trainees felt they were exposed to much more responsibility than contemporaries in big London firms. One who advised employers directly on redundancies and another attending trial in London on their own reported that they saw the work through from the initial stages to the end of the trial. A trainee seconded to a Paris law firm for a corporate seat used her French degree to act as interpreter in meetings, as well as grappling with French legal terms, and preparing seminars on tax at the Palais de Justice. This trainee has since been invited back to France for an office party at a chateau.

WEIGHTMANS
Weightmans is a large insurance-based Liverpool firm with an office in Birmingham. All trainees sit with a partner who supervises their work schedule. In the contentious seats, up to fourteen trainees are placed on the 'court clerk rota.' This is a computerised diary system which is used to allocate applications before district judges. This gives trainees great negotiation and advocacy experience.

Trainees felt that in allocating seats the firm "listens to your views and tries to tailor your training to suit you." They liked the nature of the training which is quite structured but "you are not too cosseted and are expected to muck in and get on with it."

All interviewees commented that they would like their own PC (these are currently available only to qualified staff apart from in the "more organised" commercial property department). They felt particularly that it impacted on the computerised court clerk rota.

The firm has recently acceded to trainees' requests to introduce a formalised three month written appraisal system, which allows them

more time to respond to the firm's comments on their performance. The commercial property department hands new trainees a booklet which details what is expected from them during that seat; some felt this system would be useful if extended throughout the firm.

WILDE SAPTE
This finance firm has recently been in the news over its failed merger talks with accountants Arthur Andersen. Although this caused some nerves amongst fee-earners at the time "it has all pretty much blown over" and trainees did not feel particularly affected.

In their first year trainees do one contentious and one non-contentious seat. In the second year they can go back to a previous seat if they want to specialise early. "This particularly applies to mature students with experience in an industry area." The majority of trainees will go through either a general banking or asset finance seat – "although if you have a particular preference not to then you can avoid it." However, in view of the firm's finance bent, interviewees felt it was helpful to do at least one such seat.

There are client secondments and overseas seats available in Paris and Tokyo, usually taken in the third or fourth seats. Lots of free language classes are available and trainees are encouraged to take them up. The firm's Lloyd's office also takes two or three trainees.

Training generally receives a round of applause. Each department has an information and support lawyer. Their job includes organising training, which includes a "big chunk" of internal lectures and a number of outside lectures by, for example, barristers in the litigation department. Smaller departments may not be so organised. Trainees felt that client exposure was good. "You have to learn how to deal with clients quite quickly. You are not protected from them. The firm is keen to give trainees as much independence as possible."

The firm is overwhelmingly viewed as friendly – "it does not have the same kind of City mentality you hear of in other firms." There is a strong view that Wilde Sapte is more open-minded than most about recruiting older trainees. "They do not take on clones. Lots of trainees have previously done something else and are entering the law as their second profession."

WRAGGE & CO

A Birmingham commercial firm which used to run its training with the recently-disbanded Norton Rose M5 Group. They now co-ordinate their own PSC courses in conjunction with the College of Law and BPP Law School. This is a week off-site, which allows trainees to get to know each other.

Inside the firm, training is ongoing and there is a useful introduction into each seat. New trainees appreciated the fact that second year trainees who join the same department on the same day act as 'minders.'

Trainees do property, corporate and litigation

seats. The best training in the firm is deemed to be in the corporate department. Each trainee has a principal – "a partner who will keep an eye on you and see how you're doing over the two years." Trainees sit with a departmental supervisor and appraisals are formal and written. The principal "usually fights my side – I am always very happy with that", commented one trainee. There are no overseas seats or formal secondments to other firms. Plans to organise one to a large manufacturing client have not taken off.

Trainees highlighted the team culture and the fact that they are encouraged to air their grievances on the spot. "There is very much an attitude of 'put up or shut up' – if you've got a problem you get it out in the open and say your piece – you sort it out and don't harbour grudges." The positive attitude to the more mature candidate was also highlighted. "They like the fact that you've got useful experience and that's very encouraging." ■

FIRMS RANKED BY TRAINING CONTRACTS PER YEAR

Firm	Contracts	Firm	Contracts
Clifford Chance	130	Trowers & Hamlins	12–15
Linklaters	120	Beachcroft Stanleys	12
Eversheds	100–120	Kennedys	12
Allen & Overy	100	Olswang	12
Freshfields	90	Titmuss Sainer Dechert	up to 12
Cameron McKenna	80	Charles Russell	10–12
Herbert Smith	80	Manches & Co	10–12
Lovell White Durrant	80	Watson, Farley & Williams	10–12
Slaughter and May	75	Nicholson Graham & Jones	10–11
Norton Rose	60–70	Field Fisher Waterhouse	10
Simmons & Simmons	60	Ince & Co	10
Dibb Lupton Alsop*	50	Paisner & Co	10
Garretts*	50	Penningtons	10
Ashurst Morris Crisp	45–50	Withers	10
Nabarro Nathanson*	30	Biddle	8
Wilde Sapte	30	Bristows	8
S J Berwin & Co	28	Fisher Meredith	8
Denton Hall	25–30	Mishcon de Reya	8
Rowe & Maw	25	Sinclair Roche & Temperley	8
Stephenson Harwood	25	Bird & Bird	7
Baker & McKenzie	22	White & Case	7
Taylor Joynson Garrett	22	Capsticks	6–8
Berwin Leighton	20	Farrer & Co	6
Gouldens	20	Hempsons	6
Macfarlanes	20	Holman, Fenwick & Willan	6
Richards Butler	20	Jay Benning & Peltz	6
Theodore Goddard	20	Lewis Silkin	6
Travers Smith Braithwaite	20	Russell Jones & Walker	5–6
Davies Arnold Cooper	up to 20	Edward Lewis	5
Clyde & Co	16	Harbottle & Lewis	5
Reynolds Porter Chamberlain	16	Speechly Bircham	5
Masons*	15–17	Vizards	5
Berrymans Lace Mawer	14	Orchard	4–6
Lawrence Graham	14	Sidley & Austin	4–6
D J Freeman	12–15		

The table represents London firms providing more than 4 training contracts per year. For those firms marked with an asterisk the number may include contracts available in regional branches. For further details see A-Z section.

Training contracts available per year: Regional firms

Firm		Firm	
Pinsent Curtis	35	Hugh James	5
Edge Ellison	30	Lester Aldridge	5
Addleshaw Booth & Co	20–25	Silverbeck Rymer	5
Bond Pearce	20	Veale Wasbrough	5
Hammond Suddards	20	Walker Smith & Way	5
Bevan Ashford	19	Dolmans	5
Wragge & Co	18–20	Donne Mileham & Haddock	4–5
Shoosmiths & Harrison	16	Shadbolt & Co	4–5
Burges Salmon	15	Attey Bower & Jones	4
Hewitson Becke + Shaw	15	B.P. Collins & Co	4
Irwin Mitchell	15	Battens (with Poole & Co)	4
Wansbroughs Willey Hargrave	15	Bell Lax Litigation	4
Mills & Reeve	10–14	Clarks	4
Martineau Johnson	10–12	Cunningham, John & Co	4
Osborne Clarke	10–12	Donns Solicitors	4
Blake Lapthorn	10	Elliott & Company	4
Edwards Geldard	10	Foot & Bowden	4
Walker Morris	8–10	George Davies & Co	4
Weightmans	8–10	Hart Brown	4
Browne Jacobson	8	Iliffes Booth Bennett	4
Clarke Willmott & Clarke	8	James Chapman & Co	4
Cripps Harries Hall	8	Mace & Jones	4
Dickinson Dees	8	Marshall & Galpin	4
Freeth Cartwright Hunt Dickins	8	McCormicks	4
Lawrence Tucketts	8	Rees Page	4
Pannone & Partners	8	Ormerod Heap & Marshall	4
Lyons Davidson	7	Palmer Wheeldon	4
Bower & Bailey	6	Perkins & Co	4
Cobbetts	6	Prettys	4
Davies Wallis Foyster	6	Robert Muckle	4
Halliwell Landau	6	Shakespeares	4
Howes Percival	6	T.G. Baynes & Sons	4
Ward Hadaway	6	Taylor Vinters	4
Cartwrights	5	Wilsons Solicitors	4

The table represents regional firms providing 4 or more training contracts per year. For further details see A-Z section.

52

TRAINING WITH AMERICAN FIRMS

There are about 65 US firms in London. Most opened their offices in the last five years and were staffed initially by US attorneys practising American law, principally in capital markets and project finance. Now, however, they are seeking to diversify and many are starting to handle more mainstream corporate work together with litigation and even property. They are recruiting English lawyers and are offering "dual capability" to their global clients. Some market themselves as English firms with an international focus. "We are in fact an English firm aiming to offer a full-service English law capability" says Linda McDonald of Coudert Brothers.

US firms began their expansion in the UK by poaching experienced staff from top City practices. They were not interested in more junior lawyers and often employed paralegals to handle less important work. Now, though, as the number of English partners starts to swell, the next logical step is to expand at junior level and that includes taking on trainees. As Elizabeth Sanderson of Weil Gotshal says: "It was recognised that we needed assistance at junior level."

Law Society regulations mean that US firms are restricted in their recruitment of trainees to a certain degree. "If you have only two English qualified partners, then you can take on only four English trainees," comments Elizabeth Normand of White & Case. Perhaps more restrictive is the fact that English trainees must cover at least three different areas of law; for example – corporate, litigation and property. Until recently, many US firms could not offer broad enough training. However, times are changing; the Law Society reports an increase in the number of US firms gaining authorisation and the number of places available at each firm is also on the increase.

White & Case, Coudert Brothers, Sidley & Austin and Leboeuf Lamb Greene & Macrae remain the best known US firms with English trainees and a structured training programme.

What is it that attracts English students to US firms? "I would like the opportunity to do a secondment in the US rather than anywhere else in the world," says Jasmine Cansell who is currently being interviewed by seven US firms for a training contract. Ironically, because of the lack of English staff in the US offices, she is more likely to have that opportunity at a big City firm. Also US firms want their English trainees in the London office. "We want our English trainees to stay in England," comments Elizabeth Normand of White and Case. However, the global nature of much of the work at US firms means that contact with foreign countries and travel will inevitably be part of your job post-training. "Students like the excitement of an international firm plus the opportunity to get in on the ground floor of a growing operation," says Leboeuf's James Johnson. Those who like the idea of handling high quality work in a small office, rather than at a large City practice also find US firms attractive.

Last, but certainly not least, is money. The US firms want good staff and they are paying good money to get them. Average salaries for trainees are higher than at City firms and qualification salaries are considerably higher. Mayer, Brown & Platt, for example, pay first year trainees £26,000 and second year qualified lawyers £68,000. Other firms run incentive schemes: Cadwalader offer a bonus for trainees who manage the imposing target of 2,000 billable hours per year. The financial rewards are definitely tempting.

The good news is there are increasing opportunities to join US firms, and as their training schemes become more established, so respect for them will grow. At the moment, the safe option is still to choose a trusted UK practice, but for the more adventurous, the US firms are an exciting prospect. ■

TRAINEES ABROAD

Many trainees join large firms hoping to spend up to six months of their training in an overseas seat. Traditionally favourite destinations have been Hong Kong, New York and Paris. However, Hong Kong's change of status and the emergence of the far Eastern markets mean that firms are moving to centres such as Singapore, Beijing or even Ho Chi Minh City. It is also becoming more common for Middle East and Eastern European seats to arise. These seats may not be as obviously glamorous or popular, but can give equally valuable experience as well as an insight into a culture which one is not likely to experience in a holiday situation.

If you arrive at your chosen firm and are determined to try for an overseas seat, how can you achieve your goal? Sitting and hoping for your track record to speak for you will not always work. One former trainee at a leading City firm was convinced that her excellent reports would ensure her a seat in Hong-Kong. "In fact I discovered that pretty good friends of mine were secretly lobbying partners. I didn't get a seat. I soon realised that I had been very naive. It's an important lesson to learn that who you know and who can use influence on your behalf is at least as important as your ability."

This may be a cynical view but most trainees will agree that when there is hot competition for a place, a proactive response is definitely called for. Being friendly with the personnel department also helps. Of course if you have relevant language skills or have lived and worked in the region, you stand a much better chance of being chosen.

Clifford Chance leads the field in terms of numbers of placements with 82 places abroad per year. Linklaters follows closely with 80 places, while Freshfields and Slaughter and May follow behind with less than half that number. Regional firms offering seats abroad include Hammond Suddards in Leeds, Osborne Clarke in Bristol and Dickinson Dees in Newcastle (see table opposite).

Most seats abroad are taken in the second year, after trainees have gained experience of working in the firm and have had time to con-sider where they would like to go. The foreign seat tends to be in company/commercial law, often with an international finance bias. (Finance makes up a large proportion of the international work of the largest firms.) However, a seat in Brussels will often be in EC competition law, and Hong Kong may count as litigation.

Hong Kong is always a popular choice with trainees. It's lively, the local law is close to English law and there's a large and flourishing community of trainees – about 50 at any one time. Their time in Hong Kong will be "work hard, play hard." Late nights and Saturday mornings at work and late nights out on the town are par for the course. Social life is well-organised, even down to a directory of trainees out there. One trainee from Freshfields found the working environment quite different from that in the London office. "It's a smaller office, much more friendly and hierarchy is less important. I got very good client contact but the work is more limited. Because of the small-er number of support staff the worst of the pho-tocopying and proofing was in Hong Kong."

No other overseas location has such a com-plement of young English lawyers. In Bahrain, for example, there is room for only one English trainee. Alex Pallett of Norton Rose was there in his fourth seat. "From a trainee perspective the work is better than in the London office," he commented, "I was doing banking work and was able to handle some small deals on my own – I ran my own loan for example." Although the first week was a little lonely with no trainee network to fall back on, there is a large group of expatriates who are "amazingly welcoming and keen to meet new people." Alex soon built up a group of friends and "the last four months were just mad – absolutely brilliant," he said. And contrary to popular belief the country is not alcohol-free – in fact they have drive-thru' off-licences

Not all trainee experiences abroad are to branches of the firm. They may be to associate offices or clients. One trainee from a large regional firm spent time in an associated Paris

TRAINEE SALARIES

Trainee salaries: London firms

Firm Name	1st year trainee salary	2nd year trainee salary	Qualification salary
White & Case	£25,000	£25,000	£45,000
Gouldens	£24,000	£26,000	£36,750
Rowe & Maw	£21,500	£24,500	£33,000
Baker & McKenzie	£21,000	£23,500	£34,000
Cameron McKenna	£21,000	£23,100	£34,000
Nabarro Nathanson	£21,000	£24,000	£33,000
Theodore Goddard	£21,000	£24,000	£33,000
Travers Smith Braithwaite	£21,000	£24,000	£33,000
Watson Farley & Williams	£21,000–£22,000	£23,000–£24,000	£33,000
Barlow Lyde & Gilbert	£21,000	£23,000	£33,000
Clifford Chance	£21,000	£24,000	£32,000
Freshfields	£21,000	£24,000	£32,000
Linklaters	£21,000	£24,000	£32,000
Macfarlanes	£21,000	£24,000	£32,000
Norton Rose	£21,000	£23,500	£32,500
Simmons & Simmons	£21,000	£24,000	£32,000
S J Berwin & Co	£21,500	£24,500	£31,000
Slaughter and May	£21,000	£24,000	£32,000
Berwin Leighton	£21,000	£23,000	£33,500
Taylor Joynson Garrett	£21,000	£23,000	£33,000
Titmuss Sainer Dechert	£21,000	£23,000	£33,000
Watson, Farley & Williams	£21,000–£22,000	£23,000–£24,000	£33,000
Ashurst Morris Crisp	£21,000	£23,500	£32,000
Bird & Bird	£21,000	£22,500	£33,000
Denton Hall	£20,500–£21,500	£22,500–£23,500	£32,500
Lovell White Durrant	£21,000	£23,000	£32,500
Paisner & Co	£20,500	£23,000	£33,000
Lawrence Graham	£20,000	£23,000	£33,000
Richards Butler	£21,000	£23,500	£31,500
Trowers & Hamlins	£20,500	£22,500	£33,000
Warner Cranston	£21,500	£23,000	£31,500
Allen & Overy	£21,000	£24,000	£30,500
Withers	£20,500	£22,600	£32,000
Herbert Smith	£21,000	£24,000	£30,000
Dibb Lupton Alsop	£21,000	£22,000	£32,000
Manches & Co	£20,550	£23,000	£30,600
Coudert Brothers	£20,500	£22,500	£31,000
Farrer & Co	£20,000	£22,000	32,000

The table shows firms in decreasing order of average salary for the three headings listed. The table only includes firms which have supplied figures for all three headings. Salaries represent the most up-to-date figures provided by the firms. See A-Z section for further details.

Trainee salaries: London firms (cont.)

Firm Name	1st year trainee salary	2nd year trainee salary	Salary on qualification
Ince & Co	£21,000	£23,000	£30,000
Clyde & Co	£20–£20,500	£21,000–£22,000	£31,500
Fox Williams	£20,000	£22,000	£31,000
Holmes Hardingham	£21,000	£22,000	£30,000
Sinclair Roche & Temperley	£20,000	£21,000	£31,500
Biddle	£20,000	£22,000	£30,000
Stephenson Harwood	£20,000	£22,000	£30,000
Tarlo Lyons	£20,000	£22,000	£30,000
D J Freeman	£19,000	£21,500	£31,000
Nicholson Graham & Jones	£20,000	£21,500	£31,000
Capsticks	c£20,500	c£22,500	£28,000+
Reynolds Porter Chamberlain	£19,000	£21,000	£31,000
Harbottle & Lewis	£19,500	£20,500	£30,500
Peter Carter-Ruck and Partners	£19,750	£22,500	£28,000
Edge Ellison	£19,500	£20,500	£30,000
Edward Lewis	£19,000	£21,000	£29,500
Beachcroft Stanleys	£19,000	£20,000	£30,000
Bristows	£18,500	£20,500	£30,000
Field Fisher Waterhouse	£20,000	£21,000	£27,500
Hill Taylor Dickinson	£18,500	£20,000	£30,000
Speechly Bircham	£18,000–£19,000	£19,500–£20,000	£30,000
Collyer-Bristow	£18,500	£20,500	£28,500
Payne Hicks Beach	£18,500	£20,000	£29,000
Penningtons	£19,500	£20,500	£27,500
Lewis Silkin	£19,000	£20,000	£28,000
Lane & Partners	£19,000	£20,000	£27,000
Radcliffes	£18,500	£19,500	£28,000
Rosling King	£19,000	£20,500	£26,000
Davenport Lyons	£19,000+	£20,000+	£26,000
Russell Jones & Walker	£18,000	£19,750	£27,000
Le Brasseur J Tickle	£17,500	£18,500	£28,500
Sheridans	£18,500	£19,250	£26,500
Lee Bolton & Lee	£18,000	£19,000	£27,000
Dawson & Co	£18,000	£19,000	£26,000
Pritchard Englefield	£17,500	£18,000	c£27,000
Townleys	£18,250	£19,250	£25,000
Druces Attlee	£17,250–£17,750	£18,250–£19,000	£26,000
Magrath & Co	£16,000	£20,000	£26,000
Teacher Stern Selby	£17,000	£18,000	£26,000
Hamlin Slowe	£16,000	£18,000	£26,000
Berrymans Lace Mawer	£13,000–£19,500	£14,000–£20,500	£22,000–£30,000
Ross & Craig	£15,000	£17,000	£27,000
Seddons	£16,000	£17,500	£25,000
Cumberland Ellis Peirs	£15,000	£16,000	£22,000
Anthony Gold, Lerman & Muirhead	£13,750	£15,400	£23,350
Edward Fail Bradshaw & Waterson	£12,250	£13,000	£19,000

Trainee salaries: Regional firms

Firm Name	1st year trainee salary	2nd year trainee salary	Salary on qualification
Wiggin and Co, *Cheltenham*	£21,200	£24,700	£31,000
Shadbolt & Co, *Reigate*	£17,500	£21,000	£27,000
Hammond Suddards, *Leeds*	£16,000	£18,000	£31,000
Wragge & Co, *Birmingham*	£15,000	£17,000	£25,500
Walker Morris, *Leeds*	£15,750	£17,500	£24,000
Burges Salmon, *Bristol*	£15,500	£16,500	£25,000
Dibb Lupton Alsop, *vaious*	£15,500	£16,500	£25,000
Edge Ellison, *Birmingham*	£15,500	£16,500	£25,000
Martineau Johnson, *Birmingham*	£15,500	£16,500	£25,000
Addleshaw Booth & Co, *Leeds*	£15,000–£15,500	£16,500–£17,000	£25,000
Pannone & Partners, *Manchester*	£15,000	£17,000	£24,000
Osborne Clarke, *Bristol*	£15,000–£15,500	£16,000–£16,500	£23,500
Shoosmiths & Harrison, *Northampton*	£14,750	£15,750	£24,000
Boyes Turner & Burrows, *Reading*	£15,000	£16,000	£23,500
Halliwell Landau, *Manchester*	£15,000	£16,000	£23,000
Mills & Reeve, *Cambridge*	£14,250	£15,250	£23,500
Dickinson Dees, *Newcastle-upon-Tyne*	£14,750	£15,750	£22,250
Cartwrights, *Bristol*	£14,000–£14,600	£15,200–£15,800	£22,500
Linnells, *Oxford*	£13,300	£14,750	£23,500
Browne Jacobson, *Nottingham*	£14,000	£15,500	£21,500
Cobbetts, *Manchester*	£13,400	£14,800	£22,500
Freeth Cartwright Hunt Dickins, *Nottm*	£13,000	£16,000	£21,000
Bevan Ashford, *Bristol*	£13,250	14,250	£22,000
Cripps Harries Hall, *Tunbridge Wells*	£13,000	£15,000	£21,500
Foot & Bowden, *Plymouth*	£12,500	£14,000	£23,000
Thomson Snell, *Tunbridge Wells*	£12,750–£13,500	£14,250–£15,000	£21,500
Brachers, *Maidstone*	£12,750	£13,875	£22,500
Bond Pearce, *Plymouth*	£13,500	£14,500	£21,000
Stevens & Bolton, *Guildford*	£13,000	£14,000	£22,000
Buller Jeffries, *Birmingham*	£13,500	£15,000	£20,000
Greenwoods, *Peterborough*	£13,135	£15,000	£20,000
Birketts, *Ipswich*	£13,500	£14,500	£20,000
Furley Page Fielding & Barton, *Canterbury*	£13,650	£15,015	£19,000
Blake Lapthorn, *Fareham*	£13,000	£14,000	£20,000
Clarke Willmott & Clarke, *Bristol*	£13,000	£14,500	£19,500
Donne Mileham & Haddock, *Brighton*	£12,500	£15,000	£19,500
George Green & Co, *Warley*	£12,000	£14,000	£21,000
Fennemores, *Milton Keynes*	£13,000	£14,000	£19,500
Iliffes Booth Bennett, *Uxbridge*	£13,000	£13,500	£20,000
Reynolds Parry-Jones, *High Wycombe*	£13,000	£13,500	£20,000

Trainee salaries: Regional firms (cont.)

Firm Name	1st year trainee salary	2nd year trainee salary	Salary on qualification
Wilsons Solicitors, *Salisbury*	£12,750	£14,000	£19,000
Challinors Lyon Clark, *West Bromwich*	£11,250	£13,000	£21,350
Clarkson Wright & Jakes, *Orpington*	£12,825	£13,500	£19,000
Matthew Arnold & Baldwin, *Watford*	£13,000	£14,000	£18,000
Walker Smith & Way, *Chester*	£12,500	£14,000	£18,500
Hugh James, *Cardiff*	£12,240	£12,750	£19,910
Lester Aldridge, *Bournemouth*	£12,000	£12,600	£20,000
Lyons Davidson, *Bristol*	£11,884–£12,484	£13,084–£13,684	£19,000+
Wansbroughs Willey Hargrave, *Bristol*	£10,000	£13,000	£21,000
Knight & Sons, *Newcastle-under-Lyme*	£11,250	£12,000–£13,000	£19,204
Kent Jones and Done, *Stoke-on-Trent*	£12,000	£13,390	£18,500
Howells, *Sheffield*	£12,500	£13,500	£16,800
Cuff Roberts, *Liverpool*	£10,850	£11,850	£20,000
Gosschalks, *Hull*	£10,850	£11,850	£20,000
Lupton Fawcett, *Leeds*	£10,850	£11,850	£20,000
Twitchen Musters & Kelly, *Southend*	£11,200	£12,200	£19,000
Stephens & Scown, *Exeter*	£11,250	£12,000	£18,000
Coffin Mew & Clover, *Portsmouth*	£10,850	£11,350	£17,750
Hawkins Russell Jones, *Hitchin*	£11,500	£13,000	£15,250
Huttons, *Cardiff*	£10,850	£10,850	£18,000
Turbervilles with Nelson Cuff, *Uxbridge*	£10,850	£10,850	£18,000
Higgs & Sons, *Brierley Hill*	£10,850	£11,350	£17,000
Richmonds Solicitors, *Doncaster*	£11,000	£11,000	£17,000
Crombie Wilkinson, *York*	£10,400	£11,200	£16,000

The table shows firms in decreasing order of average salary for the three headings listed. The table only includes firms which have supplied figures for all three headings. Salaries represent the most up-to-date figures provided by the firms. See A-Z section for further details.

Perks: Nationwide (cont.)

Firm Name	Sponsorship and Awards	Benefits	Sports Facilities
Theodore Goddard	CPE and LPC fees paid in full £3,900 maintenance p.a. in London and Guildford, £3,300 elsewhere	Permanent employment offered from the outset. Contributory pension, PHI, private medical insurance, death in service benefit, subsidised staff restaurant	Sports club membership
Titmuss Sainer Dechert	LPC fees and £4,000 maintenance p.a. for those living in London and £3,750 for those outside (where LA grants unavailable)	Free PHI and life assurance, and interest free season ticket loans	Gym membership
Travers Smith Braithwaite	LPC and CPE fees paid and £4,000 maintenance p.a.	PHI, season ticket loans, LVs	Sports club membership
Wilde Sapte	CPE and LPC fees; £4,000 maintenance p.a.	Interest free season ticket loan, death in service benefit, PPP, PRP, contributory pension at age 28 after qualification, staff restaurant	Gym membership
Wragge & Co	CPE and LPC fees paid and £3,500 maintenance grant	Life assurance, permanent health scheme, pension, interest free travel loans	

The table shows approximately the top 50 firms nationwide in alphabetical order. For further details and information on smaller firms, see the A-Z section. Where there are gaps, full information has not been supplied.

Private practice: South East		
	High Street	**Commercial**
Newly qualified	£17,500 - £20,000	£21,000 - £26,500
1-2 years	£19,500 - £23,500	£23,000 - £28,500
2-3 years	£22,500 - £26,000	£28,000 - £32,500
3-4 years	£25,000 - £30,500	£32,000 - £45,000

Private practice: Midlands		
	High Street	**Commercial**
Newly qualified	£17,000 - £19,000	£22,000 - £25,500
1-2 years	£18,500 - £22,000	£23,000 - £28,000
2-3 years	£20,000 - £26,000	£28,000 - £31,500
3-4 years	£23,000 - £29,000	£32,000 - £45,000

Private practice: North	
Legal Aid firms (1-12 partners)	
Newly qualified	£17,000 - £21,500
1-2 years	£18,500 - £23,000
2-3 years	£20,000 - £27,000
3-4 years	£23,500 - £31,000

Commercial practice		
	Manchester	**Leeds**
Newly qualified	£22,000 - £24,000	£22,000 - £25,000
1-2 years	£22,000 - £26,000	£22,000 - £27,000
2-3 years	£25,000 - £33,000	£25,000 - £34,000
3-4 years	£35,000 - £46,000	£35,000 - £48,000

Lawyers in Industry	
Newly qualified	£28,350
1-2 years	£31,500
2-3 years	£38,000
3-4 years	£42,000

Lawyers in Banking		
	Average salary	Average bonus (as % of annual salary)
Newly qualified	£35,000	18%
1 year	£42,000	22%
2 years	£48-50,000	33%
3 years	£55-60,000	38%
4 years	£65-68,000	45%
5 years	£70-75,000	58%

ALTERNATIVE CAREERS

Not all law students are able to obtain training contracts, and indeed not all want to. If you fall into this category, rest assured, your knowledge of the law will never go to waste. The skills you have acquired will give you a head start in a surprising range of jobs. Many employers favour law students even for positions with no legal dimension. They value a proven intellectual ability, an eye for detail, and the ability to identify salient points within complex issues. Below we outline some of the options available. The majority provide scope for drawing on your legal knowledge. Some require new skills to be learnt, either on the job or through formal qualifications.

For students trying to obtain training contracts:

Paralegal Work

Paralegal posts in private practice and local authorities are often filled by law students who have done their LPC but failed to secure training contracts. The work is usually administrative, often helping with discovery in large litigation matters, but paralegals sometimes undertake the same work as trainees. It can be a useful insight into different firms.

Outdoor Clerk

Working as an outdoor clerk is another way of gaining some first-hand legal experience. Tasks usually include delivering documents to court and barristers' chambers, lodging and sealing documents with the appropriate court office, attending hearings before masters on administrative issues and taking notes during proceedings.

Becoming a paralegal or an outdoor clerk can be a back door route to a training contract, although this depends very much on the attitude of the firm. If this is your hope, be sure to research the track record of any firms you apply to.

Voluntary work

Voluntary work in a Citizens Advice Bureau or a Law Centre alongside qualified lawyers, pro-

vides good experience in legal aid work. Legal issues centre on welfare, housing, employment, and crime. Environmental and Civil Rights Groups also welcome volunteers.

The Law Commission

The Law Commission often needs assistants for its research teams which review specific areas of law and make recommendations for law reforms. Most researchers will have completed the LPC, but there are opportunities for law graduates. Contracts typically last a year, but can go on for three.

European Parliament

If you can work in a European language other than English and are interested in EC law, you could do a 'stage' within the European Parliament and Courts of Justice. Such posts offer excellent experience and invariably impress recruiters from Europe-oriented law firms.

For students considering alternative careers:

Legal Executives

One of the obvious alternatives is to become a legal executive for a law firm, for an in-house legal department or for the Civil Service. These positions arise mainly in litigation, conveyancing or probate. Senior legal executives can expect a good level of remuneration, but cannot become a partner in a private practice firm.

Licensed Conveyancing

Licensed conveyancing is another option. You could work as a freelance, or with a local authority, an in-house department or a private practice firm.

Scrivener Notary

If you speak two or more foreign languages, you might consider the specialised role of a scrivener notary, which entails certifying legal documents for use in other jurisdictions. Graduate training includes spending up to a year in a recognised country.

Finance

If you have a head for finance or figures, then accountancy, insurance, banking or financial services might be the most appropriate alternative careers. Accountancy firms are keen to recruit law students as tax specialists, because the skills and knowledge required are similar to those learnt in legal practice. Insurance opportunities include underwriting, claims, pensions, broking and loss adjustment.

The Civil Service

Several departments within the Civil Service have a strong legal flavour and thus suit law graduates. These include Customs and Excise, Immigration and the Inland Revenue. If you have an interest in policy-making and implementation, Civil Service departments such as the Home Office and the Foreign Office merit consideration. There are also usually a small number of vacancies for clerks in the two Houses of Parliament.

Human resources

The role of personnel manager requires a good understanding of employment law issues such as equal opportunities, sexual discrimination and termination conditions. Good administration and communication skills are also needed. Advancement in this field increasingly depends upon formal personnel qualifications.

Administration

Administrative posts, largely concerned with the running and co-ordination of the internal administration of an organisation, require a methodical, efficient approach, and good communication skills. Most opportunities are in the public sector, such as the Civil Service, Local Government, Health Service, or Further and Higher Educational Institutions.

Welfare and Community Work

If working for the community rather than the commercial sector appeals to you, then a career in social work, probation, housing, or welfare advice, could be the answer. All require an understanding of the relevant legal issues. Voluntary work or further training may be needed to break into these fields.

For lawyers considering a career change:

Company secretary

Qualified solicitors are often employed in company secretarial roles. Their job is largely administrative, but they require a sound grounding in company law. The work involves close contact with management, and thus offers scope for diversification later on. There are opportunities to work for companies while simultaneously studying through the Institute of Chartered Secretaries and Administrators.

Legal Recruitment

Legal recruitment is a competitive market these days, but is still potentially lucrative. Contacts within the legal profession are crucial, so solicitors who have practised in more than one firm are often favoured.

Legal publishing

Opportunities for legal publishers and journalists are increasing as the number of legal publications grows. Those considering a career in publishing should have a good general knowledge of the law and a good commercial sense, and journalists should obviously have good writing and communication skills.

Legal Marketing

Legal marketing for law firms or for barristers' chambers is another fast-growing and increasingly sophisticated area. The job involves liaising internally with partners and externally with the press. Although most departmental heads have professional marketing qualifications, many like to have law graduates or qualified lawyers working alongside them.

Teaching Law

Teaching or lecturing law at higher education level is a popular career move for disenchanted solicitors. Some colleges require teaching qualifications as well as legal training, but it is worth approaching individual institutions. The College of Law, for example, employs junior solicitors with no extra qualifications. ∎

change
the way you think about your future

If you think a career in tax outside a law firm is just about numbers and preparing routine tax returns, think again.

The mental stimulation, intellectual challenge and sheer variety of tax work will surprise and impress you.

A career in tax consultancy involves advising clients on how to achieve specific business objectives; offering advice that directly affects their future actions. On very complex areas of the law we will go to seek Counsel's advice – just like solicitors.

Graduates joining the London tax practice this year started on £22,000 plus overtime. In addition to training towards a choice of professional qualifications, our tax practice has its own comprehensive technical and personal development programme. This takes place on an international basis. After qualification, trainees move smoothly into a full time career: no nervous anticipation of "Will I be kept on?".

If you are interested in joining one of our UK tax practices, please send a copy of your CV to:

The Tax Graduate Recruiting Manager
Arthur Andersen
1 Surrey Street
London WC2R 2PS
Tel: 0171 438 3000
http://www.arthurandersen.com

ARTHUR ANDERSEN

Invest in your future

Robson Rhodes is the first national firm of chartered accountants to achieve simultaneous Investors in People accreditation throughout all of its offices. This reflects our commitment to the highest standards of development and training for everyone.

We are equally committed to delivering the highest standards of performance to our clients. Ensuring that you take responsibility for your own development helps us to achieve this.

If you join us as an ACA student in audit, tax or corporate recovery or as a CIPFA student in public sector audit, you will work alongside acknowledged experts in these fields and in corporate finance, forensic accountancy and management consultancy.

Only exceptional people can help us to continue to deliver the best thinking in the profession.

If you think you are up to the challenge, please contact the Graduate Recruitment Manager, Robson Rhodes, 186 City Road, London, EC1V 2NU.

ROBSON RHODES

Chartered Accountants

RSM
international

Specialist Practice Areas

ADMINISTRATIVE & PUBLIC LAW
(including Local Government, Education, Immigration and Civil Liberties)

Area of law

Under this heading we include administrative law in the commercial sector, local government law, education, immigration and civil liberties. All these are separate subjects in their own right, requiring particular skills and personal qualities, but administrative and public law is an important aspect of them all.

Administrative and public law is concerned with the activities of public bodies and, in particular, whether their actions are lawful. It involves central government, local government and other bodies such as the Advertising Standards Authority, the Securities and Investments Board and the Take-Over Panel. Challenging the decisions of public authorities by way of judicial review is an important common thread in education, immigration and civil liberties work. Equally in the commercial sector, greater awareness of what judicial review can achieve and increasing regulation of commercial activity have resulted in more judicial review applications. Lawyers involved in local government work see the other side of the coin – advising public authorities on their powers and defending their decisions.

Administrative Law
in the Commercial Sector

Type of work

Administrative law is an important weapon in the armoury of any commercial entity seeking to maintain a competitive advantage. However, you will not find lawyers in commercial firms who specialise exclusively in administrative law. There are a number, though, who devote a significant amount of time to it, often acting for both applicants and regulators. Peter Watson is a commercial litigator at Allen & Overy and around 25% of his workload is judicial review/administrative law. The firm has a long history of defending the Independent Television

Commission (the regulator of commercial television) against challenges to its decisions – for example it recently successfully defended a claim by the Referendum Party relating to the allocation of party political broadcasts during the 1997 election campaign.

At Herbert Smith, Andrew Lidbetter combines public and administrative law and other contentious regulatory matters with general commercial litigation. A typical day for Lidbetter might involve preparing an affidavit for a court case, advising a client on the rules of natural justice in a disciplinary case, considering a possible challenge to a regulator in the utilities sector, and discussing with the firm's banking section whether a particular transaction is within the powers of a local authority.

Skills needed

"Administrative law is a rapidly evolving subject", says Andrew Lidbetter, "so anyone wanting to specialise in it should have an interest in monitoring legal developments". In the commercial sector, those handling administrative law matters will require general commercial litigation skills. They should possess a good tactical mind and be confident, articulate and persuasive both orally and in writing. They must also be creative, think laterally and be able to appreciate, for example, the potential relevance in a commercial context of a recent case involving immigration or prisoners' rights.

Career options

In a City firm, administrative and public law will probably be a specialist area within the firm's general commercial litigation practice, and prospects are much the same as for commercial litigators. It is rare for a firm with a strong commercial and local government practice to deal with social security, human rights or immigration cases as well. So if you want to specialise in the less commercial side of administrative and public law, you should think about going to a smaller practice which has expertise in these areas. There is more scope at the bar to specialise in "across-the-board" administrative law. Some sets (notably 4–5 Gray's Inn Square and Blackstone Chambers) specialise in administrative law, with barristers handling all types of commercial and non-commercial cases. Making the change from solicitor to barrister is not unknown.

Outside private practice there is little scope to specialise in the commercial side of administrative law.

Local Government

Type of work

Law firms act for local authorities on a whole range of matters, from development and urban regeneration projects to new methods of service delivery through third parties.

Léonie Cowen & Associates, for example, a leading local government firm, recently acted in the transfer of Hounslow's leisure, sports and cultural services to a group of not-for-profit companies. Lawrence Graham have recently advised the London Borough of Enfield on the £200 million regeneration of Edmonton Town Centre.

Other work includes housing stock transfers, advising on local authority finance and vires (powers), and acting in relation to planning appeals and judicial reviews. A typical day for Tony Curnow, head of the Public Sector Group at Ashurst Morris Crisp, might include drafting heads of terms for a local authority regeneration project, meeting with clients to discuss a housing transfer agreement, reviewing a compulsory purchase order case and chasing the Department of Transport for the issue of a draft road closure order.

Skills needed

To succeed as a local government lawyer, says Tony Curnow, you need "an ability to get on with people at all levels, from chief executives to lowly officers". You need to be flexible and modulate your approach depending on who you're dealing with. Furthermore, you need to be politically aware, and understand the relationship between central and local government. A head for statutory interpretation and an ability to master a complex regulatory regime are essential. Self-motivation and a common sense approach are also vital attributes.

Career options

The obvious starting point for someone wishing to specialise in local government law is to apply for a training contract with a local authority legal department. You then have the option to stay at the authority or move into private practice. "Somebody who'd done their training in a local authority, stayed on for a year or so, and then applied to us – would be an attractive package " says Tony Curnow. "They might be more attractive than someone who'd been solely in the private sector, but it depends on the individual."

On the other hand, firms like Nabarros, Eversheds or Ashursts may be able to offer broader commercial experience during training, as well as good quality local government work. A wider range of options may then remain open on qualification. You could continue in a commercial private practice, transfer into more general public law work or move into a local authority.

Salaries are generally higher in private practice, but hours are often longer to match. The good news about local authorities is that pay and conditions are perceived to be improving.

Education

Type of work

Type of work depends on type of client and there are two kinds of client: institutions and individuals. Commercial firms tend to act for institutions including universities, schools, colleges and funding organisations. Smaller, niche firms act for individuals, including pupils and their parents, university students and special needs children.

Advice to institutional clients covers more than just education law. Eversheds for example, advises universities and colleges on employment law, industrial relations, constitutional issues, funding matters, student relations and discipline. At Beachcroft Stanleys, Julian Gizzi was involved in the Dearing Committee inquiry into the running of Further Education colleges and is also involved in funding and franchising issues.

David Ruebain, meanwhile, at David Levene & Co, might spend his morning with the parents of a disabled child trying to sort out funding for transport to school. His afternoon could be spent on the telephone arguing against an examining board on behalf of a special needs pupil. Jack Rabinowicz at Teacher Stern Selby may have to deal with the parents of a child bully one day and the parents of a child who has been bullied the next.

Skills needed

Julian Gizzi emphasises the importance of a commercial outlook when acting for educational institutions. "Universities are businesses like any other business these days. The people we're dealing with have their feet firmly on the ground and expect to receive commercial advice like any other organisation". An aptitude for statutory interpretation is important in the public law side of the work he says, and because education law is a fast changing area, with new legislation every year, "having the self-confidence to stick your neck out and take a view" is vital.

"I don't think there's any point in doing this work if you don't take a rights-based perspective" says David Ruebain of education work for individuals. "And you've got to have decided that earning as much money as possible is not your priority, otherwise you'd be acting for institutions." As for particular skills, it's important to have a head for statute and case law, but "it's not sufficient to have an encyclopaedic knowledge of rules and regulations if you don't have an instinct for when judges will consider certain behaviour unacceptable, even though there isn't a rule that says it's unacceptable". A feel for the way public policy is developing is also important.

Career options

There are a number of opportunities to practice education law outside private practice. Joining a local authority legal department is one obvious option – a significant part of local authority legal work involves educational institutions. There are also posts within the Department for Education, and some universities now have their own legal units.

Immigration

Type of work

There are two types of immigration work: personal and business. Personal immigration work includes political asylum cases, nationality issues, marriage applications and family reunion cases. Much of this work is legally aided and is carried out by small firms. Business or corporate immigration includes advising national and multinational corporations on work permits and investor applications and advising employers on avoiding criminal liability under the Immigration and Asylum Act 1996. Large and medium-sized commercial firms undertake this work.

A typical day, says Peter Alfandary, head of Corporate Immigration at Warner Cranston, might involve advising the English arm of a foreign company wanting to bring staff from New York to work in the UK, drafting an application for a work permit on behalf of a multi-national client, advising a foreign investor on setting up a business in the UK, advising a human resources department on whether a potential employee has a legal right to work in the UK and telephoning the British Embassy in Beijing to sort out entry clearance for the wife of a Chinese executive.

A typical day for personal immigration expert Wesley Gryk could involve encounters with a whole range of clients. He may spend the morning with a lesbian couple advising them on same sex immigration issues, followed by an emergency meeting with a foreign wife abandoned by her husband. The afternoon could involve simple work permit advice to someone who is not likely to have a problem, then more complicated advice to someone who has virtually no right to be in the country and has been 'underground' for twenty years. A junior lawyer's day may be just as varied – they may start the morning filing, but then be sent off on their own for a five hour interview at Gatwick airport or the Home Office, in sole charge of looking after the interests of an asylum seeker.

Skills needed

"Communication skills are of overriding importance" emphasises Peter Alfandary. "They are an absolute prerequisite. There is an enormous amount of client contact and a lot of telephone work and if you can't communicate effectively you won't get past first base". Communicating with senior executives, government departments and embassies requires tact, diplomacy and patience. Good drafting and advocacy skills are also essential if you are to present a convincing case on behalf of your client.

In personal immigration, Wesley Gryk looks for an interest in current affairs and politics, liberalism (with a small 'L'), but also a healthy scepticism. "You're not doing clients any favours by assuming that everything they tell you is true and repeating it verbatim to the Home Office" he says. "In some ways you need to do a tougher cross-examining job than the government to get to the core of their true story so you can present it well to the authorities. It's not good enough to be well-intentioned and to offer a cup of tea and sympathy." Personal immigration lawyers must also be true team players – the offices are often small and busy and there is no standing on ceremony – everyone has to be prepared to chip in.

Career options

Personal immigration, like civil liberties work, doesn't offer the financial rewards enjoyed by those in more commercial disciplines, including those specialising in business immigration. But would-be personal immigration specialists are unlikely to be motivated by financial gain anyway. Alternatives to private practice include working for a Law Centre or bodies such as the UN or the Joint Council for the Welfare of Immigrants. Leading immigration lawyer Alison Stanley, for example, was articled at

Winstanley Burgess, then spent several years as the solicitor to the JWCI before returning to private practice with Bindman & Partners. It is also possible to come to this type of work from a more commercial background. Wesley Gryk began his career as a corporate lawyer with large US firm Shearman & Sterling.

Civil Liberties

Type of work

Civil liberties is a broad concept covering suspected miscarriages of justice, actions against the police, prisoners' rights, public order, discrimination and free speech issues. Redress will often be sought by way of judicial review. There is considerable cross-over between civil liberties work and other areas such as crime and immigration.

At Bindman & Partners, Stephen Grosz's work is characterised by its variety. A morning's work might include studying a European directive on freedom of access to information on the environment, advising a client on a school closure, meeting a student who failed exams because of insufficient provision for dyslexia, and considering new instructions from a homosexual naval officer.

Skills needed

An imaginative legal mind, an ability to adapt to different areas of law and an interest in using the law creatively and strategically are all important qualities in a civil liberties lawyer, according to Stephen Grosz. "You need to try and push back the boundaries, and if you're working with campaigning organisations, as you frequently are, you have to understand their needs and priorities." Grosz also looks for a sympathetic and understanding nature and a broad world view, as opposed to a narrow legalistic outlook.

Career options

As with immigration work, a career as a civil liberties lawyer is unlikely to be lucrative. Law Centres, campaigning groups and voluntary organisations (such as Liberty, Justice, The

Public Law Project, Child Poverty Action Group and Amnesty International) offer alternatives to private practice.

The Firms

There isn't really a 'market' in administrative and public law work, as opposed to, say, local government law work. Firms handling administrative and public law matters normally specialise in either applicant or respondent work, but rarely handle both. Exceptions to this rule are Bindman & Partners and Bates Wells & Braithwaite, both London based.

Commercial sector

Few firms outside London handle this type of work. Herbert Smith and Allen & Overy, already mentioned above, are the leading practices. Clifford Chance has a good reputation for judicial review and advisory work in the commercial sphere, particularly media, sports, and regulatory/financial services disciplinary cases. Also strong in this area is Lovell White Durrant, whose recent work has included *British Steel plc* v *Commissioners for Customs & Excise*, a Court of Appeal challenge to the rule of procedural exclusivity. Originally seen as an applicant firm with a reputation for freedom of information and immigration cases, Bates Wells & Braithwaite increasingly acts for respondents in more commercial cases (ICSTIS, the premium rate telephone service regulator, for example).

Central and Local Government

Sharpe Pritchard act as agents for numerous respondent local authorities in judicial reviews, statutory and planning appeals. TV Edwards, by contrast, handle a large number of community care and mental health cases involving judicial review of the policies of local authorities. Nabarro Nathanson have the biggest local authority practice in London, advising over 120 local authority clients on a range of matters. The firm was recently involved in the first PFI (Private Finance Initiative) schools project and advised Bournemouth City Council on the first PFI library project. (For further details on PFI projects see the Projects section).

From their offices in Leeds and Manchester, Eversheds dominate local government work in the North, and PFI work in particular, having acted in the first four local goverment PFI deals to reach financial close. In the Midlands Pinsent Curtis have a strong team of 12 local government lawyers. The firm recently acted for seven West Midlands councils on the £150m refinancing of Birmingham International Airport. Their main rivals in the region, Dibb Lupton Alsop, recently advised Malvern Hills District Council on the establishment of the Malvern Hills Science Park.

Education

The firms handling education work divide into those which act for individuals, and those which represent institutions.

On the institutional side, Eversheds London office has a substantial practice focused on further and higher education. Also strong are Beachcroft Stanleys, who offer a one-stop-shop service to universities in alliance with Price WaterhouseCoopers.

Outside London, Veale Wasbrough (Bristol) have a sizeable education unit, and the largest national practice acting for independent schools. Martineau Johnson (Birmingham) act for grant-maintained schools and new universities in matters involving academic performance and disciplinary procedures. Their clients include the universities of Birmingham, Coventry and Warwick.

Of the firms acting for individuals Teacher Stern & Selby have a particularly good reputation and have been involved in a number of cutting edge cases. David Levene & Co are well known for disability and special needs work.

Regional firms which act for individuals in education matters include Young & Lee in Birmingham, Hunt & Coombs in Peterborough and Hugh James in Cardiff.

Immigration

Several of the large London firms have sizeable business immigration practices, notably Cameron

McKenna (2 partners, 11 assistants) and Simmons & Simmons (1 partner, 6 assistants). Other top firms include Kingsley Napley, who act for a number of clients in the hotel and catering industry, entertainers and sports people, and Warner Cranston, whose clients include Hitachi, TI Group and Courtaulds.

Winstanley Burgess have a longstanding reputation for their personal immigration work, which includes frequent judicial review actions. The firm's recent work includes representation of Czech Romany asylum seekers and the *Radiom* ECJ case (national security and EC nationals). Wesley Gryk and his firm also have excellent reputations, especially for gay rights cases and refugee law. Notable firms outside London include Darbys in Oxford, known for political asylum, family reunion, same sex cases and judicial review, and David Gray & Co in Newcastle, with a reputation for political asylum and refugee law, family settlement, student work and nationality law.

Linnells in Oxford, Trethowan Woodford in Southampton and Davis Blank Furniss in Manchester are all firms with well regarded personal and business immigration practices.

Civil Liberties

Bindman & Partners and B.M. Birnberg & Co are the outstanding London firms for civil liberties work. Bindmans' ongoing work includes the ban on gays in the armed forces and the Hanratty and Silcott miscarriage of justice cases. Birnbergs are also highly rated for miscarriage of justice and death in custody cases.

Tyndallwoods are widely acknowledged as the leading players in the Midlands. The firm's recent work has included cases concerning transsexuals in the police and the liability of the DSS to damages for breach of statutory duty after failing to pay benefits on time. AS Law of Liverpool is the leading firm in the north, specialising in prisoners' rights cases, particularly those serving life sentences.

Leading Firms

London Firms	Admin. & Public Law	Civil Liberties	Education	Immigration & Nationality	Local Govt.
Allen & Overy	****				
Anthony Gold	**				
Ashurst Morris Crisp					****
B.M. Birnberg & Co		******		******	
Baker & McKenzie				***	
Barnett Alexander Chart					***
Barnett Sampson	*				
Bartram & Co, Hounslow				*****	
Bates, Wells & Braithwaite	****			*****	
Beachcroft Stanleys			*****		
Berwin Leighton					*****
Bindman & Partners	******	******	*****	******	
Cameron McKenna	*			******	
Campbell Hooper				***	
Christian Fisher		***			
Clifford Chance	***				***
D J Freeman					***

Firms and their star ratings are based on Chambers' Directory 1998–1999. Six stars represent a top-ranked firm, five stars a second-ranked firm, etc. See page 3 for further details.

BANKING
(including Capital Markets & Derivatives)

Area of law
Banking as an area of law is really the practice of commercial law for the banking and financial industry. It is about finance in its broadest sense, from loans, bonds, swaps and derivatives, through to regulation. In private practice, being a banking lawyer means giving advice to lenders and borrowers. It also means being a deal maker, preparing the documentation and understanding the regulations that lie behind a deal. Deals vary depending on the type of bank, and the complexity of the transaction. International merchant banks, for example, use sophisticated City firms, whereas the retail banks will also be able to use provincial firms. There is also a strong regulatory side to the business which, with the formation of new banks, is increasing in importance every year.

Type of work
Banking work varies from firm to firm reflecting a market that is polarised and dynamic. It is essentially concentrated in the hands of the City firms, due to their expertise, client connections and international networks. Outside London the number of firms doing complex transactions is limited, with the notable exception of some national firms such as Dibb Lupton Alsop.

In the largest leading firms in London – Allen & Overy and Clifford Chance – banking work is cutting edge. The deals are vast in terms of value and complexity, and lawyers in these two firms often devise precedents and techniques that are used by other firms. Deals are international and are often allied to the capital markets and the projects market. At the international finance end of the scale the work is varied – different countries, different structures, different law in some cases. Being a linguist at this end of the market is an asset.

Allen & Overy's banking department numbers over 200 lawyers worldwide. The large teams involved in their deals can mean that trainees

and junior lawyers rarely see the client; however the technical skills acquired will be of the highest calibre. Working in teams, whatever the size, is an important feature of transactions. At the large firms part of the buzz comes from working on deals that are worth unimaginable sums of money – such as arranging $10.2 billion of debt for ICI when they decided to buy Unilever's chemicals business. A mistake on a deal of this size can be worth millions – which all adds to the stimulation and adrenalin kick.

Doing the deal is the heart of banking work, for both large and small firms. "Having sweated blood for what could be months, pulling the final thing together and seeing the loan signed, that's the real buzz," says Geoffrey Wynne of Denton Hall. Although considerably smaller than some of the other City firms, Denton Hall's banking department acts for banks and borrowers in all areas of practice from regulation to securitised financings.

Much is made of the glamour attached to being a banking lawyer. High finance deals are international, involving intense client contact. This can mean a lot of travelling, centred around fast-paced deals. Time spent on planes is critical for preparing for meetings or for catching up on nights of lost sleep. Geoffrey Wynne has recently been doing "hellish amounts" of travelling. One fortnight saw him fly from London to Zurich to West Africa and back again; the next week, he was in Latin America! "If clients are prepared to travel, they expect the lawyer to travel." But he would warn anyone against thinking it glamorous.

Technical skills, as for other areas, are important. Putting together the documents can be boring especially if you are reviewing other people's documents. However, most banking lawyers will say that as no deal is ever the same, neither are the documents. "You get to love a document because it lives and breathes and you've perhaps fought over many of its words," comments

Geoffrey Wynne, "You can spend hours taking it apart and putting it back together again."

At Clifford Chance technical drafting skills are important but the firm puts as much emphasis on client handling, team management, communication and writing skills. The amount of drafting a Clifford Chance lawyer will do varies, depending on the area. For example, in the fixed income area, the work may be more project management, making sure the listings are in place, and making sure all the paperwork is signed. "It's a great big organisational job," says Chris Bates at Clifford Chance. On the other hand, "If you're working on a structured finance matter, you might be allocated one piece of the contract which requires extensive original drafting." Working on an advisory project will involve little drafting but a lot of synthesising opinions from counsel, gathering information, chasing people up and getting the advice together in a suitable form for the client.

Regulations form the other side of banking law. Lawyers specialising in this work are similar to company tax advisors. They need to be able to interpret the regulations in a manner favourable to their client. Regulatory lawyers may not receive or desire the buzz of doing the deal, but their role is key to the transaction.

Skills needed

Banking lawyers need to understand and enjoy finance and business. Without an interest in these areas, the work is difficult and boring. They also need to understand their clients' business needs. The ever-changing ways of raising capital mean that lawyers have to acquire new knowledge all the time and keep up-to-date with high finance in order to move effectively with the market.

The deal makers in this field were described by one practitioner as 'deal-junkies', who thrive on the mentally and physically demanding nature of high-profile, complex deals. These lawyers are generally outgoing and dynamic, with plenty of stamina, often reflecting the bankers themselves.

Regulatory lawyers require different skills – they are generally superb technicians with a fine attention to detail and a head for figures and rules.

Career options

Becoming a banking lawyer enables you to move into related financial areas such as project, asset or acquisition finance. There are also opportunities to move in-house. Most major banks have in-house legal departments and compliance departments which employ lawyers with corporate and banking backgrounds. Some lawyers move out of their legal role and become bankers or financial analysts themselves. A recent major move was that of Robert Palache. He headed the Capital Markets Group at Clifford Chance, but recently announced his decision to move away from the law altogether to become a deal maker at Nomura Bank. Remuneration in any of these areas is high.

The Firms

There is no such thing as a 'banking' firm *per se*. Two City firms, Allen & Overy and Clifford Chance, stand out ahead of the other firms in the sophistication and size of their banking practices. For these firms, banking work is the engine driving their international expansion. Clifford Chance is a global law firm with offices all over the world. A banking lawyer here would have the opportunity to be involved in multinational deals from Vietnam to Moscow. Allen & Overy does not have as many offices worldwide, but lawyers here work on cutting edge deals involving all the latest financing techniques. The banking departments in both firms are impressive: Clifford Chance fields 60 partners and 250 assistants worldwide and Allen & Overy has 43 partners and 200 assistants.

There are other City firms which also have highly developed banking practices. Freshfields, for example, has a long history of acting for the Bank of England. Its work is therefore often skewed to the regulatory or litigious aspects of the business, although it does also work on large deals. Other notable City firms include Linklaters who have a strong reputation acting for banks and companies, and Lovell White Durrant who do a lot of work for Barclays.

A recent development in the City has been the advent of the American firms who are rapidly developing their banking practices. Shearman & Sterling have recently recruited much of the former Ashurst Morris Crisp banking practice, and now have a sizeable team handling cross-border European and transatlantic deals.

As expected, the cutting edge banking work is handled by the City firms. However, most of the large commercial regional firms also have banking practices. Much of their work is centred around acting for the major clearing banks, although in the main commercial centres such as Leeds, firms also handle considerable deals.

Key firms include Osborne Clarke in Bristol who handle work for Nat West and were appointed to the panel of 3i in 1997. Their team compared to the large City firms is small – one partner and three assistants but all are pure transactional lawyers and work full time on deals. In the north, Addleshaw Booth & Co are the leading banking firm with offices in Manchester and Leeds. They have a good reputation acting for lenders and in the equity market.

Leading Firms

London Firms	Banking	Capital Markets & Derivatives
Allen & Overy	★★★★★★	★★★★★★
Ashurst Morris Crisp	★★★★	★★★
Baker & McKenzie	★	★★
Berwin Leighton	★	★★
Cameron McKenna	★★★	
Cleary, Gottlieb, Steen & Hamilton		★★★★★★
Clifford Chance	★★★★★★	★★★★★★
Cravath, Swaine & Moore		★★★★★★
Davis Polk & Wardwell		★★★
Denton Hall	★★	
Dibb Lupton Alsop	★★	
Dundas & Wilson CS/Garretts	★★	
Field Fisher Waterhouse	★	
Freshfields	★★★★★	★★★★★★
Gouldens	★★	
Herbert Smith	★★★	★★★
Linklaters	★★★★★	★★★★★★
Lovell White Durrant	★★★★★	★★★★★
Macfarlanes	★★	
Nabarro Nathanson	★	
Norton Rose	★★★★★	★★★
Shearman & Sterling		★★★★★★
Sidley & Austin		★★★
Simmons & Simmons	★★	★★★★★
Simpson Thatcher & Bartlett		★★★★★★
Slaughter and May	★★★★	★★★★★
Stephenson Harwood	★★	

Firms and their star ratings are based on Chambers' Directory 1998–1999. Six stars represent a top-ranked firm, five stars a second-ranked firm, etc. See page 3 for further details.

Leading Firms

London Firms (cont.)	Banking	Capital Markets & Derivatives
Sullivan & Cromwell		★★★★★★
Taylor Joynson Garrett	★★	
Theodore Goddard	★★	
Travers Smith Braithwaite	★★	
Watson, Farley & Williams	★	
Weil, Gotshal & Manges	★★	★★★
Wilde Sapte	★★★★	
Withers	★	

Leading Firms

Regional Firms – Banking

Firm	Rating	Firm	Rating
Addleshaw Booth & Co, *Leeds*	★★★★★★	Garretts, *Manchester*	★★★★★★
Addleshaw Booth & Co, *Manchester*	★★★★★★	Gateley Wareing, *Birmingham*	★★★
Bevan Ashford, *Exeter*	★★★	Halliwell Landau, *Manchester*	★★★★★
Bond Pearce, *Plymouth*	★★★★★	Hammond Suddards, *Leeds*	★★★★★
Burges Salmon, *Bristol*	★★★★★	Hammond Suddards, *Manchester*	★★★★
Cameron McKenna, *Bristol*	★	Leathes Prior, *Norwich*	★★★★
Chaffe Street, *Manchester*	★★★★	Lester Aldridge, *Bournemouth*	★★★★
Cobbetts, *Manchester*	★★	Lyons Davidson, *Bristol*	★
Davies Wallis Foyster, *Manchester*	★	Martineau Johnson, *Birmingham*	★★★
Dibb Lupton Alsop, *Birmingham*	★★	Mills & Reeve, *Cambridge*	★★★★★
Dibb Lupton Alsop, *Leeds*	★★★★	Mills & Reeve, *Norwich*	★★★★★
Dibb Lupton Alsop, *Liverpool*	★★★★★★	Morgan Bruce, *Cardiff*	★★★★
Dibb Lupton Alsop, *Manchester*	★★★★★★	Osborne Clarke, *Bristol*	★★★★★★
Dickinson Dees, *Newcastle-upon-Tyne*	★★★★	Pinsent Curtis, *Birmingham*	★★★★★
Edge Ellison, *Birmingham*	★★★★	Pinsent Curtis, *Leeds*	★★★★★
Edwards Geldard, *Cardiff*	★★★	Robert Muckle, *Newcastle-upon-Tyne*	★★
Eversheds, *Birmingham*	★★★★	Shoosmiths & Harrison, *Northampton*	★★
Eversheds, *Cardiff*	★★★★★	Slater Heelis, *Manchester*	★★★★
Eversheds, *Leeds*	★★★★★	Stephens & Scown, *Exeter*	★
Eversheds, *Manchester*	★★★★★★	Walker Morris, *Leeds*	★★★★
Eversheds, *Newcastle-upon-Tyne*	★★	Ward Hadaway, *Newcastle-upon-Tyne*	★★
Eversheds, *Norwich*	★★★★★	Wragge & Co, *Birmingham*	★★★★★
Garretts, *Leeds*	★★★★		

Firms and their star ratings are based on Chambers' Directory 1998–1999. Six stars represent a top-ranked firm, five stars a second-ranked firm, etc. See page 3 for further details.

CORPORATE FINANCE / COMPANY

Area of law

All commercial law firms are keen to be involved in corporate work. Transactions in this area command large fees and receive coverage in the national and regional press. Experienced corporate lawyers are much in demand and are among the highest paid in the profession earning in some instances six figure salaries.

Corporate work relates primarily to company mergers and acquisitions (M&A) or the financing of companies. Companies wishing to acquire other businesses often need to raise finance by floating on the Stock Exchange, selling new shares or arranging loans from banks. Other areas of corporate practice are joint ventures and management buy-outs. Joint ventures are where two or more companies collaborate together (often through a new company) for a specific purpose, such as the agreement between the Bank of Scotland and Sainsbury's to set up Sainsbury's bank. A management buy-out (MBO) is where a company agrees to sell part of itself to a team of managers such as the recent MBO of Soda Stream from Cadbury Schweppes who decided they no longer wanted to pursue the soda business.

Type of work

Corporate work depends on the size and location of the firm. Large City firms act for listed companies on the Stock Exchange, and deal with household names such as BT, Guinness and Grand Metropolitan. For example, top City firms Slaughter and May, Linklaters and Freshfields act for the majority of the FTSE 100 companies. Smaller City and regional firms tend to advise leading regional private companies.

The distinction between stock exchange and private company work is more than just the size of the company. Private companies' M&A work tends to be consensual because the deal can only proceed if all parties agree to it, whereas stock market companies can be subject to hostile takeovers.

Lawyers advising on private company acquisitions will draft the sale and purchase agreements, help arrange the financing for the deal and carry out a process known as 'due diligence.' The sale, purchase and financing negotiations are usually carried out between company executives and lawyers. Trainees are not expected to take a lead role in negotiating the agreement, although they may be asked to prepare the first draft, participate in due diligence and attend meetings. A private company sale takes about a month to complete.

Trainees and students on work experience inevitably get involved in the due diligence – a time consuming process but necessary to ensure equality of information between a purchaser (known as a bidder) and a company being purchased (known as a target). If a target claims to be the largest widget manufacturer in the country, then it could be the trainee's job to check this is true. Trainees may also be expected to help check that the target is not involved in outstanding litigation and does not have damaging 'change of control' clauses, which could harm profitability after a take over.

Stock exchange deals are different. Private companies have few shareholders (owners). Stock Exchange registered companies can have millions. This makes them vulnerable to hostile takeover bids from rival companies who can buy shares and thereby obtain a controlling stake.

To help public companies combat this threat, the Stock Exchange has developed a detailed takeover code to govern both friendly and hostile M&A activity. The code sets a strict timetable for companies to make and respond to potential bidders and sets out detailed guidelines for the treatment of shareholders. Lawyers advising these companies know this code inside out, and will explain what company directors should be doing at every stage of a potential acquisition.

Skills needed

Corporate work is not for the faint-hearted. Clients are willing to pay premium rates to have transactions completed quickly and the takeover code lays down strict timetables for the completion of deals involving major plcs. Lawyers involved in M&A or hostile takeovers can find themselves attending news conferences and being quoted in daily newspapers. Freshfields, for example, is advising Manchester United in its proposed merger with BSkyB. But this high-profile work does come at a price. Evening, weekend and even overnight work is common, and corporate lawyers routinely work from eight in the morning to eight at night. By way of compensation, five year qualified corporate lawyers in City firms earn up to £80,000 per year, and corporate partners at these firms can earn more than £500,0000.

The hours a trainee is expected to work depends on the type of deal and the individual managers. One assistant from a midlands firm described her supervising partner as a 'workaholic' who expected her to work the same hours as him, whereas a partner in a medium-sized London firm said trainees could expect to work an average of five-and-a-half days a week. Tales of assistants collapsing at four in the morning after working three twenty-hour days in a row may be unusual, but should not be dismissed out of hand. Some firms offer their lawyers a 'shirt allowance', so they can buy a new shirt after an 'all-nighter' and continue work the next day without a break.

Because corporate work is often a whole new world for trainees, they can find it takes time to adjust. But Mark Rawlinson, corporate partner with Freshfields would urge trainees not to be put off in their first few months. "I found my first six months in the corporate department really difficult", says Rawlinson. "But a senior property lawyer who had been a captain in the marines said to me that I'd make a good corporate lawyer, so I went back and tried it again. After the first 18 months, it began to get more interesting. The trouble is as a trainee everything moves at 100mph and there's such a lot to take in. That said, law school training is now much more City-geared. Before I started, I'd never heard of the City Code or the Yellow Book, but nowadays trainees seem better prepared."

Many corporate lawyers find they get a 'buzz' out of their work. Nigel Boardman, who heads the corporate department at top City law firm Slaughter and May, admits corporate lawyers tend to have a 'macho' attitude. "If you enjoy seeing the deals you do in the newspapers and meeting high quality, high profile people on deals where there's a lot of money at stake – then you'll enjoy corporate law." Mark Rawlinson agrees. "In your early 20s you are meeting all sorts of people who are headline news – and in your early 30s you can be a partner advising them. It's demanding, but enjoyable."

Boardman also comments: "You spend much of your time in meetings, so you need good presentation skills. You must be able to think on your feet, make a decision and justify it. This could include telling a government minister or company director that they don't have the power to do what they want to do. You need to have confidence, tact and clear communication skills to say no to Robert Maxwell at two in the morning."

Many of the leading corporate lawyers in the City have firm views about the sort of trainees they want to recruit. Topping all their lists is strength of personality and backbone. Guy Beringer, head of corporate at Allen & Overy tends to prefer people who have not done law as their first degree, but acknowledges that the pressures are more intense on graduates to evince a focus on law from the beginning. "I look for people out of the stereotypical mould who have had to demonstrate themselves in a way that maybe others haven't, people who have been tested in some way." Anthony Salz, senior partner of Freshfields, looks for curiosity, "It's a good originating instinct," he says. "I like people who are interested in how and why things work, such as the inter-relationship between law and business and what clients want to achieve."

Career options

A sound grounding in corporate finance makes an excellent springboard for working in industry.

Many lawyers move in-house to major companies in the early years post qualification, tempted by salaries comparable with private practice or better (at that stage), but with more predictable hours. Moves in-house do occur at partner level, but they are less common.

Another popular move among young corporate finance lawyers is to join the banking world, either as an in-house lawyer or as a corporate finance executive or analyst. This is a chance to move from 'lawyer' to 'client'. Those who have made the transition seem to enjoy the dynamic pace of life and are glad to have shed the advisory role. Such moves generally occur early on, but there are notable exceptions every year. The head of corporate at Clifford Chance, Peter Brooks, has recently moved to Deutsche Bank as a deal maker, showing that it is never too late to make the move.

Becoming a company secretary and advising board members on their internal legal compliance procedures is an alternative route. This position is suitable for senior lawyers with a general range of company and commercial skills and salaries can be in excess of £100,000.

Although an in-house career is increasingly common for corporate lawyers, the majority of lawyers are happy working in private practice. Mark Rawlinson joined Freshfields in 1982 as an articled clerk, qualified in 1984, became a partner in 1990 and has never worked for anyone else. If you enjoy corporate work, it seems you get reluctant to leave the lifestyle behind. "It's demanding," says Mark Rawlinson, "but enjoyable. There are personal sacrifices, but balances can be achieved."

The Firms

As you might expect corporate finance work is dominated by City firms such as Freshfields, Linklaters and Slaughter and May. These three firms – sometimes referred to as the 'Magic Circle' – act for most of the major corporates and have the largest departments in the country – Freshfields has 40 partners and 96 assistants and Linklaters numbers 60 partners and 199 assistants. Sixty per cent of Slaughter and May's

whole practice is corporate. The top firms will be involved in most of the major business transactions that go on in the UK. For example, six out of the top ten largest firms in London were involved in the £5 billion deal to form Cable & Wireless Communications.

Medium sized City firms such as Macfarlanes and Travers Smith Braithwaite act for major corporates but as secondary advisers, although they are also involved in transactions for medium-sized companies. Travers Smith, for example, will handle deals in new markets such as the flotation of Esprit Telecom on the new European IT stock exchange EASDAQ. Other firms in this size band such as Berwin Leighton will act for clients such as fashion retailer Monsoon plc.

Most City firms, regardless of size, do corporate work of some form. Smaller firms such as Lewis Silkin and Warner Cranston also handle corporate transactions The former acted for Abbott Mead Vickers on a series of six acquisitions worth £26million. The numbers are smaller but the work is as interesting and the scope for involvement as a trainee can be higher. Even a reasonably small West End media firm such as Olswang gets involved in high profile corporate work such as acting for Chris Evans in the £81m Virgin Radio deal. Firms at this end of the market may also handle more AIM (Alternative Investment Market) flotations.

Corporate work in the regions varies in quality and intensity. The major commercial centres such as the midlands and the north west have a concentration of sophisticated firms involved in this type of work. Examples are Wragge & Co in Birmingham and Addleshaw Booth & Co in Manchester and Leeds. Both have sizeable corporate departments – Wragges have 13 partners and 24 assistants and Addleshaw Booth & Co have 16 corporate partners and 30 assistants in Manchester alone. Their client lists are also impressive including such companies as AT&T, Cadbury Schweppes and AMEC.

Most commercial firms around the country will have some corporate capability, although the complexity and size of the work is smaller. Corporate transactional work is generally still seen as the preserve of the 'City' firms, although regional firms will be able to handle routine acquisitions and disposals for their larger clients.

Leading firms

London Firms	Number of Fee-earners		
	250+	125–250	1–125
Allen & Overy	★★★★★		
Allison & Humphreys			★
Ashurst Morris Crisp	★★★★★		
Baker & McKenzie		★★★★★	
Barnett Alexander Chart			★
Beachcroft Stanleys		★★	
S J Berwin & Co		★★★★★	
Berwin Leighton		★★★★★	
Biddle			★★
Bird & Bird			★★
Cameron McKenna	★★★		
Charles Russell			★
Clifford Chance	★★★★★		
Clyde & Co		★★	
Coudert Brothers			★
Davies Arnold Cooper		★★	
Denton Hall	★★★		
Dibb Lupton Alsop		★★★	
D J Freeman		★★	
Eversheds		★★★	
Field Fisher Waterhouse		★★★	
Forsyte Saunders Kerman			★
Fox Williams			★★★★★★
Frere Cholmeley Bischoff		★★★★	
Freshfields	★★★★★★		
Gouldens		★★★★★	
Hammond Suddards			★★★★★★
Harbottle & Lewis			★★
Herbert Smith	★★★★★		
Hobson Audley Hopkins & Wood			★★
Howard Kennedy			★★★
Lawrence Graham		★★★	
Laytons			★
Lewis Silkin			★★★
Linklaters	★★★★★★		
Lovell White Durrant	★★★★		
Macfarlanes		★★★★★★	
Manches & Co			★
Marriott Harrison			★★

Firms and their star ratings are based on Chambers' Directory 1998–1999. Six stars represent a top-ranked firm, five stars a second-ranked firm, etc. See page 3 for further details.

Leading firms

London Firms (cont.)	Number of Fee-earners		
	250+	125–250	1–125
Memery Crystal			★★★
Middleton Potts			★
Nabarro Nathanson	★★		
Nicholson Graham & Jones		★★★	
Norton Rose	★★★★		
Olswang			★★★★★★
Osborne Clarke			★★★
Paisner & Co			★★★★★
Pinsent Curtis			★★★★★
Radcliffes Crossman Block		★★	
Rakisons			★
Richards Butler		★★★★★	
Rowe & Maw		★★★★★	
Simmons & Simmons	★★★★		
Sinclair Roche & Temperley		★★	
Slaughter and May	★★★★★★		
Speechly Bircham		★★★	
Stephenson Harwood		★★★★	
Taylor Joynson Garrett		★★★★	
Theodore Goddard		★★★★	
Titmuss Sainer Dechert		★★★★	
Travers Smith Braithwaite		★★★★★★	
Warner Cranston			★★★★★
Watson, Farley & Williams		★★★	
Wedlake Bell			★
Wilde Sapte	★		

Leading Firms

Regional Firms

Aaron & Partners, *Chester*	★★	Berry Smith, *Cardiff*	★★★★
Addleshaw Booth & Co, *Leeds*	★★★★★★	Berrymans Lace Mawer, *Liverpool*	★★
Addleshaw Booth & Co, *Manchester*	★★★★★★	Bevan Ashford, *Bristol*	★★★★
Andrew M. Jackson & Co, *Hull*	★★	Birketts, *Ipswich*	★★★
Archers, *Stockton-on-Tees*	★	Blake Lapthorn, *Fareham*	★★★
Attey Bower & Jones, *Doncaster*	★	Bond Pearce, *Exeter*	★★★★★
B.P. Collins & Co, *Gerrards Cross*	★★	Bond Pearce, *Plymouth*	★★★★★
Band Hatton, *Coventry*	★	Bond Pearce, *Southampton*	★★★
Barker, Booth & Eastwood, *Blackpool*	★★	Boyce Hatton, *Torquay*	★
Beor Wilson & Lloyd, *Swansea*	★★	Brabner Holden Banks Wilson, *Liverpool*	★★
Bermans, *Liverpool*	★★★★	Bremner Sons & Corlett, *Liverpool*	★★

Leading Firms

Regional Firms (cont.)

Firm	Rating
Bretherton Price Elgoods, *Cheltenham*	★
BrookStreet Des Roches, *Witney*	★★
Bullivant Jones & Co, *Liverpool*	★★★★★
Burges Salmon, *Bristol*	★★★★★★
Cartwrights, *Bristol*	★★
Chaffe Street, *Manchester*	★★
Charles Russell, *Cheltenham*	★
Clarke Willmott & Clarke, *Taunton*	★★★★
Clarks, *Reading*	★★
Cobbetts, *Manchester*	★★★★★★
Coffin Mew & Clover, *Portsmouth*	★
Cole & Cole, *Oxford*	★
Colemans, *Maidenhead*	★
Crawford Owen, *Bristol*	★★★★
Cripps Harries Hall, *Tunbridge Wells*	★★
Cuff Roberts, *Liverpool*	★★★★
Davies and Partners, *Gloucester*	★★
Davies Wallis Foyster, *Liverpool*	★★★★★
Dean Wilson, *Brighton*	★
Denison Till, *Leeds*	★
Denton Hall, *Milton Keynes*	★★★
Dibb Lupton Alsop, *Birmingham*	★★
Dibb Lupton Alsop, *Leeds*	★★★★★
Dibb Lupton Alsop, *Liverpool*	★★★★★★
Dickinson Dees, *Newcastle-upon-Tyne*	★★★★★
Dolmans, *Cardiff*	★
Donne Mileham & Haddock, *Brighton*	★★★
Edge Ellison, *Birmingham*	★★★★
Edwards Geldard, *Cardiff*	★★★★★★
Elliott & Company, *Manchester*	★★
Ellison & Co, *Colchester*	★
Eversheds, *Birmingham*	★★★★★
Eversheds, *Bristol*	★
Eversheds, *Cardiff*	★★★★★★
Eversheds, *Leeds*	★★★★★
Eversheds, *Manchester*	★★★★★★
Eversheds, *Newcastle-upon-Tyne*	★★★
Eversheds, *Norwich*	★★★★
Few & Kester, *Cambridge*	★★
Field Cunningham & Co, *Manchester*	★★★★★
Foot & Bowden, *Plymouth*	★
Freeth Cartwright, *Nottingham*	★
Garretts, *Leeds*	★★★
Gordons Wright & Wright, *Bradford*	★★
Gorna & Co, *Manchester*	★★
Gosschalks, *Hull*	★★★
Gotelee & Goldsmith, *Ipswich*	★★
Greenland Houchen, *Norwich*	★★
Greenwoods, *Peterborough*	★★
H. Montlake & Co, *Ilford*	★★★
Halliwell Landau, *Manchester*	★★★★★★
Hammond Suddards, *Leeds*	★★★
Hammond Suddards, *Manchester*	★★★★
Hancock & Lawrence, *Truro*	★
Harold Benjamin & Collins, *Harrow*	★★
Harvey Ingram Owston, *Leicester*	★
Hawkins Russell Jones, *Hitchin*	★
Hewitson Becke + Shaw, *Cambridge*	★★★
Hewitson Becke + Shaw, *Northampton*	★★
Higgs & Sons, *Brierley Hill*	★★
Hill Dickinson, *Liverpool*	★★★
Hugh James, *Cardiff*	★★★★
Irwin Mitchell, *Sheffield*	★★★
Jacksons, *Stockton-on-Tees*	★★
Jones Maidment Wilson, *Manchester*	★★★
Kenneth Elliott & Rowe, *Romford*	★★★
Kitsons, *Torquay*	★
Knight & Sons, *Newcastle-under-Lyme*	★★
Kuit Steinart Levy, *Manchester*	★★
Laceys, *Bournemouth*	★
Lawrence Tucketts, *Bristol*	★★
Laytons, *Hampton Court*	★
Leathes Prior, *Norwich*	★★
Lee Crowder, *Birmingham*	★★
Lester Aldridge, *Bournemouth*	★★
Linnells, *Oxford*	★★
Lyons Davidson, *Bristol*	★★★
Manby & Steward, *Wolverhampton*	★★
Martineau Johnson, *Birmingham*	★★★
McGuinness Finch, *Leeds*	★★
Michelmores, *Exeter*	★★★★
Mills & Reeve, *Norwich*	★★★★
Moore & Blatch, *Southampton*	★
Morgan Bruce, *Cardiff*	★★★★★
Morgan Bruce, *Swansea*	★★★★★
Nabarro Nathanson, *Sheffield*	★★★
Napthen Houghton Craven, *Preston*	★★★
Needham & James, *Stratford upon Avon*	★★
Osborne Clarke, *Bristol*	★★★★★
Oxley & Coward, *Rotherham*	★

Leading Firms

Regional Firms (cont.)

Palser Grossman, *Cardiff Bay*	★★★		Thomas Eggar, *Chichester*	★★★
Pannone & Partners, *Manchester*	★★		Thomas Eggar, *Horsham*	★★★
Paris Smith & Randall, *Southampton*	★★★		Thomas Eggar, *Reigate*	★★★
Penningtons, *Basingstoke*	★		Thomas Eggar, *Worthing*	★★★
Pictons, *St. Albans*	★		Thomson Snell & P, *Tunbridge Wells*	★★
Pinsent Curtis, *Birmingham*	★★★★		Tolhurst Fisher, *Chelmsford*	★
Pinsent Curtis, *Leeds*	★★★★		Tolhurst Fisher, *Southend-on-Sea*	★
Pitmans, *Reading*	★★		Townsends, *Swindon*	★
Porter Dodson, *Yeovil*	★		Trethowan Woodford, *Salisbury*	★
Prettys, *Ipswich*	★★		Trumps, *Bristol*	★★
Rawlison & Butler, *Crawley*	★★		Veale Wasbrough, *Bristol*	★★★★★
Read Hind Stewart, *Leeds*	★★★		Walker Morris, *Leeds*	★★★★★
Rickerby Watterson, *Cheltenham*	★		Walker Smith & Way, *Chester*	★★
Robert Muckle, *Newcastle-upon-Tyne*	★★		Wansbroughs, *Bristol*	★★★
Robertsons, *Cardiff*	★★		Wansbroughs, *Manchester*	★★★★★
Rollit Farrell & Bladon, *Hull*	★★		Ward Hadaway, *Newcastle-upon-Tyne*	★★
Sherwin Oliver, *Portsmouth*	★★		Watson Burton, *Newcastle-upon-Tyne*	★★
Shoosmiths & Harrison, *Northampton*	★		Weightmans, *Liverpool*	★★★
Shoosmiths & Harrison, *Southampton*	★★		Willmett & Co, *Windsor*	★
Slater Heelis, *Manchester*	★★★★★		Wolferstans, *Plymouth*	★
Stamp Jackson and Procter, *Hull*	★		Wollastons, *Chelmsford*	★★
Steele Raymond, *Bournemouth*	★		Wragge & Co, *Birmingham*	★★★★★★
Stevens & Bolton, *Guildford*	★★★		Wright Hassall & Co, *Leamington Spa*	★
Taylor Vinters, *Cambridge*	★★			

Firms and their star ratings are based on Chambers' Directory 1998–1999. Six stars represent a top-ranked firm, five stars a second-ranked firm, etc. See page 3 for further details.

CRIME
(including Fraud)

Area of law

General criminal lawyers act for defendants in magistrates courts, Crown Courts and courts martial. They may also undertake civil liberties work. In addition to expertise in criminal law and procedure, they need to be familiar with mental health, immigration and extradition issues. Fraud work requires a knowledge of insolvency law, financial services regulations and commercial litigation (particularly Mareva injunctions and Anton Piller orders). This chapter deals mainly with general criminal work.

Type of work

Criminal lawyers lead a hectic life. In a typical day, you might get into the office at 8.30am, having already spent some of the night at the police station as duty solicitor. At 9.30 it's off to the magistrates court for procedural and remand hearings, or perhaps a plea in mitigation. Lunch is on the hoof, and the afternoon spent interviewing clients and conferring with Counsel. After that, there may still be paperwork to deal with and you could be back at the police station that night. When at last you get home, you'll have to spend some of your 'free' time preparing for the next day's court hearing.

It can be a thankless task. "As a duty solicitor at court, you've only got five minutes with your client," says Girish Thanki, partner with niche firm Thanki Novy Taube. "They want bail, which you know isn't an option, but you still put in an application. At the end of this futile exercise, you must convince the client that the magistrate was dreadful and the prosecution was a slimeball. And, above all, that you did your best."

On the bright side, cases have a quick turnover. Even murder cases are usually dealt with in under a year. "There is a lovely rhythm to criminal work," says Thanki, "You finish it, you bill it, you get the money within a couple of months. Whether you're upbeat because you got the desired result or annoyed because you failed to, it's all over quickly and things are moving on."

Just as well given the harrowing nature of some cases. "A murder case came to us on appeal where a man killed his own mother," says Thanki. "I was expecting a big fat file but when it arrived it was thin, what you'd expect with a burglary. He'd pleaded guilty to murder, which sounded very strange until we looked into his psychiatric history – he was clearly unfit to plead."

Certainly, criminal work requires a strong stomach. Unless you specialise in white collar fraud, many of your clients will come from deprived backgrounds and some will have psychiatric problems. "Clients have been known to walk into firms, threatening to kill staff and burn down their offices," says Stephen Hewitt of Fisher Meredith. Criminal practitioners have to be social workers as well as lawyers.

But criminal law is more intrinsically interesting than many areas of law. Thanki says: "I recently had great fun arguing that a black defendant could not get a fair trial in Missouri. The American government was furious, but was forced to produce documentation on how they could prevent jury bias. We got extensive media coverage in the US."

Offices of niche criminal firms are generally small, understaffed and hectic. Trainees are thrown in at the deep end with their own case loads and will be interviewing suspects at police stations, visiting defendants in prison and attending scenes of crime from day one. "You are very much expected to learn as you go along," said one trainee who spent a seat in the crime department of a leading northern litigation firm. "It teaches you to think on your feet. It can seem rather intense to start with, very client-oriented with little desk-work." Trainees may also get to assist senior lawyers and barristers in more serious assault, rape and murder cases, and sit through Old Bailey trials if they are lucky.

essential and can sometimes be the saving grace in particularly difficult client meetings.

The work is all about people, agrees Nickson, and it concerns live issues. "At parties, if you let slip that you're an employment lawyer, someone always asks for advice about a problem – it's far safer to say you're a dentist." Having said that, Nickson would not do anything else, "apart perhaps from opening a wine bar in Sydney!"

Lawyers working for union firms obviously need to be sympathetic to their clients' interests and, according to Stephen Cavalier, they need to realise that a legal solution may not always be the best approach. "Many cases are not simply about compensation," he comments, "but perhaps a wider industrial issue that needs resolving."

Career options

Janet Gaymer read law at Oxford in the late 1960s and then did a part-time masters degree (LLM) at LSE while working at Simmons & Simmons, where she was admitted in 1973. She started specialising in employment law "purely accidentally – I just got handed an unfair dismissal case," and hasn't looked back since. She has been a partner since 1977.

Michael Short qualified at Lovell White & King (now Lovell White Durrant) and was enjoying work as a civil litigator in the City firm. Then, "someone who knew my political interests and background (my family has strong connections with the Labour party) told me about a job at Rowley Ashworth involving employment law and working with trade unions." Short made the move and now advises those considering a career in employment law to look beyond the City for their training. "At Rowley Ashworth we often find that applicants from the City have worked on a lot of very similar cases. Other firms may offer more variety."

There are options to go in-house, but as Sue Nickson comments, "few companies have a large enough legal team to include a full-time employment lawyer". It is more likely that a move in-house would combine employment law with perhaps general commercial litigation. If the idea of working for a company rather than a law firm appeals, an alternative step is to work more generally in a human resources department. There are openings in the academic world for employment experts, and lawyers considering this path should gain as much lecturing experience as possible. Towards the top end of the professional scale, lawyers may apply to chair employment tribunals;many partners in leading employment practices combine their practice with part-time tribunal chairs.

Remaining in private practice seems to be the popular choice among the lawyers we interviewed and they expressed confidence in the choice of employment law as a career. "Employment law's stability in economically turbulent times has obvious irony, but it provides comforting reassurance for those in the field," says Michael Short. "Like most litigation, the volume of our work increases in times of recession."

The Firms

Employment Law

Simmons & Simmons leads the field among the employer firms in London. In the past year the team has been involved in setting up the European Employment Forum. Also well-respected is international practice Baker & McKenzie. With 57 offices worldwide the firm has been at the forefront in advising large UK plcs and foreign multi-national companies on European Works Councils. Lovell White Durrant have a respected practice as do smaller firms, Rowe & Maw and Fox Williams. Eversheds has a leading practice in London and around the country, particularly in Wales and the Midlands.

The leading employee practice in London is Pattinson & Brewer, a firm whose Trade Union credentials date back to the turn of the century. It has offices throughout the country as do the other leading firms Rowley Ashworth, Russell Jones & Walker and Thompsons.

Cole & Cole dominate in the South East of the country. The firm's major clients include the Equal Opportunities Commission and Oxford

University. In the West Country, Bristol's largest firms (Osborne Clarke and Burges Salmon) hold sway. Bond Pearce in Plymouth are also strong and have been involved in test cases involving the Disability Discrimination Act and health and safety law in the last year.

Manchester's large commercial firms – Addleshaw Booth & Co, Dibb Lupton Alsop and Hammond Suddards are key players. However, a five-partner niche firm, Short Richardson & Forth, is considered the outstanding employment law practice in Newcastle. The firm does a lot of tribunal work and has a nationwide practice with an equal amount of contentious and non-contentious work. In Leeds, Pinsent Curtis are strong, particularly in discrimination law.

Pensions and Employee Benefits

The large City firms are all active in pensions and employee benefits, especially Linklaters, Clifford Chance and Freshfields who have good reputations for both types of work, although Linklaters leads the field in employee benefits. Niche firm Sacker & Partners is very well-known for pensions work.

In the regions, it is the large commercial firms with corporate clients who specialise in these areas, with Pinsent Curtis being the key player in employee benefits outside London. Addleshaw Booth & Co have a strong presence in Leeds and Manchester, and Dibb Lupton Alsop are strong on the pensions side.

Leading Firms

London Firms	Employment	Employee Benefits	Pensions
Allen & Overy	**	****	******
Ashurst Morris Crisp		****	
Baker & McKenzie	*****	*	***
Beachcroft Stanleys	**		
Biddle			***
Bindman & Partners	***		
Boodle Hatfield	*		
Cameron McKenna	***		***
Charles Russell	**		
Clifford Chance	**	*****	*****
D J Freeman	*		
Denton Hall	*		
Dibb Lupton Alsop			*
Eversheds	****		*
Field Fisher Waterhouse		**	
Fox Williams	****		
Freshfields	*	*****	******
Hammond Suddards			***
Herbert Smith	***	****	**
Hodge Jones & Allen	***		
Langley & Co	*		
Lawford & Co	**		
Lewis Silkin	***		
Linklaters	*	******	******
Lovell White Durrant	****	****	******
Macfarlanes	*		

Firms and their star ratings are based on Chambers' Directory 1998–1999. Six stars represent a top-ranked firm, five stars a second-ranked firm, etc. See page 3 for further details.

Leading Firms

London Firms (cont.)	Employment	Employee Benefits	Pensions
Nabarro Nathanson			★★★★★
Nicholson Graham & Jones		★★	
Norton Rose	★	★★★	
Osborne Clarke	★		
Paisner & Co	★★★		
Pattinson & Brewer	★★★★★★		
Richards Butler	★★		★
Rowe & Maw	★★★★		★★★★★★
Rowley Ashworth	★★★★★		
Russell Jones & Walker	★★★★		
S J Berwin & Co	★		
Sacker & Partners			★★★★★★
Salans Hertzfeld & Heilbronn HRK	★★★		
Simmons & Simmons	★★★★★★		★★
Slaughter and May	★★★	★★★★	★★★★★
Speechly Bircham	★		
Stephenson Harwood	★★		
Taylor Joynson Garrett	★		
Theodore Goddard	★★		
Thompsons	★★★★		
Titmuss Sainer Dechert	★		
Travers Smith Braithwaite		★★★	★★★
Warner Cranston	★★★		

Leading Firms

Regional Firms	Employment	Employee Benefits	Pensions
Addleshaw Booth & Co, *Leeds*	★★★★★	★★★★★	★★★★★★
Addleshaw Booth & Co, *Manchester*	★★★★★★	★★★★★	★★★★★★
Bevan Ashford, *Bristol*	★★★		
Bond Pearce, *Plymouth*	★★★★★★		
Brachers, *Maidstone*	★★		
Bridge McFarland Solicitors, *Grimsby*	★★		
Browne Jacobson, *Nottingham*	★★★		★★★★
Burges Salmon, *Bristol*	★★★★★★	★★	★★★★★★
Cartwrights, *Bristol*	★★		
Clarks, *Reading*	★★		★★★★
Clarkson Wright & Jakes, *Orpington*	★★		
Cobbetts, *Manchester*	★★★		
Cole & Cole, *Oxford*	★★★★★★		
Cripps Harries Hall, *Tunbridge Wells*	★★		
Davies Arnold Cooper, *Manchester*			★★★
Davies Wallis Foyster, *Liverpool*	★★		★
Davies Wallis Foyster, *Manchester*			★
Dibb Lupton Alsop, *Birmingham*	★★★★★		

Leading Firms

Regional Firms (cont.)	Employment	Employee Benefits	Pensions
Dibb Lupton Alsop, Leeds	*****		******
Dibb Lupton Alsop, Liverpool			******
Dibb Lupton Alsop, Manchester	*****	*****	******
Dibb Lupton Alsop, Sheffield			******
Dickinson Dees, Newcastle upon Tyne	****		***
Donne Mileham & Haddock, Brighton	***		
Edge Ellison, Birmingham	*****		******
Edwards Geldard, Cardiff	**		
Eversheds, Birmingham	******	****	*****
Eversheds, Bristol	***		
Eversheds, Cardiff	******		*****
Eversheds, Derby			******
Eversheds, Ipswich	******		
Eversheds, Leeds	****		******
Eversheds, Manchester	****		*****
Eversheds, Newcastle-upon-Tyne	****		
Eversheds, Norwich	******		***
Ford & Warren, Leeds	***		
Garretts, Birmingham			***
Garretts, Leeds		**	
Gordons Wright & Wright, Bradford	**		
Greenwoods, Peterborough	***		
Halliwell Landau, Manchester	***		***
Hammond Suddards, Leeds	*****	**	*****
Hammond Suddards, Manchester	******		***
Hay & Kilner, Newcastle-upon-Tyne	*		
Henmans, Oxford	***		
Hewitson Becke + Shaw, Cambridge	******		
Hewitson Becke + Shaw, Northampton			****
Higgs & Sons, Brierley Hill	****		
Irwin Mitchell, Sheffield	**		
Jacksons, Stockton-on-Tees	***		
Leathes Prior, Norwich	**		
Leo Abse & Cohen, Cardiff	***		
Lester Aldridge, Bournemouth	**		
Mace & Jones, Liverpool	****		
Malcolm Lynch, Leeds		***	
Martineau Johnson, Birmingham	***		
Mills & Reeve, Cambridge	******		
Mills & Reeve, Norwich	******		
Morgan Bruce, Cardiff	****		
Nabarro Nathanson, Sheffield	***		***
Osborne Clarke, Bristol	******	**	******
Pannone & Partners, Manchester	**		
Pattinson & Brewer, Bristol	***		
Pattinson & Brewer, Chatham	**		
Pickworths, Hemel Hempstead	**		

Leading Firms

Regional Firms (cont.)	Employment	Employee Benefits	Pensions
Pinsent Curtis, *Birmingham*	★★★★★	★★★★★★	★★★★★
Pinsent Curtis, *Leeds*	★★★★★★	★★★★★★	★★
Prettys, *Ipswich*	★★		
Read Hind Stewart, *Leeds*	★★★		
Rollit Farrell & Bladon, *Hull*	★★★★		
Shakespeares, *Birmingham*	★★		
Short Richardson & Forth, *Newcastle*	★★★★★		
Steele & Co, *Norwich*	★★★★★★		
Stephens & Scown, *Exeter*	★★		
Stevens & Bolton, *Guildford*	★★		
Stone King, *Bath*	★★		
Taylor Vinters, *Cambridge*	★★★		
The Lewington Partnership, *Birmingham*	★★		
Thompsons, *Bristol*	★★★		
Thompsons, *Cardiff*	★★		
Thompsons, *Ilford*	★★		
Thompsons, *Newcastle-upon-Tyne*	★★★★		
Thrings & Long, *Bath*	★★		
Tyndallwoods, *Birmingham*	★★★		
Underwoods, *St. Albans*	★★		
Veale Wasbrough, *Bristol*	★★★★★		
Walker Morris, *Leeds*	★★★		★★★
Wansbroughs Willey Hargrave, *Bristol*	★★		
Wansbroughs Willey Hargrave, *Sheffield*	★★★		
Ward Hadaway, *Newcastle upon Tyne*	★★		
Whittles, *Liverpool*	★★★★★		
Whittles, *Manchester*	★★★★★		
Wragge & Co, *Birmingham*	★★★★★	★★★★★	★★★★★★
Wrigleys, *Leeds*			★★

Firms and their star ratings are based on Chambers' Directory 1998–1999. Six stars represent a top-ranked firm, five stars a second-ranked firm, etc. See page 3 for further details.

ENVIRONMENTAL LAW

Area of law

Anyone who thinks that practising environmental law is all about saving the planet and making polluters pay should remember that the great majority of environmental lawyers spend their time representing corporate clients. There are lawyers who act for the Environment Agency, environmental pressure groups, and individuals, but they are the minority.

It would be wrong to suggest, however, that advising corporate clients means simply finding ways for them to evade their responsibilities. Effective corporate environmental law advice is always aimed at prevention rather than cure.

All the larger full-service firms have an environmental law capability, usually a cross-departmental group involving planners, litigators and corporate lawyers. Leading environmental law firms like Simmons & Simmons and Allen & Overy have dedicated teams with several specialists handling 100% environmental law.

Type of work

Environmental lawyers deal with contentious and non-contentious work. Non-contentious lawyers handle environmental aspects of the sale and purchase of businesses, properties and other assets. Environmental issues have moved up the agenda in such transactions to rank alongside tax and corporate matters. The work includes advising clients on potential environmental liabilities, and drafting contractual provisions for the allocation of risk. Environmental work also takes the form of 'stand alone' work, advising clients on their obligations under all types of environmental law, for example waste, pollution control, water abstraction and nature conservation. On the contentious side, environmental law involves both civil and criminal litigation – from battles over environmental warranties in corporate sale agreements, to defending pollution prosecutions.

In many firms dealing with defendant environmental litigation such work is handled by firms' commercial litigation departments. In plaintiff litigation, there is often a cross-over between environmental law, health and safety, product liability (especially involving tobacco and asbestos) and personal injury. Some firms handle particular specialisms within environmental law – environmental insurance, for example. Such work includes the drafting of specialist environmental insurance policies and handling environmental claims in relation to professional indemnity and public liability policies.

Skills needed

"Fundamentally, what one is looking for is a good all-round lawyer," says Stephen Tromans, head of Simmons & Simmons' Environmental Law Department. "The work we do can range from criminal to civil litigation, drafting of environmental indemnities on corporate transactions, to general regulatory advice. You have got to be a jack of all trades – a versatile lawyer."

Given the nature of much non-contentious environmental law, gaining a sound knowledge of how business and corporate structures work is essential. It is important to have a good corporate seat during your training contract. As an environmental lawyer you may easily find yourself consulting the Stock Exchange's Yellow Book rules, for example.

A common theme among the leading environmental lawyers we spoke to was that commercial clients want pragmatic and robust advice. Good non-contentious environmental lawyers apply themselves to each transaction to produce the most effective result for the client, rather than just sending out standard environmental warranties and indemnities. They are able to draft agreements which protect their own clients' interests, without promoting those interests to a degree unacceptable to the other side. They are good communicators who can inspire confidence in their clients.

Environmental lawyers need to gain a grasp of the technical as well as the legal aspects of environmental audits. An understanding of physical geography and the environment is certainly an asset. It helps to know, for example, what an aquifer is, or a little about how river or atmospheric systems work.

"People often ask whether scientific qualifications are useful," says Stephen Tromans. Some advertisements for environmental lawyers do mention that a science degree would be regarded as advantageous. Tromans himself thinks they are "helpful, but by no means essential. Where it helps is that people don't get put off by reading reports with lots of numbers and chemical formulae in them. Having said that I didn't do science myself beyond 'O' level, and once you've read a few consultants' reports you get to know your way around them."

The qualities required to be a successful environmental litigator are the qualities essential for general commercial litigation. Commercial awareness is obviously a priority, as well as confidence, tenacity, a tactical approach and an ability to communicate clearly.

Career options

Environmental law experience during training can generally only be gained at the bigger London firms, and a smattering of firms elsewhere like Dibb Lupton Alsop and Addleshaw Booth & Co. These firms offer environmental advice to corporate clients and can afford to run specialised teams. A training seat in an environmental law department provides useful and varied experience, according to a trainee at Simmons & Simmons, "We've got civil litigation going on, corporate and regulatory work, EC and international law matters, as well as criminal litigation which you don't normally get in a City firm. You get such broad experience here that even if you decided you didn't want to do environmental law you wouldn't be shooting yourself in the foot."

Although environmental law is a growing area, with more prosecutions and more legislation, this hasn't yet been fully reflected in the number of job opportunities for recently qualified lawyers in private practice. Again it is generally only the larger firms who have space for more than one or two dedicated environment lawyers. Nevertheless, if you are lucky enough to get a job in this field, you will probably be thrown in at the deep end and, as part of a small team, be given as much responsibility as you can handle. As Stuart Wardlaw, an environmental specialist at Nabarro Nathanson in Sheffield, observes: "Because you'll be in a small department, it's very much all hands on deck. It's not like being in a large department – you'll be one of a small number of specialists, so if a lot of work comes through the door, you have to deal with it."

An alternative route is to apply for a training contract or position with a local authority. Much work here is regulatory and you will handle environment-related planning inquiries, waste issues and air pollution problems. You may also handle more corporate-type work, such as advising on potential liabilities in relation to the property and business interests of the authority. There are quite a number of lawyers in private practice who began their careers in local authorities.

Opportunities to practise environmental law in-house are limited, but they do exist. Very few company legal departments have lawyers who handle mainly or exclusively environmental law, but many in-house departments have to deal with environmental issues – particularly those in the water industry and the chemicals, power, oil, mining/quarrying and construction sectors.

A number of companies employ in-house lawyers, part of whose responsibility is environmental law matters. Anthony Smith, legal manager and company secretary at Exxon Chemicals, for example, handles contract, competition and employment law as well as advising on health and safety and environmental issues generally. Paul Kelly at Northumbrian Water deals with environmental law matters, commercial contracts, civil and criminal litigation as well as water and drainage law.

Work will often be outsourced – specialist regulatory advice and heavyweight litigation for example – but more routine environmental law matters may well be handled by in-house departments.

The Department of the Environment, Transport and the Regions also employs around 100 lawyers in three main locations in London. These lawyers are generally recruited from the Government Legal Service, with a small number coming from private practice. There are opportunities for legal trainees on GLS-funded training schemes to work within the Department. It also takes a couple of students each year on vacation schemes.

Another career option is the Environment Agency. The Agency took over the enforcement powers of the National Rivers Authority, Her Majesty's Inspectorate of Pollution, and the waste regulation authorities in April 1996. It currently employs a total of 81 solicitors and barristers, 3 legal executives and 36 paralegals. These are spread between the head office in Bristol and eight regional offices. As well as recruiting qualified lawyers, the Agency does employ and train staff, with a view to them qualifying as solicitors in the future. Anyone interested should contact the Regional Solicitor at the relevant office.

The Firms

Simmons & Simmons and Freshfields are the market leaders in environmental law work, closely followed by Allen & Overy and Cameron McKenna. The larger firms all handle both contentious and non-contentious work, though the emphasis placed on each will vary.

Non-contentious and regulatory work

Non-contentious work includes transaction-related, advisory and regulatory matters. Simmons & Simmons acted for General Utilities on its £116m acquisition of Leigh Interests plc (the largest waste industry transaction of 1997) and is also advising the government on a project for the disposal of radioactive waste. Freshfields advised ICI on its acquisition of the chemical business of Unilever.

Plymouth-based Bond Pearce is the leading firm in the south west, with a national reputation for work on renewable energy projects, especially wind farms. In the midlands the pre-eminent firm for environmental law is Wragge & Co, whose practice focuses on manufacturing industry and involves roughly equal amounts of contentious and non-contentious work. Edge Ellison and Pinsent Curtis also have strong environmental law practices, especially in waste-related matters. Nabarro Nathanson remain Eversheds' main competitors in the north. The firm's reputation is based on work for the mining, coal and waste industries.

Environmental litigation

Freshfields, as well as possessing a good non-contentious practice, is the leading London firm acting for corporate clients in environmental litigation. Clifford Chance also has a strong practice and recent work includes defending a case against Anglo United over alleged dioxin contamination of land. Outside London, Eversheds' offices in Leeds and Manchester have recently been defending over 500 toxic tort claims brought against Monsanto and Flexsys following a leak of hydrogen sulphide.

Leigh Day & Co is the pre-eminent plaintiff firm for environment-related litigation. Many of its cases have a personal injury element, such as alleged links between electromagnetic fields from power lines and leukaemia, and asthma caused by traffic pollution. Tyndallwoods in Birmingham has also developed a reputation for acting for plaintiffs and third parties in high profile public law matters (eg judicial reviews of incineration of hazardous waste by the cement and lime industry).

Specialisms

Other firms are known for particular specialisms within environmental law – Berrymans Lace Mawer and Barlow Lyde & Gilbert, for example, in the field of environmental insurance. This work includes the drafting of specialist insurance policies and handling environmental claims in relation to professional indemnity and public liability policies. ▶

Leading Firms

London Firms

Allen & Overy	★★★★★	Leigh, Day & Co	★★★★
Ashurst Morris Crisp	★★	Linklaters	★
Baker & McKenzie	★	Lovell White Durrant	★
Barlow Lyde & Gilbert	★	Nabarro Nathanson	★
Berrymans Lace Mawer	★	Nicholson Graham & Jones	★★
Berwin Leighton	★★★	Norton Rose	★★
Bristows	★★★	Rowe & Maw	★
Cameron McKenna	★★★★★	S J Berwin & Co	★★
Clifford Chance	★★★	Simmons & Simmons	★★★★★★
Denton Hall	★★★	Slaughter and May	★
Freshfields	★★★★★★	Stephenson Harwood	★
Gouldens	★	Trowers & Hamlins	★
Herbert Smith	★★	Wiseman Solicitors	★
Lawrence Graham	★★		

Leading Firms

Regional Firms

Addleshaw Booth & Co, *Leeds*	★★	Eversheds, *Manchester*	★★★★★★
Addleshaw Booth & Co, *Manchester*	★★★	Eversheds, *Norwich*	★★★★★
Andrew Bryce & Co, *Colchester*	★★★★★★	Fynn & Partners, *Bournemouth*	★★
Bevan Ashford, *Bristol*	★★★	Griffith Smith, *Brighton*	★★
Blake Lapthorn, *Fareham*	★★★	Hammond Suddards, *Leeds*	★★★
Bond Pearce, *Plymouth*	★★★★★★	Hammond Suddards, *Manchester*	★★★
Bond Pearce, *Southampton*	★★	Hewitson Becke + Shaw, *Cambridge*	★★★★★
Brachers, *Maidstone*	★★★	Kent Jones & Done, *Stoke-on-Trent*	★★
Browne Jacobson, *Nottingham*	★★★	Knight & Sons, *Newcastle-u-Lyme*	★★
Burges Salmon, *Bristol*	★★★★★	Lawrence Tucketts, *Bristol*	★★★
Clarke Willmott & Clarke, *Taunton*	★★★★	Leigh, Day & Co, *Manchester*	★★★
Dibb Lupton Alsop, *Manchester*	★★★★★★	Lester Aldridge, *Bournemouth*	★★
Dibb Lupton Alsop, *Sheffield*	★★★	Lyons Davidson, *Bristol*	★★★★
Dickinson Dees, *Newcastle*	★★★	Masons, *Manchester*	★★★★★★
Donne Mileham & Haddock, *Brighton*	★★	Mills & Reeve, *Norwich*	★★★★★
Edge Ellison, *Birmingham*	★★★★★	Morgan Bruce, *Cardiff*	★★★
Edwards Geldard, *Cardiff*	★★	Nabarro Nathanson, *Sheffield*	★★★★★
Eversheds, *Birmingham*	★★★★	Osborne Clarke, *Bristol*	★★★★★
Eversheds, *Cardiff*	★★★	Pinsent Curtis, *Birmingham*	★★★★★
Eversheds, *Leeds*	★★★★★★	Pinsent Curtis, *Leeds*	★★★

Firms and their star ratings are based on Chambers' Directory 1998–1999. Six stars represent a top-ranked firm, five stars a second-ranked firm, etc. See page 3 for further details.

Leading Firms

Regional Firms (cont.)

Firm	Rating	Firm	Rating
Richard Buxton, *Cambridge*	★★★★★★	Wake Dyne Lawton, *Chester*	★★★
Rollit Farrell & Bladon, *Hull*	★★	White & Bowker, *Winchester*	★★
Stephens & Scown, *Exeter*	★★	Wilbraham & Co, *Leeds*	★★★
Tyndallwoods, *Birmingham*	★★★	Wragge & Co, *Birmingham*	★★★★★★
Veale Wasbrough, *Bristol*	★★★		

Firms and their star ratings are based on Chambers' Directory 1998–1999. Six stars represent a top-ranked firm, five stars a second-ranked firm, etc. See page 3 for further details.

FAMILY/MATRIMONIAL

Area of law

Family law comes into play when relationships break down or where there are concerns about children. It covers divorce, separation, co-habitation, domestic violence, private children work (such as residence, contact, adoption, surrogacy and child abduction) and public childcare (where local authorities are involved). These diverse areas involve knowledge, not only of family law (and, increasingly the law relating to co-habitation), but also an understanding of property, tax, pensions and trusts (on the high-income side) and a grounding in criminal law, welfare law, education law and mental health issues (on the low-income side). Most family lawyers will end up acting either for 'high net worth' individuals at City or smart West End firms, or for low income clients on legal aid at smaller London and high street practices. Public childcare will generally be handled at the high street practices.

Type of work

It is the job of a divorce lawyer to guide people through one of the most stressful periods of their life. It is no surprise that their clients are often emotional, bitter and oblivious to logical argument. One family lawyer says he negotiates with his clients as much as he negotiates with the opposition. Clients range from individuals with substantial property and assets to people with very little money, but a painful contact battle to fight. The well-known London firms acting for wealthy and often high-profile clients must deal with media interest in their cases. Farrer & Co, for example, represent many members of the Royal family and acted for Prince Charles in his divorce.

In any family department, few days will go according to plan. Monday morning is often the busiest time of the week, comments Miranda Baker of London firm, Kingsley Napley: clients have had a bad weekend arguing about an affair or about the children and they phone up wanting immediate advice and solutions. In other cases, clients might walk in off the street needing immediate help – their child has been abducted and you need emergency injunctions and port alerts to prevent the other parent unlawfully taking the child out of the country. "Such cases move at a rapid pace and often involve the media," comments Sandra Davis of Mishcon de Reya. "Problems of domestic violence require paperwork to be swiftly lodged at court and advocacy work undertaken with little time to prepare." Margaret Bonner advises clients against rushing to court, but inevitably many cases will end up there. "I'm frequently in court," comments Philip Kidd, "because orders have to be renewed every 28 days."

Public childcare work can be the most disturbing of all types of family law. Parents of children taken into care often have a history of violence, alcoholism or mental illness. The children themselves could have the same problems and could also be victims of mental, physical or sexual abuse. Philip Kidd of Exeter firm Tozers, recently had to interview two children with armed police standing by because the father was looking for them with a gun. Acting for children, he says, requires particular skill and experience and solicitors can't act for children in care until they have three years' experience of work in this field. "You have to remember you're acting for a vulnerable human being," says Kidd, "My youngest child client was just seven days old, and the rest range from toddlers to teenagers. I see older children more often to check whether they continue to give the same instructions as their guardians. You can get into close relationships – but not too close, obviously, because you walk away at the end of the case."

Samantha Little is a childcare specialist with Croydon firm, Atkins Hope. She has recently been accepted onto the Law Society's Children Panel which means she can now represent children in court and comments "representing children is very challenging and there are many skills to learn." Little's work is mostly legal aid and she has a mixed caseload of public law work, private law disputes and adoption cases.

As a trainee in a West End family department your job will involve taking notes in client interviews, drafting documents, researching points of law and court work. The court work can vary from preparing bundles, to running to court to lodge documents in time, to attending court with counsel. In addition you will usually have a structured training programme, plenty of supervision and support and earn a reasonable salary.

In a high street practice you are more likely to be thrown in at the deep end and given more responsibility early on. You might arrive at work with nothing scheduled and within an hour have to make emergency applications to court on behalf of a woman who was assaulted by her partner the previous evening. The afternoon may involve assisting counsel on your own.

Skills needed

Family work is as much about human behaviour as it is about the law. Miranda Baker believes that family lawyers must develop the right balance between showing sympathy, while not becoming overly involved. "Clients need to feel they can trust you – not only that you will give them appropriate advice but also that you will remain objective at all times."

You'll need a great deal of patience and understanding. It is crucial to recognise when a client is not taking in your advice, says Baker. They may simply not understand or they may not want to hear the advice being given. Baker often has to follow up a meeting with a letter if she senses that a client has not understood a particular point.

Baker also believes that the ability to prioritise is crucial. "Many clients like to think they're your only client," she says, admitting that she has on occasion wanted to remind a pushy client of their likely total fees in relation to her annual fee target. "One has to make decisions every day about which case is most urgent. It can be very difficult."

Childcare work requires particular skills. "As a childcare lawyer working in a high street practice you have to keep an open mind," says Samantha Little, "As well as law there's an element of social work and situations are very complicated and can be distressing for the solicitor. It is however very rewarding work." Parents automatically get legal aid if their child is taken into care so childcare specialists have to be fully conversant with the legal aid system and dealing with a wide variety of people.

"You need to be able to get on your hands and knees and play around with a five year old child for an hour to find out what they want," comments Philip Kidd. Many childcare cases also involve medical experts such as family paediatricians, consultant child psychiatrists and radiographers. "If you ask a consultant neurosurgeon whether a child's bilateral subdural haematoma was likely to be an accidental injury, you need a fair amount of medical knowledge," says Kidd.

Kidd also warns that family work requires a 'strong stomach'. Children have often been subjected to years of abusive behaviour and the evidence can be disturbing. Kidd himself has recently settled a traumatic case concerning three generations of sadistic sexual abuse of children.

For the more financial side of matrimonial work, you'll need a reasonable commercial acumen and a head for figures. But above all, whatever type of family work you're doing, you must be comfortable spending the majority of your time with troubled, emotional and, often, angry people. It can be tough, but this humanitarian aspect is what makes family law so rewarding for the right type of lawyer.

Career options

In the prestigious London firms, trainees may be able to do a family seat as part of their training. The work will generally be for wealthy private clients and will focus on divorce and financial disputes. In the high street, work will be a mixture of private and legal aid cases. Some high street family departments are mixed with conveyancing or criminal departments, so you will receive a grounding in several areas. There will be more opportunity to handle childcare work and you'll have client contact from day one.

There is no typical career path into family law. But because it is such an emotional and demanding field, most family lawyers have been committed to it from very early on in their careers. Samantha Little is in the unusual position of having trained as a commercial lawyer at Allen & Overy, before leaving to pursue her dream of being a family lawyer. Some of her earliest experiences of family law were at law centres where she volunteered as a trainee. "It's a great way to gain exposure to the more 'down-to-earth' situations which you'll be dealing with as a family lawyer," she says. Rather than being put off (as many people are), Little spent some time talking to lawyers at Croydon firm Atkins Hope to see if it was what she really wanted to do. Five years later, she is still there.

William Longrigg of Charles Russell agrees that you have to be extremely committed to succeed in family law, and explains what keeps his interest. "Family law is inextricably linked with social trends and lawyers can get involved in the development of the law to reflect these social changes. One of my partners has just been involved in submissions to the House of Commons Select Committee and the SFLA continues to advise the Lord Chancellor on family issues." For those interested in campaigning and law reform, family law provides plenty of opportunities, particularly in the development of the law relating to co-habitation and lesbian and gay issues. There are also opportunities to extend your study of the law. Miranda Baker's academic work took her to the International Bar Association conference in Delhi last November to present a paper on surrogacy.

The alternatives to private practice are limited, but qualified lawyers can work in-house for local authorities and charities such as the NSPCC. In rare cases, those with good advocacy skills might go to the bar, but this is preferably done at an early stage in their career.

Family lawyers occasionally move into mediation or social work, but the remuneration in these fields is poor and the pressure can be just as great as private practice.

The Firms

Manches & Co (5 partners/8 assistants) and Withers (6 partners/7 assistants) have the largest and most prestigious family departments in London. They both specialise in high net worth clients, complex private children cases and have an international dimension to their work. Bates, Wells & Braithwaite (2 partners/4 assistants), Charles Russell (5 partners/6 assistants) and Sears Tooth (4 partners/2 assistants) also have large well-known departments. Dawson Cornwell & Co are another prestigious London firm, but their clients range from those whose net worth is in excess of £30 million to those who are legally aided.

In the south east, Blandy & Blandy (Reading) lead the field and have recently launched 'Stepahead' - a one-stop counselling, mediation and legal advice survey. Darbys (Oxford) also have a respected department, particularly for ancillary relief. They were involved in a Court of Appeal adoption case this year. In the south west, Lester Aldridge (Bournemouth) is the pre-eminent firm with a reputation for cases with an offshore and foreign element; while Clarke Willmott & Clarke (Taunton) handle mainly the financial side of private cases and public law Children's Act work. In the midlands, Barbara Carter (Birmingham) is well known for her public and private work and larger firm, Freeth Cartwright Hunt Dickens (Nottingham) are specialists in ancillary relief and childcare. Norwich firm Fosters and Buckle Mellows in Peterborough are well-known East Anglia practices. The former has a 24 hour helpline to deal particularly with domestic violence. In the north west, Pannone & Partners (Manchester) has a very strong reputation, especially for high profile children cases. Addleshaw Booth in Leeds is unusual in being a leading commercial firm which also has the top family department in the area. Dickinson Dees and Jones Myers Gordon are also strong. ▶

Leading Firms

London Firms

Anthony Gold	★★★	Kingsley Napley	★★★★
Barnett Sampson	★★★	Levison Meltzer Pigott	★★★★
Bates, Wells & Braithwaite	★★★★★	Manches & Co	★★★★★★
Bindman & Partners	★★	Margaret Bennett	★★
Charles Russell	★★★★★	Miles Preston & Co	★★★★
Collyer-Bristow	★★★★	Mishcon de Reya	★★★★
David du Pré & Co	★★	Osbornes	★★
David Truex and Company	★★	Payne Hicks Beach	★★★
Dawson & Co	★★	Penningtons	★★
Dawson Cornwell & Co	★★★★	Reynolds Porter Chamberlain	★★★
Druces & Attlee	★★	Russell Jones & Walker	★★
Edward Fail Bradshaw & Waterson	★	Russell-Cooke, Potter & Chapman	★
Farrer & Co	★★★★	Sears Tooth	★★★★★
Fisher Meredith	★★★	Stephenson Harwood	★★
Forsters	★	The Family Law Consortium	★★★
Goodman Ray	★★★	The Simkins Partnership	★
Gordon Dadds	★★★★	Withers	★★★★★★
Hodge Jones & Allen	★★	Wright Son & Pepper	★
Hunters	★		

Leading Firms

Regional Firms

Addleshaw Booth & Co, *Leeds*	★★★★★★	Buss Murton, *Tunbridge Wells*	★★★★
Adie Evans & Warner, *Birmingham*	★★	Challinors Lyon Clark, *West Bromwich*	★★
Andrew M. Jackson & Co, *Hull*	★★★	Clarke Willmott & Clarke, *Taunton*	★★★★★
Archers, *Stockton-on-Tees*	★	Coffin Mew & Clover, *Portsmouth*	★★★★
Askews, *Redcar*	★	Cole & Cole, *Oxford*	★★★★★★
Barbara Carter, *Birmingham*	★★★	Coodes, *St. Austell*	★★★★
Battens (with Poole & Co), *Yeovil*	★★★	Cozens-Hardy & Jewson, *Norwich*	★★
Berrymans Lace Mawer, *Liverpool*	★★★	Cranswick Watson, *Leeds*	★★★
Berrymans Lace Mawer, *Manchester*	★★★	Cripps Harries Hall, *Tunbridge Wells*	★★★★
Blacks, *Leeds*	★★	Crombie Wilkinson, *York*	★
Blair Allison & Co, *Birmingham*	★★★	Cuff Roberts, *Liverpool*	★★
Blakesley Rice, *Chesterfield*	★★	Darbys, *Oxford*	★★★★★
Blandy & Blandy, *Reading*	★★★★★★	Dickinson Dees, *Newcastle-upon-Tyne*	★★★★★
Blythe Liggins, *Leamington Spa*	★	Donne Mileham & Haddock, *Brighton*	★★★★
Bond Pearce, *Plymouth*	★★★★★	E. David Brain & Co, *St. Austell*	★★★★
Brachers, *Maidstone*	★★★★	Elliot Mather Smith, *Chesterfield*	★★
Buckle Mellows, *Peterborough*	★★★	Eversheds, *Norwich*	★★★
Burges Salmon, *Bristol*	★★★★★	Farleys, *Blackburn*	★★★
Burnetts, *Carlisle*	★★	Faulkners, *Frome*	★★★★

Firms and their star ratings are based on Chambers' Directory 1998–1999. Six stars represent a top-ranked firm, five stars a second-ranked firm, etc. See page 3 for further details.

Computer/IT

Many firms with leading IP practices are strong in IT work too, particularly Bird & Bird, who have a team of 15 partners and 25 assistants. Baker & McKenzie (5 partners and 14 assistants) are seen as one of the leading computer litigation firms in London and are active in emerging areas such as electronic commerce and year 2000 compliance. Also top ranked are Clifford Chance, who undertake some of the biggest deals and specialise in international transactions, the internet and e-commerce. By contrast, Masons' reputation in the field is based on its outstanding IT litigation practice, acting for clients such as WH Smith and the ICL Group.

Nabarro Nathanson's Reading office has one of the leading IT practices in the south of England, the others being niche firms Clark Holt in Swindon and The Law Offices of Marcus J. O'Leary in Bracknell. In the Midlands and East Anglia, Wragge & Co and Hewitson Becke + Shaw (whose clients include Microsoft Research Ltd, Pegasus and Novell) continue to lead in IT as well as in IP. Pinsent Curtis in Birmingham also have a good reputation and client base.

In the north, Masons offices in Leeds (1 partner, 6 assistants) and Manchester (1 partner, 2 assistants) are pre-eminent and have particular expertise in outsourcing deals. Other firms with leading IT practices are Addleshaw Booth & Co and Rotherham-based Oxley & Coward, who are known for their NHS work.

Telecoms

This sector is dominated by large London practices, but much of the global work is handled by New York firms and niche Washington specialists. The leaders in London are Allen & Overy, Baker & McKenzie, Bird & Bird, Clifford Chance and Simmons & Simmons. At Allen & Overy, 9 corporate partners, 6 finance partners, 13 corporate assistants and 12 finance assistants handle the work. Clifford Chance has 12 partners and 40 assistants undertaking telecoms work. They are currently advising on the liberalisation of the Caribbean telecoms sector. Baker & McKenzie have a core team of 2 partners and 4 assistants but draw on the experience of 5 other partners when needed. They advised Energis on a joint venture with Deutsche Telekom and France Telecom. The smaller firms with expertise in this area include Rakisons and Charles Russell. Outside London, only Eversheds in Leeds and Wiggin & Co in Cheltenham have any major telecoms work.

Leading Firms

London Firms	IP Patent	IP Non-Patent	Computer/ IT	Telecoms
Allen & Overy	★★★	★★★★★	★★★★	★★★★★★
Ashurst Morris Crisp		★★★	★★	★★★★★
Baker & McKenzie	★★	★★★★★	★★★★★★	★★★★★★
Bird & Bird	★★★★★★	★★★★★★	★★★	
Briffa & Co		★★		
Bristows	★★★★★★	★★★★★		★★★
Cameron McKenna		★★★		
Charles Russell		★	★★★★★★	★★★★★★
Clifford Chance	★★★★	★★★★★★		★★★★★
Collyer-Bristow		★		
Debevoise & Plimpton				★★★★★★
Denton Hall		★★★	★★★★	★★★★★
Dibb Lupton Alsop		★★★	★★★★	

Firms and their star ratings are based on Chambers' Directory 1998–1999. Six stars represent a top-ranked firm, five stars a second-ranked firm, etc. See page 3 for further details.

Leading Firms

London Firms (cont.)	IP Patent	IP Non-Patent	Computer/ IT	Telecoms
Eversheds	★★	★★★★★★		
Field Fisher Waterhouse		★	★★★	★★
Freshfields		★★★		★★★
Garretts			★★	
Gouldens		★		
Hammond Suddards	★★	★★★	★★★	
Harbottle & Lewis			★★★	
Henry Hepworth		★	★★★★	
Herbert Smith	★★★★	★★★		
Hobson Audley Hopkins & Wood		★		
Kemp & Co			★★★	
Linklaters	★★★★★	★★★★★	★★★	★★★★★
Llewelyn Zietman		★★★		
Lovell White Durrant	★★★★★	★★★★★★	★★★★	★★★
Macfarlanes		★★		
Masons			★★★★★	
Maycock's		★★		
Morrison & Foerster				★★★★★★
Nabarro Nathanson		★★	★★	
Needham & Grant	★★★★★	★★★★★		
Norton Rose		★★		
Olswang		★★	★★★★	★★★
Osborne Clarke			★★★★	
Rakisons				★★
Reynolds Porter Chamberlain		★★		
Robertson & Co			★★	
Roiter Zucker		★★		
Rowe & Maw	★	★★★	★★	
Sidley & Austin				★★
Simmons & Simmons	★★★★★★	★★★★★★	★★★	★★★★★★
Slaughter and May		★★★	★★★	
Squire Sanders & Dempsey				★★★★★★
Stephenson Harwood		★★		
Tarlo Lyons			★★	
Taylor Joynson Garrett	★★★★★	★★★★★★	★★★	★★
Theodore Goddard			★★	
Titmuss Sainer Dechert		★★		
Wilde Sapte		★		
Willoughby & Partners		★★★★★		

Leading Firms

Regional Firms	IP	Computer/IT	Telecoms
Addleshaw Booth & Co, *Leeds*	★★★★★★	★★★★★	
Addleshaw Booth & Co, *Manchester*	★★★★★★	★★★★★	
Anstey Sargent & Probert, *Exeter*		★★★	
Bevan Ashford, *Bristol*	★★★★		
Boyes Turner & Burrows, *Reading*		★★★	
Browne Jacobson, *Nottingham*	★★★		
Burges Salmon, *Bristol*	★★★★		
Clark Holt, *Swindon*		★★★★★★	
Clarke Willmott & Clarke, *Taunton*	★★★★		
Clyde & Co, *Guildford*		★★★	
Davies Wallis Foyster, *Liverpool*	★★		
Dibb Lupton Alsop, *Birmingham*	★★★★	★★★★	
Dibb Lupton Alsop, *Leeds*	★★★★★★		
Dibb Lupton Alsop, *Liverpool*	★★		
Dibb Lupton Alsop, *Sheffield*	★★★★★★	★★★	
Dickinson Dees, *Newcastle-upon-Tyne*	★★		
Donne Mileham & Haddock, *Brighton*	★★★	★★★	
Edge Ellison, *Birmingham*	★★★★★		
Edwards Geldard, *Cardiff*	★★★	★★★★	
Eversheds, *Cardiff*	★★★	★★★	
Eversheds, *Leeds*	★★★	★★★★	★★
Eversheds, *Norwich*	★★★★★		
Eversheds, *Nottingham*	★★	★★★★	
Freeth Cartwright Hunt Dickins, *Nottingham*	★★★		
Garretts, *Leeds*		★★	
Garretts, *Reading*	★★★★★	★★★★★	
Greenwoods, *Peterborough*	★★★		
Halliwell Landau, *Manchester*	★★★★★★	★★★	
Hammond Suddards, *Leeds*	★★★		
Hammond Suddards, *Manchester*	★★		
Hewitson Becke + Shaw, *Cambridge*	★★★★★★	★★★★★	
Hewitson Becke + Shaw, *Northampton*	★★★	★★★★★	
Hill Dickinson, *Manchester*	★★★★★		
Humphreys & Co, *Bristol*	★★★★		
Kuit Steinart Levy, *Manchester*	★★		
The Law Offices of Marcus J. O'Leary, *Bracknell*	★★★★★★		
Lawson Coppock & Hart, *Manchester*	★★		
Laytons, *Bristol*	★★★★★	★★★	
Lester Aldridge, *Bournmouth*		★★★	
Lochners Technology Solicitors, *Godalming*	★★★		
Lupton Fawcett, *Leeds*	★★★★★		
Manches & Co, *Oxford*		★★★★★	
Martineau Johnson, *Birmingham*	★★★★★		
Masons, *Leeds*		★★★★★★	
Masons, *Manchester*		★★	
Mills & Reeve, *Norwich*	★★★★★		

Leading Firms

Regional Firms (cont.)	IP	Computer/IT	Telecoms
Morgan Bruce, *Cardiff*	★★	★★★	
Nabarro Nathanson, *Reading*	★★★★★	★★★★★★	
Osborne Clarke, *Bristol*	★★★★★★	★★★★★	
Oxley Coward, *Rotherham*		★★★★★	
Pinsent Curtis, *Birmingham*	★★★★★	★★★★★	
Pinsent Curtis, *Leeds*	★★★★★	★★★★★	
Shoosmiths & Harrison, *Northampton*	★★★		
Singletons, *Pinner*		★★	
Taylor Vinters, *Cambridge*	★★★★★		
Taylors, *Blackburn*	★★		
The Law Offices of Marcus J. O'Leary, *Bracknell*		★★★★★★	
Walker Morris, *Leeds*	★★★★★		
Wansbroughs Willey Hargrave, *Birmingham*	★★		
Wansbroughs Willey Hargrave, *Bristol*	★★★★★	★★★	
Wiggin & Co, *Cheltenham*			★
Willoughby & Partners, *Oxford*	★★★★★★	★★★★★	
Wragge & Co, *Birmingham*	★★★★★★	★★★★★★	

Firms and their star ratings are based on Chambers' Directory 1998–1999. Six stars represent a top-ranked firm, five stars a second-ranked firm, etc. See page 3 for further details.

LITIGATION

Area of law

Litigation lawyers – usually known simply as litigators – act for clients involved in disputes. There are three ways in which disputes can be pursued. Litigation itself involves recourse to the courts. This can be an expensive and time-consuming process. For this reason, contracts often provide for disputes between the parties to be referred to binding arbitration, normally by an expert in the field. Unlike court proceedings, arbitrations are confidential. They are particularly common in the shipping, insurance and construction industries. Alternative Dispute Resolution (ADR) is a cheaper alternative to both litigation and arbitration. Although it can take various forms, ADR normally involves structured negotiations between the parties directed by an independent mediator. The parties retain the right to litigate if they find it impossible to reach an agreement.

If you think that contentious work is all about court-room drama, think again. Most disputes settle before the issue of a writ. If proceedings are commenced, the odds are that the case will never reach trial. Parties to commercial litigation are not, as a rule, interested in having their 'day in court'. Litigation is much too expensive for that. The emphasis, therefore, is on reaching a commercial settlement. "If you can keep your clients out of court, they will love you much more than if you get them into a scrap," says Neil Fagan of Lovell White Durrant. "Most of our work involves trying to stop people litigating."

Type of work

General commercial litigators handle a variety of business disputes. Most cases will be contractual – everything from a dispute over the sale of a multi-million pound business, to an argument over the meaning of a term in a photocopier maintenance contract. They might also deal with negligence claims by companies against their professional advisors. Some litigators specialise in certain industry sectors – for example, construction, shipping, insurance, property or media. But most of the litigator's skills are common to all areas of commercial litigation, according to Christopher Style of Linklaters. "The procedure in running a court action or an arbitration, and the skill in negotiating an agreement is the same, whether you're talking about a dispute between the manufacturers of widgets or between accountants, stockbrokers or bankers," he says.

Litigation is a process. Once a case has been commenced, it follows a pre-determined course laid down by the rules of court – pleadings, disclosure of documents, various procedural applications and, in a small number of cases, trial. In a major case, this process can take several years. The mutual disclosure of relevant documents – the discovery process – can be a particularly protracted and expensive affair.

Managing this process is the litigator's primary role. This requires not only a mastery of the rules of court, but also a keen appreciation of tactics. If you're acting for a defendant, for example, you might ask the plaintiff for more information about its claim by means of a formal document known as a Request for Further and Better Particulars. Obtaining the information might not be your primary aim. You might know perfectly well the main thrust of the claim. But your Request may expose weaknesses in the plaintiff's case. It also has a nuisance value, forcing the plaintiff to spend time and money in providing you with further information. If you're lucky, the Request may persuade the plaintiff to settle a case. Discovery can also be used as a tactical ruse, with parties taking advantage of their disclosure obligations to swamp their opponents with largely irrelevant documents. Lord Woolf's reforms to the civil justice system, due to be implemented over the next year or so, may reduce the scope for such tactical games by simplifying procedures.

The range of the litigator's work has increased over the last few years, thanks largely to the extension of High Court rights of audience to solicitors. Although solicitors could always draft pleadings – the formal documents setting out the plaintiff's claim and the defendant's response – and act as advocates in High Court procedural hearings, they rarely did so. Instead, such work was normally referred to barristers. This is now changing. There hasn't been a flood of solicitor-advocates into the High Court. But the possibility of a career as an advocate, together with potential costs savings for the client, is encouraging solicitors to keep more work in-house. This phenomenon is particularly marked in the large City firms. The Woolf reforms are likely to accelerate this trend since they will place a greater emphasis on written advocacy and introduce a new preliminary hearing – the case-management conference – which will be more easily handled by solicitors than barristers.

As a trainee, much of your time will be spent researching points of law and procedure. In a large City firm, a qualified litigator may sometimes work on no more than two or three big cases at a time. The caseload will probably be more varied in smaller litigation departments.

As a two or three year qualified litigator, you might begin your day by dealing with correspondence. Then you're off to the High Court for a procedural application in which you've instructed counsel. You asked the other side for Further and Better Particulars but weren't satisfied with their response. So now you want the court to order them to give full answers. The hearing lasts half an hour. Afterwards, you have a short discussion with counsel on how to take the case forward. You get back to the office a little after mid-day, and spend the next hour trying to finish off a 50-page draft witness statement on which you've been working for the last week. By lunchtime, you've only got one page left to do. But you're due at a client in 45 minutes to check on a team of paralegals working on discovery in a big case. So you stop work on the witness statement, and shoot off to the Underground, munching a sandwich on the way. When you arrive at the client, your heart sinks. Contrary to your instructions, the paras have been including privileged documents among the material to be disclosed to the other side. Instead of being there for only half an hour as

planned, you're there for two hours trying to sort out the mess. You look at your watch – it's 4pm. You suddenly remember that in an hour you're supposed to be attending a conference with leading and junior counsel in another major case. You phone up the partner in charge of the action, and tell him that you'll meet him and the client at counsel's chambers. You miss your connection and run to chambers from the Underground station. You arrive breathless, only to find that the partner and the client haven't yet arrived. You settle your nerves over a cup of black coffee. The partner and the client then stroll in, and tell you you're looking peaky. The conference itself lasts for three hours. By now it's well past eight and you're starving. But you've still got that witness statement to finish off. You try to persuade yourself that it can wait till tomorrow. But you know that you'll have to spend most of tomorrow on that blasted discovery exercise. So you force yourself back to the office for another hour's hard labour. It's almost ten when you leave. You fall asleep on the train home, have a nightmare about the discovery exercise and wake up in a cold sweat three stops too late. What a day.

Skills needed

Litigators require drive, commercial-mindedness, a grasp of tactics and a certain natural toughness and competitiveness. "You need to like to win," says Linklaters' Christopher Style. "You have to have that drive. It's no use being some academic who sits back thinking clever thoughts. You have to be able to roll up your sleeves and really get stuck in."

The sheer scale and complexity of many commercial disputes, usually involving a huge volume of documentary evidence, places a premium on the ability to assimilate information quickly and see the big picture. "The best litigators are those with strong commercial awareness and an ability to think laterally around the immediate dispute," says Anthony Bourne of Glovers. "They must be able to spot the salient points early and allow more trivial matters to drop." And while litigators will fight their client's corner, they must also know when discretion is the better part of valour. "If, as proceedings progress, the client's case is looking bad, you have to work out how much can be salvaged. Knowing which points are worth pursuing and which can be negotiated away, requires a detailed understanding of arguments for and against your client."

Negotiating skills are essential. According to Lovell's Neil Fagan, "verve and panache are important when getting your view across." However, litigators also need a hard edge. "Charm takes you a long way," says Paul Bowden of Freshfields. "But clients and opponents need to know that you can bite."

Career options

All commercial practices in London and the provinces have litigation departments, and most trainees do at least one litigation seat. Herbert Smith are generally reckoned to have the leading general commercial litigation practice in the City, followed by Clifford Chance, Freshfields, Linklaters and Lovell White Durrant. Among the specialist industry sectors, Masons lead the field in construction litigation. The insurance firms are strong, not only in insurance litigation, but also in professional negligence work and shipping litigation. Other niche areas of litigation include property, banking, employment, media, defamation, personal injury and medical negligence.

In-house opportunities are somewhat thin on the ground. Insurance, construction and shipping companies sometimes employ specialist litigators. Only the very largest in-house departments field general commercial litigators.

The Firms

Large scale commercial litigation cases can only really be handled by the big City firms. The sheer logistics of these cases, where discovery alone can take years, mean that huge teams of lawyers are required (increasingly supplemented with large numbers of short-term contract paralegals).

Herbert Smith field a large team of 50 partners and 100 assistants. They are known for their highly skilled and aggressive approach. They

handle cases worth millions of pounds and recently represented Jyske Bank in a £56 million international fraud action. Linklaters has a smaller full-time team of 16 partners and 50 assistants. They masterminded Co-op's defence of the hostile take-over bid by Andrew Regan, and acted for Natwest Group in relation to £90.5 million interest rate derivatives losses. The other City firms handle deals of a similar size and all have considerable teams.

Medium-sized City firms with good practices include Barlow Lyde & Gilbert (25 partners/42 assistants), SJ Berwin & Co (11 partners/18 assistants), DJ Freeman (8 partners/14 assistants), Macfarlanes (5 partners/20 assistants) and Stephenson Harwood (9 partners/28 assistants). They also handle major commercial cases. SJ Berwin acted for American Express against the BCCI liquidators. Stephenson Harwood represented Wang (UK) Ltd in a multi-million pound computer dispute. Barlow Lyde & Gilbert acted for Macdonalds in the McLibel trial.

Smaller London firms with good departments include Reynolds Porter Chamberlain, Warner Cranston, Glovers and Goodman Derrick.

In the regions, Pinsent Curtis and Wragge & Co lead the field in the midlands. The former acted for Nottingham County Council in a £10 million claim for misfeasance in public office and the latter for 125 farmers against the NFU for compensation for loss of milk quota. In the north, Dibb Lupton Alsop in Liverpool and Leeds; and Eversheds, Addleshaw Booth & Co and Hammond Suddards in Manchester and Leeds are the leaders. Eversheds in Manchester successfully recovered £8 million for 236 investors against a stockbroker following the collapse of an investment scheme. Addleshaws in Leeds acted in a £20 million "retrospective taxation" case in the European Court of Human Rights on behalf of Yorkshire Building Society. In East Anglia, Eversheds and Mills & Reeve lead the field and in the south, Bond Pearce in Plymouth, Burges Salmon and Osborne Clarke in Bristol, Donne Mileham & Haddock in Brighton and Blake Lapthorn in Fareham are the major practices.

▶

Leading firms

London Firms	Overall Leaders	100+ Solicitors	40–100 Solicitors	Under 40 Solicitors
Allen & Overy	★★★★			
Ashurst Morris Crisp	★★★			
Baker & McKenzie		★★		
Barlow Lyde & Gilbert		★★★		
Berrymans Lace Mawer			★★★	
Berwin Leighton		★★		
Biddle			★★	
Bower Cotton				★
Cameron McKenna	★★★			
Clifford Chance	★★★★★			
Clyde & Co		★★		
D J Freeman		★★★		
Davies Arnold Cooper		★★		
Denton Hall	★★			
Dibb Lupton Alsop		★		
Eversheds		★★		
Field Fisher Waterhouse		★		
Fladgate Fielder			★	
Freshfields	★★★★★			
Glovers				★★
Goodman Derrick				★★
Gouldens		★★		
Hamlin Slowe				★★
Hammond Suddards		★		
Harbottle & Lewis			★★★	
Herbert Smith	★★★★★★			
Holman, Fenwick & Willan			★★★	
Howard Kennedy			★	
Jeffrey Green Russell			★	
Kennedys			★	
Kingsford Stacey Blackwell				★★
Lane & Partners				★
Lawrence Graham		★		
LeBoeuf, Lamb, Greene & MacRae				★
Lewis Silkin			★★	
Linklaters	★★★★★			
Lovell White Durrant	★★★★★			
Macfarlanes		★★★		
Mackrell Turner Garrett				★
Manches & Co			★	
Memery Crystal			★	
Mishcon de Reya			★	
Nabarro Nathanson		★★		
Nicholson Graham & Jones			★★	

Firms and their star ratings are based on Chambers' Directory 1998–1999. Six stars represent a top-ranked firm, five stars a second-ranked firm, etc. See page 3 for further details.

Leading Firms

London Firms (cont.)	Advertising & Marketing	Defamation	Film & Broadcasting	Digital Media	Music	Theatre	Publishing
Stephens Innocent		****					
Swepstone Walsh		****					
Tarlo Lyons						*****	
Taylor Joynson Garrett					**		***
Theodore Goddard	**	*****	****			****	
Townleys	*						
Wiggin and Co			****				

Leading Firms

Regional Firms	Advertising & Marketing	Defamation	Entertainment
Bevan Ashford, *Bristol*		**	
Brabner Holden Banks, *Liverpool*		**	
Cobbetts, *Manchester*		**	
Dibb Lupton Alsop, *Leeds*	***		**
Dickinson Dees, *Newcastle*			**
Edge Ellison, *Birmingham*			**
Edge Ellison, *Leicester*	**		
Eversheds, *Birmingham*	**		**
Eversheds, *Cardiff*		*	**
Eversheds, *Leeds*			**
Eversheds, *Manchester*			**
Foot & Bowden, *Plymouth*		***	
Frances Anderson, *Birmingham*			***
Hart-Jackson & Hall, *Newcastle*			**
Knights, *Tunbridge Wells*		**	
Lea & Company, *Stockport*			**
Leathes Prior, *Norwich*			*
Lester Aldridge, *Bournemouth*	**		
Manches & Co, *Oxford*			*
McCormicks, *Leeds*			**
Morgan Bruce, *Swansea*			**
Pannone & Partners, *Manchester*		*	
Ramsbottom & Co, *Blackburn*			**
Sean Redmond, *Stafford*			**
Wiggin and Co, *Cheltenham*		***	***
Wragge & Co, *Birmingham*		*	**

Firms and their star ratings are based on Chambers' Directory 1998–1999. Six stars represent a top-ranked firm, five stars a second-ranked firm, etc. See page 3 for further details.

PERSONAL INJURY & MEDICAL NEGLIGENCE

Area of law

Personal injury and medical negligence work often take place in the same department and firms usually specialise in either plaintiff or defendant work. Plaintiff firms are instructed by private individuals, legal expenses insurers and trade unions. Defendant firms act for private individuals, health authorities, hospitals, trusts, insurance companies, public bodies and self-insuring companies. A small number of firms represent both plaintiffs and defendants.

Personal injury cases range from simple "slipper tripper" cases (such as falling over uneven paving stones) to disaster litigation (the King's Cross fire) and group industrial disease actions (such as asbestosis litigation).

Medical negligence actions vary from minor injuries to serious disability, brain-damaged babies and fatalities.

Type of work

PI and medical negligence lawyers spend the majority of their time gathering information from clients, obtaining expert evidence, reading up on the technicalities of their cases and generally preparing for litigation. However they also offer pre-litigation advice, advising on the best method of defence or sometimes persuading a client that their case is not strong enough to take action. Most settlements are reached out of court, so time actually spent at trials is minimal. Four or five trials a year is about the maximum.

Personal Injury

The staple diet of a PI lawyer is the road traffic accident and non-specialist firms devote much time to such straightforward, low-value work. The specialist plaintiff firms, on the other hand, have expertise in a variety of niche areas. Leigh Day & Co specialise in aviation disasters and also have expertise in horse-riding accidents.

Russell Jones & Walker handle deafness cases, and represent police officers deafened by motor-cycle and gunfire noise, and an office worker deafened by a faulty fire alarm. They also have a special unit for victims of sexual assault. Hodge Jones & Allen have particular expertise in multi-party cases following their involvement in the King's Cross and Marchioness disasters.

Defendant firms are often instructed by insurers, but they require as much specialist knowledge as their plaintiff counterparts. "Shortly after qualifying I bought myself a Teach Yourself Anatomy book and read it from cover to cover," says Steve Daykin, head of defendant PI at Nabarro Nathanson in Sheffield. He has been defending British Coal in the "Vibration White Finger" (a condition where vibrating machinery causes fingers to turn white and go numb) litigation in the Court of Appeal, and in a group respiratory disease claim. He obviously needs to be fully aware of the medical conditions allegedly suffered by the plaintiffs.

This type of work takes lawyers from the factory floor to the coal mine, from the scene of an accident to the hospital, and from the home to the sports field. They become mini-experts in a number of activities. Terry Lee, partner with Evill & Coleman, had to learn the ins and outs of the rules of rugby as well as draw on his knowledge of head and spinal injuries, when he represented the rugby player, Ben Smolden, in his ground-breaking action against two rugby referees. Smolden sustained severe injuries during a match and one of the referees was held liable for those injuries.

Medical Negligence

Like PI, medical negligence work ranges from the simple injury to the action worth a million pounds in damages. The more complex cases require an in-depth knowledge of medical technicalities. Katie Hay, a consultant with the defendant firm, Capsticks, explains that the doctors and experts can tell you much of what you need to know, but that with most specialist cases, "you just have to sit down and learn it for yourself."

Hay defended Merton, Sutton and Wandsworth Health Authority in an action brought by a patient who became pregnant after she had supposedly been sterilised. Following detailed gynaecological, histological and video evidence, it was established that the doctor who performed the sterilisation had not been at fault. The lawyers knew as much about the medical complications as the doctors by the end of the trial.

An awareness of mental as well as physical illness is often required by the lawyers. Specialist plaintiff firm, Pritchard Englefield, acted for Mr and Mrs Tredget in their test case against Bexley Health Authority, which established that a father who witnessed the mismanaged birth of his son (who died shortly afterwards) could recover damages for his own psychological injury.

Magi Young, partner with plaintiff firm, Parlett Kent, last year achieved a settlement of £1.2 million for a psychiatric patient who managed to take an overdose while under one-to-one observation. For 12 hours, the hospital failed to realise that she had lapsed into a coma.

These cases are at the top end of the scale and a trainee or recently qualified solicitor would obviously play only a junior role in such matters. Nevertheless, this role could still involve liaising with clients and doctors. As a trainee with Parlett Kent, points out: "I already have a lot of client contact, and give advice and support on the 'phone, as well as taking witness statements and attending consultations with counsel." He also undertakes advocacy for his firm and sometimes finds himself up against a partner on the other side.

Medical negligence and PI are intense and absorbing fields and require hard work and long hours just to keep up to speed with advances in medicine and technology. According to Steve Daykin, those at the top of the profession, routinely work a 60–70 hour week.

Skills needed

It goes without saying that lawyers entering these fields must be interested in medical issues. They need a knowledge of anatomy and medical conditions, and an understanding of how the NHS works so they can ask relevant questions about hospital forms and records. An awareness of the professional relationships between doctors, nurses, managers and patients is also essential. It is not surprising then that many medical negligence lawyers have worked in the medical profession prior to practising law. The leading firms contain a number of doctors, nurses, dentists, medical secretaries and registrars. "We are here to carry out the day-to-day procedures of the law," says Katie Hay, "but a number of us come here with some sort of medical background and many people have wanted to be a doctor at some time." Bedtime reading will include not only legal updates, but also the latest issues of GP News, Health Service Journal and Healthcare Management.

An interest in medical issues must be accompanied by a "non-squeamish" nature. Most firms send their lawyers to hospitals to observe surgical procedures. As one partner commented, "Witnessing first hand what a hysterectomy involves can be pretty useful."

Good communication skills are essential for translating complicated medical issues into simple terms for clients, or for giving detailed accounts to increasingly cost-conscious health service bodies.

A sensitive and sympathetic approach, coupled with great strength of character are required in what can quite literally be life or death situations. As one trainee said: "You have to be able to empathise with people who have suffered a great deal. The fact that they may be badly treated by institutions which they see as powerful and secretive can add insult to injury."

Defendant solicitors must also employ tact and sensitivity. "We have to calm down agitated doctors as much as plaintiff solicitors have to calm down their clients," says Katie Hay. "Our job is no less stressful and we have to be reassuring and assertive at the same time. We must also weigh up the commercial considerations involved in conducting this type of litigation. A good defendant lawyer must have the ability to form an early view on whether a case should be settled or fought."

With so much emphasis on medical issues, it would be easy to forget that at the end of the day, the tactics of litigation are obviously at the forefront of this field, as with any contentious area. The usual qualities of confidence, tenacity and common sense (for knowing when to back down) are required.

Above all, successful lawyers in this field show an emotional commitment and dedication to their work, not often witnessed in drier areas of law. There are a lot of enthusiastic PI and medical negligence lawyers, comments Magi Young. She herself finds the work "phenomenally interesting", "very rewarding" and is "totally committed".

On a day-to-day basis, the lawyers stress that they appreciate a partner or opponent who is "reasonable, practical and easy to deal with".

Career options

Magi Young has always acted for plaintiffs. She trained in a small legal aid practice where she tackled personal injury, medical negligence, mental health, housing, immigration, crime and family law. She then moved to Pannone Napier (now Pannone & Partners), where she immediately specialised in personal injury and medical negligence and became a partner after four years. She has been a partner with Parlett Kent for the past seven years and recently set up a branch of the firm in Exeter.

After training with Robert Muckle, Steve Daykin joined British Coal as an assistant solicitor to experience the public sector. In 1986, he became British Coal's area solicitor for the North East and was in charge of 20 lawyers. In 1990, Nabarro Nathanson took over part of British Coal's legal department and Daykin moved to join the firm. He now heads their PI department. He had this to say of his field: "You talk to commercial lawyers who think their jobs are more demanding because they earn more money, but

acting for defendants in PI is a hell of a challenge and no less intellectually demanding."

There are very few in-house options for lawyers in this field. When pressed, Steve Daykin suggested that there may be openings for defendant solicitors with health authorities and the Post Office, but commented that "such opportunities are getting rarer all the time, with the majority of work being referred to specialist practices." Magi Young knows of no in-house lawyers in this field and stressed that as it is such a demanding and highly-focused area, "it is only for those whose commitment is total and career changes on the inside are extremely rare." Katie Hay agrees: "This is a popular area of law as it involves commercial decision-making in a human context. Those who succeed in breaking into it tend to be here to stay."

Their advice is to make focused applications to specialist firms, because the trend within private practice is towards increasing specialisation in a small number of niche firms.

The Firms

Personal Injury

Many specialist personal injury firms, particularly in London, act either for plaintiffs or defendants. Leading plaintiff firms include Leigh Day & Co, Thompsons and Russell Jones & Walker. Leigh Day & Co are renowned for their expertise in complex personal injury matters and multi-party actions (e.g. tobacco litigation); Thompsons are known for industrial disease cases, acting for union clients; and Russell Jones & Walker were involved in Page v Sheerness, the leading House of Lords case on damages and collateral benefits. All these firms also have offices around the country.

Other regional plaintiff firms include Osborne Morris & Morgan in Leighton Buzzard, who have a particular specialism in neurological injuries; Rowley Ashworth in Exeter and Leeds (another firm acting for union clients, particularly in industrial disease cases); and Irwin Mitchell in Leeds, Birmingham and Sheffield, who have ongoing involvement in the miners' respiratory disease litigation against British Coal.

The leading defendant firms in London are all insurance/healthcare practices. Beachcroft Stanleys recently defended a case for a South African company in relation to alleged mercury exposure suffered by miners; while Kennedys are instructed by the British Railways Board in two test actions involving claims for industrial diseases.

Defendant firms outside London include Davies Lavery in Maidstone, Wansbroughs Willey Hargrave in Bristol, Buller Jeffries in Birmingham, Mills & Reeve in Norwich, Keogh Ritson in Bolton and Sinton & Co in Newcastle.

Several regional firms act for both plaintiffs and defendants. They include Bond Pearce in Plymouth, Newsome Vaughan in Coventry, Colemans in Manchester and Hay & Kilner in Newcastle.

Medical Negligence

There is a trend in medical negligence work towards increasing specialisation in a small number of firms. It is particularly difficult for new defendant firms to break into this area because NHS Trusts select their legal adviser from a small panel of established firms.

Leigh Day & Co are the leading London firm for plaintiff work, acting for all types of plaintiff, but particularly children with brain injuries. On the defendant side Capsticks, Hempsons and Beachcroft Stanleys lead the field.

Firms with leading reputations for PI work are often highly rated for medical negligence as well. Osborne Morris & Morgan on the plaintiff side and newly-merged Morgan Cole on the defendant side in the south east, for example. In the south west and Wales, Bevan Ashford are the clear leaders for defendant work, and are acknowledged as having one of the best defence practices in the country. Other noteworthy firms include Alexander Harris in Altrincham who specialise exclusively in health related work on behalf of plaintiffs and have one of the largest medical negligence teams in the country; and Freeth Cartwright Hunt Dickins (Nottingham and Derby) who cover a range of plaintiff work, with particular specialisms in obstetrics, gynaecology, cancer cases and pharmaceutical product liability.

Leading Firms

London Firms	PI Plaintiff	PI Defendant	Med.Neg. Plaintiff	Med.Neg. Defendant
Anthony Gold, Lerman & Muirhead	★★			
Bannisters Solicitors		★★★		
Barlow Lyde & Gilbert		★★★★★		
Beachcroft Stanleys		★★★★★		★★★★★★
Berrymans Lace Mawer		★★★★★		
Bindman & Partners			★★★	
Bird & Bird				★★★
Bolt Burdon	★			
Cameron McKenna		★★★		
Capsticks				★★★★★★
Charles Russell			★★★	
Davies Arnold Cooper		★★★★★		
E. Edwards Son & Noice		★★		
Edward Lewis		★★		

Firms and their star ratings are based on Chambers' Directory 1998–1999. Six stars represent a top-ranked firm, five stars a second-ranked firm, etc. See page 3 for further details.

Leading Firms

London Firms (cont.)	PI Plaintiff	PI Defendant	Med.Neg. Plaintiff	Med.Neg. Defendant
Evill & Coleman	★★★		★★★★	
Field Fisher Waterhouse	★★		★★★★★	
G.L. Hockfield & Co	★			
Greenwoods		★★		
Hempsons				★★★★★★
Hextall Erskine		★★★		
Hodge Jones & Allen	★★★			
Kennedys		★★★★★		
Kingsley Napley			★★★★★	
Lawford & Co	★			
Lawrence Graham		★★★		
Le Brasseur J Tickle		★★		★★★★★
Leigh, Day & Co	★★★★★★		★★★★★★	
O.H. Parsons & Partners	★★			
Parlett Kent	★		★★★★★	
Pattinson & Brewer	★★★★★		★★	
Prince Evans	★★			
Pritchard Englefield	★		★★★★	
Rowley Ashworth	★★★			
Russell Jones & Walker	★★★★★★			
Simmonds Church Smiles	★			
Stephens Innocent	★			
Stewarts	★			
Thompsons	★★★★★★			
Vizards		★★★★★		
Wansbroughs Willey Hargrave		★★★★★		
Watmores		★★★		
Wedlake Saint		★		

Leading Firms

Regional Firms	PI Plaintiff	PI Defendant	Med.Neg. Plaintiff	Med.Neg. Defendant
A.E. Wyeth & Co, *Dartford*		★★★★★		
Abson Hall, *Stockport*	★★			
Alexander Harris, *Altrincham*	★★★★★		★★★★★★	
Allan Henderson, *Newcastle-upon-Tyne*	★★★			
Amery-Parkes, *Basingstoke*	★★★★★			
Amery-Parkes, *Birmingham*	★★	★★		
Amery-Parkes, *Bristol*	★★	★★		
Anthony Collins Solicitors, *Birmingham*			★★★★★	
Argles & Court, *Maidstone*	★	★		
Barcan Woodward, *Bristol*			★★★★★★	
Barratt Goff & Tomlinson, *Nottingham*	★★★★★			

Leading Firms

Regional Firms (cont.)	PI Plaintiff	PI Defendant	Med.Neg. Plaintiff	Med.Neg. Defendant
Bates, Wells & Braithwaite, *Ipswich*	★★★★			
Battens (with Poole & Co), *Yeovil*	★★			
Bennet Metcalfe, *Bristol*	★★	★★		
Berrymans Lace Mawer, *Liverpool*		★★★★★		
Betesh Fox & Co, *Manchester*	★★★			
Bevan Ashford, *Bristol*		★★★★		★★★★★★
Bevan Ashford, *Cardiff*				★★★★★★
Birketts, *Ipswich*	★★★	★★★		
Bishop Longbotham, *Trowbridge*	★★★			
Blackhurst Parker & Yates, *Preston*	★★★	★★★		
Blake Lapthorn, *Portsmouth*	★★★★★		★★★★	
Bond Pearce, *Plymouth*	★★★★★★	★★★★★★		
Bond Pearce, *Southampton*		★★★★★		
Boyce Hatton, *Torquay*	★★	★★		
Boyes Turner & Burrows, *Reading*	★★★★★		★★★★★★	
Brachers, *Maidstone*		★★★★★		★★★★★
Browell Smith, *Newcastle-upon-Tyne*	★★★			
Browne Jacobson, *Nottingham*		★★★★		
Buckle Mellows, *Peterborough*	★★★	★★★		
Buller Jeffries, *Birmingham*		★★★★★★		
Burroughs Day, *Bristol*	★★★★★			
Buss Murton, *Tunbridge Wells*	★★	★★		
Cartwright & Lewis, *Birmingham*		★★★★		
Cartwrights, *Bristol*		★★★★★		
Challinors Lyon Clark, *Birmingham*			★★★★★★	
Challinors Lyon Clark, *West Bromwich*	★★★			
Chapman Everatt, *Birmingham*		★★★★		
Clarkson Wright & Jakes, *Orpington*	★	★		
Cole & Cole, *Oxford*				★★★★★
Cole & Cole, *Reading*		★★★★★		
Colemans Solicitors, *Manchester*	★★★★★★	★★★★★★		
Cripps Harries Hall, *Tunbridge Wells*	★★	★★		
Crosse & Crosse, *Exeter*	★★	★★		
Crutes, *Newcastle-upon-Tyne*		★★		★★★★★★
Cunningham, John & Co, *Thetford*	★★★★★★		★★★★★★	
Darbys, *Oxford*	★★★			
David Gist & Co, *Bristol*	★★★			
Davies and Partners, *Gloucester*	★★	★★		
Davies Arnold Cooper, *Manchester*		★★★★★		
Davies Lavery, *Maidstone*		★★★★★★		
Davies Wallis Foyster, *Liverpool*		★★★★		
Davies Wallis Foyster, *Manchester*		★★★★		
Dawbarns, *Wisbech*	★★★★★		★★★★	
Deas Mallen Souter, *Newcastle*		★★		
Dibb Lupton Alsop, *Bradford*		★★		

Leading Firms

Regional Firms (cont.)	PI Plaintiff	PI Defendant	Med.Neg. Plaintiff	Med.Neg. Defendant
Dolmans, *Cardiff*		★★★		
Donne Mileham & Haddock, *Brighton*	★★	★★		
Donns Solicitors, *Manchester*	★★★★★★			
Douglas-Jones Mercer, *Swansea*	★★★	★★★		
E. Edwards Son & Noice, *Ilford*	★★	★★		
Edge Ellison, *Birmingham*		★★★★		
Edwards Geldard, *Cardiff*			★★★★	
Eking Manning, *Nottingham*		★★★★		
Elliott & Company, *Manchester*		★★		
Ensor Byfield, *Southampton*		★★★★★		
Everatt & Company, *Evesham*		★★★★		
Eversheds, *Cardiff*		★★		
Eversheds, *Ipswich*		★★★★★		
Eversheds, *Newcastle-upon-Tyne*				★★★★★★
Eversheds, *Norwich*		★★★★★		★★★★
Faulkners, *Frome*	★★			
Fennemores, *Milton Keynes*	★★★★			
Flint, Bishop & Barnett, *Derby*	★★	★★		
Ford Simey Daw Roberts, *Exeter*		★★		
Frank & Caffin, *Truro*		★★★		
Freeth Cartwright, *Derby*			★★★★★★	
Freeth Cartwright, *Nottingham*	★★★★★★		★★★★★★	
Gadsby Wicks, *Chelmsford*			★★★★★	
Geoffrey Warhurst, *Manchester*		★★★		
George Davies & Co, *Manchester*				★★★★★
George Ide, Phillips, *Chichester*	★★★★			
Goldsmith Williams, *Liverpool*	★★			
Graham Evans & Partners, *Swansea*	★★★	★★★		
Greenwoods, *Peterborough*	★★★	★★★		
Halliwell Landau, *Manchester*		★★★		
Hammond Suddards, *Leeds*		★★		
Harris & Cartwright, *Slough*	★★	★★		
Hay & Kilner, *Newcastle-upon-Tyne*	★★★★★★	★★★★★★	★	
Hempsons, *Harrogate*				★★★★★
Hempsons, *Manchester*				★★★★★★
Henmans, *Oxford*	★★	★★		
Heptonstalls, *Goole*			★★★★	
Hewitson Becke + Shaw, *Cambridge*		★★★★		
Hill Dickinson, *Liverpool*		★★★★★		★★★★★★
Hill Dickinson, *Manchester*		★★★★★		
Horwich Farrelly, *Manchester*	★★★★★	★★★★★		
Hugh James, *Bargoed*			★★★★★	
Hugh James, *Bristol*	★★★	★★★		
Hugh James, *Cardiff*		★★★★★★	★★★★★	
Hugh James, *Merthyr Tydfil*	★★★			

Leading Firms

Regional Firms (cont.)	PI Plaintiff	PI Defendant	Med.Neg. Plaintiff	Med.Neg. Defendant
Huttons, *Cardiff*	**		*****	
Iliffes Booth Bennett, *Uxbridge*	*	*		
Irwin Mitchell, *Birmingham*	******		****	
Irwin Mitchell, *Leeds*	******			
Irwin Mitchell, *Sheffield*	******		******	
Jack Thornley, *Manchester*	*****			
Jackson & Canter, *Liverpool*	**			
Jacksons, *Stockton-on-Tees*		**		
James Chapman & Co, *Manchester*		*****		
John Hodge & Co, *Weston-super-Mare*			*****	
John Pickering & Partners, *Oldham*	******			
Jones Maidment Wilson, *Manchester*			***	
Kennedys, *Brentwood*		******		
Keogh Ritson, *Bolton*		******		
Kirby Simcox, *Bristol*	**	**		
Lamport Bassitt, *Southampton*	***	***		
Langleys, *Lincoln*	*	*		
Lawford & Co, *Manchester*	***			
Le Brasseur J Tickle, *Leeds*				*****
Leathes Prior, *Norwich*	******			
Leigh, Day & Co, *Manchester*	******		***	
Leo Abse & Cohen, *Cardiff*	******			
Linder Myers, *Manchester*	*****		****	
Linsley & Mortimer, *Newcastle*		**		
Lonsdales, *Blackpool*			***	
Loosemores, *Cardiff*	**			
Lupton Fawcett, *Leeds*	*****	*****		
Lyons Davidson, *Bristol*	*****	*****		
Mace & Jones, *Liverpool*	***			
Marrons, *Newcastle-upon-Tyne*	****			
Marshall & Galpin, *Oxford*	***	***		
Maxwell Entwistle & Byrne, *Liverpool*			***	
Merricks, *Chelmsford*		***		
Merricks, *Ipswich*		****		
Metcalfe Copeman, *Wisbech*	*****			
Metcalfes, *Bristol*	**	**		
Michael W. Halsall, *Newton-le-Willows*	***			
Mills & Reeve, *Cambridge*				******
Mills & Reeve, *Norwich*		******		******
Morgan Bruce, *Cardiff*		******		***
Morgan Jones & Pett, *Great Yarmouth*			****	
Nabarro Nathanson, *Sheffield*		**		
Nash & Co, *Plymouth*	*****	*****		
Nelsons, *Nottingham*	*****			
Newsome Vaughan, *Coventry*	***	***	****	

Leading Firms

Regional Firms (cont.)	PI Plaintiff	PI Defendant	Med.Neg. Plaintiff	Med.Neg. Defendant
Osborne Clarke, *Bristol*				★★★★
Osborne Morris, *Leighton Buzzard*	★★★★★		★★★★★★	
Over Taylor Biggs, *Exeter*	★★★		★★★★★★	
Palser Grossman, *Cardiff*		★★★		
Pannone & Partners, *Manchester*	★★★		★★★★★★	
Pardoes, *Bridgwater*	★★			
Pattinson & Brewer, *Bristol*	★★★★★			
Pattinson & Brewer, *Chatham*	★★★★★			
Pattinson & Brewer, *York*	★★★★			
Penningtons, *Godalming*	★★★	★★★		
Percy Hughes & Roberts, *Birkenhead*		★★★★		
Perkins & Co, *Manchester*	★★★★★	★★★★★		
Peter Maughan & Co, *Gateshead*			★★★★★	
Peter Richbell & Co, *Chelmsford*	★★★			
Peter Rickson and Partners, *Preston*		★★★★		
Philip Hamer & Co, *Hull*	★★★			
Preston Goldburn, *Falmouth*			★★★★★★	
Prettys, *Ipswich*		★★★★★	★★★★★	
Ramsbottom & Co, *Blackburn*	★★			
Rogers and Norton, *Norwich*	★★	★★		
Rollit Farrell & Bladon, *Hull*		★		
Rowlands, *Manchester*	★★★			
Rowley Ashworth, *Birmingham*	★★★★★★			
Rowley Ashworth, *Exeter*	★★★★★★			
Rowley Ashworth, *Leeds*	★★★★★			
Rowley Dickinson, *Birmingham*		★★★		
Russell Jones & Walker, *Birmingham*	★★★★★★			
Russell Jones & Walker, *Bristol*	★★★★★★		★★★★★★	
Russell Jones & Walker, *Leeds*	★★★★★			
Russell Jones & Walker, *Manchester*	★★★★★		★★★	
Russell Jones & Walker, *Newcastle*	★★★★★			
Russell Jones & Walker, *Sheffield*	★★★★★			
Samuel Phillips & Co, *Newcastle*	★★★★★	★★★★★		★
Sansbury Hill, *Bristol*		★★★★★★		
Scrivenger Seabrook, *St. Neots*				★★★★★
Shakespeares, *Birmingham*		★★★	★★★★★	
Shoosmiths & Harrison, *Northampton*		★★★		
Shoosmiths & Harrison, *Reading*	★★★★			
Silverbeck Rymer, *Liverpool*	★★★★★	★★★★★		
Sinton & Co, *Newcastle-upon-Tyne*		★★★		
Slee Blackwell, *Barnstaple*	★★			
Smith & Graham, *Hartlepool*	★★★			★
Smith Llewelyn Partnership, *Swansea*			★★★★★★	
Stamp Jackson and Procter, *Hull*	★★★★★	★★★★★	★★★★	
Stephens & Scown, *Exeter*	★★★★★	★★★★★		

Leading Firms

Regional Firms (cont.)	PI Plaintiff	PI Defendant	Med.Neg. Plaintiff	Med.Neg. Defendant
Stones Cann & Hallett, *Exeter*	★★★	★★★		
T.G. Baynes & Sons, *Bexleyheath*	★★★			
Taylor Vinters, *Cambridge*	★★	★★		
Tayntons, *Gloucester*	★★★	★★★		
The Lewington Prtnrship, *Birmingham*				★
The Paul Rooney Prtnrship, *Liverpool*	★★★			
Thompsons, *Birmingham*	★★★★★★		★★★★	
Thompsons, *Bristol*	★★★★★★			
Thompsons, *Cardiff*	★★★★★★			
Thompsons, *Ilford*	★★★★★			
Thompsons, *Leeds*	★★★★★★			
Thompsons, *Liverpool*	★★★★★			
Thompsons, *Newcastle-upon-Tyne*	★★★★★★			
Thompsons, *Nottingham*	★★★★★★			
Thomson Snell, *Tunbridge Wells*	★★★★★		★★★★★	
Townsends, *Swindon*	★★★★★★	★★★★★★		
Tozers, *Exeter*	★★★		★★★★★★	
Trethowan Woodford, *Southampton*	★★★			
Trobridges, *Plymouth*	★★	★★		
Trumps, *Bristol*	★★★			
Vaudreys, *Manchester*		★★★★		
Veale Wasbrough, *Bristol*	★★★★★★	★★★★★★	★★★★★	
Veitch Penny, *Exeter*	★★★★★	★★★★★		
Walker Smith & Way, *Chester*	★★★★★			
Walker Smith & Way, *Wrexham*	★★★		★★★★	
Wansbroughs, *Birmingham*		★★★★		
Wansbroughs, *Bristol*		★★★★★★		★★★★★
Wansbroughs, *Leeds*		★★		
Wansbroughs, *Sheffield*				★★★★★★
Wansbroughs, *Winchester*				★★★★★★
Ward Gethin, *King's Lynn*	★★★★★			
Warner Goodman & Streat, *Fareham*	★★★★★			
Weightmans, *Birmingham*		★★★★		
Weightmans, *Liverpool*		★★★★★		
Whittles, *Leeds*	★★★			
Whittles, *Manchester*	★★★★★★			
Willcox Lane Clutterbuck, *Birmingham*		★★★		
William Hatton, *Dudley*		★★★★★		
Withy King, *Bath*			★★★★★	
Wolferstans, *Plymouth*	★★★★★	★★★★★	★★★★★	
Woollcombe Beer Watts, *Newton Abbot*	★★	★★	★★★★★	
Wynne Baxter Godfree, *Brighton*			★★★★	

Firms and their star ratings are based on Chambers' Directory 1998–1999. Six stars represent a top-ranked firm, five stars a second-ranked firm, etc. See page 3 for further details.

PRIVATE CLIENT
(including Trusts & Personal Tax, Agriculture & Bloodstock and Charities)

Area of law

Private clients – as opposed to corporate clients – are simply people, and any lawyer acting for an individual is acting for a 'private client'. In this sense, family lawyers are private client lawyers. However, as the term is now used, it refers to people of 'high net worth' ie, rich or well-to-do. These wealthy clients are then frequently categorised as 'old' or 'new' money. Long-established private client departments in firms like Withers and Farrers have well-established 'old money' client bases, but are now expanding their entrepreneurial and international 'new money' clientele. They have been helped in this by the closure of private client departments in many City firms which acted primarily for 'new money' clients.

The work of a private client department is largely tax-related and often involves advising clients on the most cost-effective use of their assets. Work cuts across the trusts and personal tax, agriculture and bloodstock, residential conveyancing and family and matrimonial sectors. In addition to tax expertise, a knowledge of land and property law is essential, and an understanding of the rules governing charities and pensions is often required. Work is generally non-contentious, but litigation is always a possibility, particularly trust litigation.

Type of work

Private client work is the most personal kind of legal work there is. Private client lawyers hear details of family life and financial matters that many people would not tell their closest friends. They must give impartial and practical advice.

John Rhodes, trusts specialist with Macfarlanes, describes a typical client: "He was divorced 20 years ago and has five children, three of them doing wonderfully on their own, but two of them complete failures. He said 'I don't know how to leave my fortune. Do I leave more money to the children who are making heavy

weather of life or do I divide it equally?'" Rhodes had only just met him, yet he opened up his heart and mind and wanted an answer.

Martyn Gowar of Lawrence Graham regularly advises clients who are unsure what to do with their fortune. "Clients are often terrified of leaving their estate to an 18-year-old who may squander it on fast cars. But they also realise that if they hang on to it, their assets will be hit by inheritance tax," comments Gowar. "We advise them to establish a trust, which might give their children a regular allowance and perhaps a bulk sum when they turn 25."

An increasing amount of private client work – especially trust work – is coming from international clients. "One of my clients is Canadian," says Rhodes, "a widow whose husband died young leaving an estate valued at $60–70 million. One of my jobs for her was to plan the most effective way of looking after that money bearing in mind Canadian and UK tax. We changed some of the trustees and created some off-shore funds to hold valuable family assets in a tax-efficient way."

Andrew Young of Lawrence Graham has also experienced an upturn in international clients. "It's partly a matter of fashion," he says. "Rich people in foreign countries know that their friends have trusts, so they want one too. The trust is becoming the ultimate fashion accessory for the seriously rich." Nevertheless the practical advantages are hard to ignore. The trust – a legal device unknown in many jurisdictions – provides wealthy foreigners with confidentiality in their business dealings, protection of their assets from creditors, a central administration for assets spread round the world, and a means of circumventing local succession laws.

Off-shore banks also seek advice from London private client lawyers because of their recognised expertise in trusts law. "When you talk to a lawyer from the Cayman islands about a difficult trusts point, he'll often ask what the answer would be in England, and then do that," says Rhodes.

An international clientele results in frequent foreign travel. "One month I travelled to Israel, Spain and Miami" commented Rhodes.

Not all international clients want trusts advice from their private client lawyers. A foreign client, new to the UK, may want a private client specialist to be their right hand man, acting in the purchase of property or shares. "If they buy an estate in England, they call on the lawyer to tie up the property and employment aspects," explains Michael Jacobs of Nicholson Graham & Jones. "They want to know where they stand on hiring and firing staff, for example." You have to draw on a wide base of knowledge.

A trainee solicitor at Lawrence Graham, says that private client work provides trainees with more client contact than other seats. It also offers trainees a better chance of seeing a project through from beginning to end. "Corporate deals might begin before trainees start their seat and end after they've gone. Private client work is on a much smaller scale," he comments. On a day-to-day basis, his work involves telephoning clients, attending meetings and drafting his own trust documents.

Agriculture and bloodstock lawyers advise on the law relating to agricultural holdings. John Moore, head of Macfarlanes' agriculture department, is well known for his work for private clients with landed estates or farms. He also does commercial work, but prefers agriculture. "It's a much smaller world with a friendly atmosphere – there are only ten top land agents so you are always dealing with the same people."

One case he remembers fondly involved a client who bought 3,000 acres from a Welsh hill farmer. After the contract was signed, the client measured his newly-acquired land and realised it only amounted to 1,500 acres. The vendor had measured around every boulder and up every cliff face on his land to arrive at the optimistic figure. When the case went to trial, the court found in favour of his client, although it took

Moore a moment to realise this since the judgment was in Welsh.

Skills needed

A private client lawyer needs to be an all-rounder – a legal jack of all trades. Although the work is primarily tax-based, lawyers require a knowledge of property, family and commercial law, in fact any law which relates to an individual's personal or company affairs. As Christopher Jessel of Farrers points out, "You will be the first person your client turns to in a moment of crisis. If they have a business dispute or a matrimonial problem, you must at least be able to talk about it intelligently and offer initial advice, even though you're not a litigator or a divorce lawyer."

Private client lawyers were also described by one partner as 'agony aunts'. They must listen to their client's problems and give all-encompassing advice, taking into account personal circumstances and family relationships. They must be flexible enough to deal with all types of individual and, as Martyn Gowar of Lawrence Graham points out, they need "enormous tolerance."

A practical approach and a creative mind for devising beneficial tax and financial solutions are always helpful.

Career options

Trainees wishing to experience private client work should aim to get training contracts with well-known private client firms such as Withers, Farrers and Boodle Hatfield. You could combine private client work with more corporate 'city-type' training at firms like Allen & Overy, Macfarlanes and Lawrence Graham, although there are limited future prospects for private client lawyers in big City firms. The recent trend is for private client work to be concentrated in 'niche' firms. This was illustrated by the move of the entire Norton Rose private client department to Charles Russell in February 1997. There are more opportunities in these smaller firms than in previous years, and private client lawyers are also increasingly setting up on their own to offer a personal service to clients.

There are limited in-house opportunities. Those which do exist are generally trust-related. Banks in the Bahamas, Cayman Islands and Jersey sometimes employ lawyers in advisory or risk control positions, and trust companies sometimes require in-house advisers.

The Firms

The leading London firms for trusts and personal tax are mostly small firms with long-established client bases of wealthy individuals and family trusts. City practice, Allen & Overy is the exception. The firm acts for many overseas clients, particularly from the Far and Middle East, and offers expertise in tax planning, off-shore trusts and trust litigation. Farrer & Co and Withers are typical examples of traditional private client firms. Both act for the landed gentry, although Withers' clients now include an increasing number of wealthy entrepreneurs and non-domiciled individuals; and off-shore trust work forms a large part of Farrers' practice. Other more corporate firms such as Macfarlanes are known for their work at the commercial end of the private client market. These three firms are also leaders in agriculture and bloodstock work. Other top-rated London firms are Lawrence Graham who are taking on the work for the estate of Diana, Princess of Wales and Charles Russell who are acting for the trustees of the Dent-Brocklehurst

estate in the sale of Poussin work to the Getty museum.

Charles Russell also have a strong presence in the south west through their office in Cheltenham. Other private client specialists in the south west range from niche practice, Wilsons, in Salisbury to Osborne Clarke in Bristol. Wiggin & Co in Cheltenham also have a growing reputation for international tax planning and asset protection. Another top London firm, Boodle Hatfield, also has a highly rated Oxford office. Together with Cripps Harries Hall, Thomas Eggar Verrall Bowles and Thomson Snell & Passmore they dominate the tax and trusts field in the south east. The pre-eminent firm in the north east is Dickinson Dees, with one of the five largest private client departments in the country. Eversheds regional offices in Cardiff, Norwich and Leeds are all respected.

Leading firms outside London for agriculture and bloodstock include White & Bowker (Winchester), whose work includes advice on quotas and farm business tenancies, as well as environmental matters. Bristol-based Burges Salmon are leaders in agricultural work, with a team of 11 partners and 36 assistants (part-time); while Roythorne & Co in Spalding, Cartmell Shepherd in Carlisle and Ward Hadaway in Newcastle are other regional leaders. ▶

Leading Firms

London Firms	Agriculture & Bloodstock	Trusts & Personal Tax	Charities
Alexanders	*		
Allen & Overy		******	*****
Badhams Thompson	***		
Bates, Wells & Braithwaite			******
Bircham & Co.		****	****
Boodle Hatfield		******	
Bristows			*
Campbell Hooper	***		
Charles Russell		******	**
Claricoat Phillips			***
Collyer-Bristow		**	
Cumberland Ellis Peirs		*	
Currey & Co		*****	
Dawson & Co	***	**	
Denton Hall			***
Edwin Coe		*	
Ellis Wood			**
Farrer & Co	******	******	*****
Field Fisher Waterhouse			**
Fladgate Fielder		*	
Forsters	**	***	
Goodman Derrick			***
Gouldens		*	
Gregory, Rowcliffe & Milners		*	*
Harbottle & Lewis			**
Hunters		***	*
Lawrence Graham		***	*
Lee & Pembertons	**	***	
Lee Bolton & Lee			**
Linklaters		*	
Macfarlanes	******	******	*
Masons		*	
Maxwell Batley		*	
May, May & Merrimans	**	*	
Nabarro Nathanson			***
Nicholson Graham & Jones		****	
Paisner & Co		**	*****
Park Nelson		*	
Payne Hicks Beach	***	****	**
Radcliffes		**	**
Rooks Rider		**	
Russell-Cooke, Potter & Chapman		*	
S J Berwin & Co			*
Simmonds Church Smiles		*	

Firms and their star ratings are based on Chambers' Directory 1998–1999. Six stars represent a top-ranked firm, five stars a second-ranked firm, etc. See page 3 for further details.

Leading Firms

London Firms (cont.)	Agriculture & Bloodstock	Trusts & Personal Tax	Charities
Simmons & Simmons		**	
Sinclair Taylor & Martin			***
Smyth Barkham		*	
Speechly Bircham		*****	***
Taylor Joynson Garrett		****	
Titmuss Sainer Dechert	*	**	
Trowers & Hamlins	*	**	***
Tweedie & Prideaux		*	
Vizards			*
Wedlake Bell		**	
Winckworth & Pemberton		**	***
Witham Weld		*	**
Withers	******	******	****

Leading Firms

Regional Firms	Agriculture & Bloodstock	Trusts & Personal Tax	Charities
A.E. Smith & Son, *Stroud*	*	****	
Adams & Remers, *Lewes*		*****	
Addleshaw Booth & Co, *Leeds*	*****	*****	**
Andrew M. Jackson & Co, *Hull*	**	*****	
Anstey Sargent & Probert, *Exeter*		******	
Anthony Collins Solicitors, *Birmingham*			***
Armitage Sykes Hall Norton, *Huddersfield*		***	
Arnold Thomson, *Towcester*	****		
Askews, *Redcar*		***	
B.P. Collins & Co, *Gerrards Cross*		***	
Baldocks, *Guildford*		***	
Bankes Ashton, *Bury St. Edmunds*	***	*****	
Barker Gotelee, *Ipswich*	*****		
Barlows, *Guildford*		***	*
Battens (with Poole & Co), *Yeovil*	***		
Beor Wilson & Lloyd, *Swansea*		***	
Berrymans Lace Mawer, *Liverpool*		******	
Bevan Ashford, *Bristol*	**		
Bevan Ashford, *Cardiff*		******	
Bevirs, *Swindon*	*		
Beviss & Beckingsale, *Chard*	*		
Birch Cullimore, *Chester*	**	*****	***
Birketts, *Ipswich*	****		
Blake Lapthorn, *Fareham*			*
Blake Lapthorn, *Portsmouth*		****	
Blandy & Blandy, *Reading*		*****	

Leading Firms

Regional Firms (cont.)	Agriculture & Bloodstock	Trusts & Personal Tax	Charities
Blythe Liggins, *Leamington Spa*		★★★★	
Bond Pearce, *Plymouth*		★★★★★★	
Bond Pearce, *Southampton*	★★★		
Boodle Hatfield, *Oxford*		★★★★★★	
Brabner Holden Banks Wilson, *Liverpool*		★★★★★★	★★★
Brachers, *Maidstone*	★★★★★★	★★★	
Brethertons, *Rugby*	★★	★★★★	
Brooke North, *Leeds*		★★★★	
BrookStreet Des Roches, *Witney*			★★
Burd Pearse, *Okehampton*		★★★★	
Burges Salmon, *Bristol*	★★★★★★	★★★★★★	★★★
Burley & Geach, *Petersfield*		★★★	
Burstows, *Crawley*		★★★	
Buss Murton, *Tunbridge Wells*		★★★★	
Butcher & Barlow, *Bury*	★		
Cartmell Shepherd, *Carlisle*	★★★★★★		
Cartwrights, *Bristol*		★★★★	
Charles Lucas & Marshall, *Newbury*			★
Charles Russell, *Cheltenham*		★★★★★★	
Chattertons, *Horncastle*	★★		
Clarke Willmott & Clarke, *Taunton*	★★★★	★★★★★	★★
Clarks, *Reading*		★★★	
Cobbetts, *Manchester*		★★★★★★	★
Cole & Cole, *Oxford*	★★★★★	★★★★★	
Coodes, *St. Austell*		★★★★★	
Cozens-Hardy & Jewson, *Norwich*		★★★	★★★
Cripps Harries Hall, *Tunbridge Wells*	★★★★★	★★★★★★	★
Cuff Roberts, *Liverpool*			★
Denison Till, *Leeds*	★		
Dickinson Dees, *Newcastle-upon-Tyne*	★★★★★★	★★★★★★	★
Donne Mileham & Haddock, *Brighton*		★★★★	
Dunnings, *Honiton*	★★		
Eastleys, *Paignton*		★★★★	
Edmondson Hall, *Newmarket*	★★★★★★		
Edward Harris & Son, *Swansea*	★★★★★		
Edwards Geldard, *Cardiff*		★★★★★★	
Elizabeth Cairns, *Maidstone*			★★★
Eversheds, *Cardiff*		★★★★★★	★★
Eversheds, *Leeds*		★★★★★	
Eversheds, *Newcastle-upon-Tyne*	★★★★★	★★★★★	★
Eversheds, *Norwich*	★★★★★	★★★★★★	★★
Every & Philips, *Honiton*	★★		
Foot & Bowden, *Plymouth*		★★★★	
Ford & Warren, *Leeds*	★		★
Freeth Cartwright Hunt Dickins, *Nottingham*		★★★★	
Furley Page Fielding & Barton, *Canterbury*			★

Leading Firms

Regional Firms (cont.)	Agriculture & Bloodstock	Trusts & Personal Tax	Charities
Gabb & Co, *Abergavenny*	★★		
Gabb & Co, *Hereford*	★★		
Gateley Wareing, *Birmingham*			★★★
George Ide, Phillips, *Chichester*		★★★	
Girlings, *Herne Bay*		★★	
Gordons Wright & Wright, *Bradford*		★★★★	
Grays, *York*	★		★★★
Greathead & Whitelock, *Pembroke*	★		
Greene & Greene, *Bury St. Edmunds*	★★★	★★★★★	
Greenwoods, *Peterborough*	★		★★
Griffith Smith, *Brighton*		★★★	★★
Hallett & Co, *Ashford*	★★★	★★★	
Halliwell Landau, *Manchester*		★★★★★★	★
Harris & Harris, *Wells*	★		
Harrowell Shaftoe, *York*		★★★	
Harvey Ingram Owston, *Leicester*			★★★
Henmans, *Oxford*	★	★★★	
Heptonstalls, *Goole*	★		
Herbert Wilkes, *Birmingham*		★★★★	
Hewitson Becke + Shaw, *Cambridge*	★★★	★★★★★★	
Hewitson Becke + Shaw, *Northampton*	★★★	★★★★★★	★★
Higgs & Sons, *Brierley Hill*		★★★★	
Hood Vores & Allwood, *Dereham*		★★★	
Hooper & Wollen, *Torquay*		★★★★★	
Howes Percival, *Norwich*	★★★		
Humphries Kirk, *Wareham*	★		
Iliffes Booth Bennett, *Uxbridge*		★★★★★	★
Irwin Mitchell, *Sheffield*		★★★★	★
Jeffreys & Powell, *Brecon*	★★★		
Jonathan Stephens & Co, *Usk*	★★★★★		
Jones Maidment Wilson, *Manchester*		★★★★★	
Knight & Sons, *Newcastle-under-Lyme*	★★★		
Knights, *Tunbridge Wells*	★★★		
Lamport Bassitt, *Southampton*		★★★	
Lanyon Bowdler, *Shrewsbury*	★★★		
Latimer Hinks, *Darlington*	★★	★★★	
Lawrence Tucketts, *Bristol*		★★★★★	
Leathes Prior, *Norwich*			★★
Lee Crowder, *Birmingham*		★★★★★	
Lees Lloyd Whitley, *Liverpool*		★★★★★	
Lester Aldridge, *Bournemouth*		★★★★★	★
Linnells, *Oxford*	★		★
Lupton Fawcett, *Leeds*		★★★★★	
Malcolm Lynch, *Leeds*			★★★★
Manby & Steward, *Wolverhampton*	★★		
Manches & Co, *Oxford*			★★★

Leading Firms

Regional Firms (cont.)	Agriculture & Bloodstock	Trusts & Personal Tax	Charities
Mander Hadley & Co, *Coventry*			**
Margraves, *Llandrindod Wells*	******		
Marshall & Galpin, *Oxford*		**	
Martineau Johnson, *Birmingham*	**	******	***
Mason & Moore Dutton, *Chester*	***		
Matthew Arnold & Baldwin, *Watford*		***	
Matthew McCloy & Partners, *Newbury*	******		
Mayo & Perkins, *Eastbourne*		**	
Meade-King, *Bristol*		*****	
Michelmores, *Exeter*		*****	**
Mills & Reeve, *Norwich*	******	******	***
Moore & Blatch, *Lymington*		*****	
Morgan Bruce, *Cardiff*			**
Morton Fisher, *Worcester*	***		
Nabarro Nathanson, *Reading*			***
Oglethorpe Sturton & Gillibrand, *Lancaster*	*****		
Osborne Clarke, *Bristol*	*	******	***
Oswald Goodier & Co, *Preston*			**
Palmer Wheeldon, *Cambridge*	****		
Pannone & Partners, *Manchester*			*
Pardoes, *Bridgwater*	**		
Paris Smith & Randall, *Southampton*		****	
Parker Bullen, *Salisbury*			**
Parrott & Coales, *Aylesbury*	*		
Penningtons, *Basingstoke*	***		
Peter, Peter & Wright, *Holsworthy*	**		
Pictons, *St. Albans*		***	
Pinsent Curtis, *Leeds*		*****	**
Porter Dodson, *Yeovil*	***		
Prettys, *Ipswich*	*	*****	
Price & Son, *Haverfordwest*	****		
Pryce & Co, *Abingdon*	***		
R. Gwynne & Sons, *Wellington*	**	****	
Rawlison & Butler, *Crawley*		**	
Rickerby Watterson, *Cheltenham*			*
Rollit Farrell & Bladon, *Hull*	*****	***	*
Roythorne & Co, *Spalding*	******	****	
Rustons & Lloyd, *Newmarket*	******		
Senior Calveley & Hardy, *Lytham St. Annes*	**		
Shakespeares, *Birmingham*		****	***
Sharman & Trethewy, *Bedford*	*		
Slee Blackwell, *Barnstaple*	*		
Sparling Benham & Brough, *Colchester*		***	
Staffurth & Bray, *Bognor Regis*		***	
Stanley Tee & Company, *Bishop's Stortford*	*****	***	
Steele & Co, *Norwich*		***	

169

Leading Firms

Regional Firms (cont.)	Agriculture & Bloodstock	Trusts & Personal Tax	Charities
Steele Raymond, *Bournemouth*		★★★★★	
Stephens & Scown, *Exeter*	★★★★		
Stevens & Bolton, *Guildford*		★★★	
Stone King, *Bath*			★★★★
Stones Cann & Hallett, *Exeter*	★★	★★★★★	
Tallents Godfrey & Co, *Newark-on-Trent*	★★		★★
Taylor Vinters, *Cambridge*	★★★★★★	★★★★★	★★★
Thomas Eggar Church Adams, *Chichester*	★★★★★★	★★★★★★	★★
Thomson Snell & Passmore, *Tunbridge Wells*		★★★★★★	★★★
Thrings & Long, *Bath*	★★★★		★★
Thursfields, *Kidderminster*	★★		
Tozers, *Exeter*			★★★
Turbervilles with Nelson Cuff, *Uxbridge*		★★★	
Ungoed Thomas & King, *Carmarthen*	★★★		
Veale Wasbrough, *Bristol*		★★★★★	
Wace Morgan, *Shrewsbury*	★★		
Walker Morris, *Leeds*		★★★	
Walker Smith & Way, *Chester*	★★★★★		
Wansbroughs Willey Hargrave, *Bristol*			★★★
Ward Gethin, *King's Lynn*		★★★★★	
Ward Hadaway, *Newcastle-upon-Tyne*	★★★★★★	★★★★	
White & Bowker, *Winchester*	★★★★★★	★★★	
Whitehead Monckton, *Maidstone*		★★★	
Wiggin and Co, *Cheltenham*		★★★★★★	
Wilkin Chapman, *Grimsby*	★		
Wilkin Chapman, *Louth*	★★		
Willcox & Lewis, *Norwich*		★★★	
Willcox Lane Clutterbuck, *Birmingham*		★★★★	
Wilsons Solicitors, *Salisbury*	★★★★★	★★★★★★	★★★
Winckworth & Pemberton), *Oxford*			★★★
Woollcombe Beer Watts, *Newton Abbot*	★	★★★★	
Wragge & Co, *Birmingham*		★★★★★	★★★
Wright Hassall & Co, *Leamington Spa*	★★★★★		
Wrigleys, *Leeds*	★	★★★★★	★★★

Firms and their star ratings are based on Chambers' Directory 1998–1999. Six stars represent a top-ranked firm, five stars a second-ranked firm, etc. See page 3 for further details.

PROJECTS
(including PFI, Construction and Energy)

Area of law

Project finance – the structuring, financing, construction and operation of infrastructure developments such as roads, power stations, bridges and telecommunications networks – is a sexy area for many of the leading UK firms. Many firms now have stand-alone project groups and the high profile, international nature of the work attracts many of the most talented lawyers in the UK and overseas. The projects are located throughout the world and project lawyers come from every major jurisdiction. However, the major projects are dominated by a few City firms and the largest US practices.

PFI/PPP

In the UK, the Private Finance Initiative (PFI), or Public Private Partnerships (PPP) as it is now called, has provided an important source of work. The objective of PFI is to introduce private funding and management into areas which were previously the domain of government, such as the building and operation of roads and hospitals. Through PFI, many smaller London firms and regional practices have become involved in projects work for the first time.

Construction

The physical building of infrastructure projects is only a small, if vital, part of project finance. Similarly, for most construction departments, project finance developments are only one of several sources of work. There are two aspects to construction work: developing the contractual arrangements prior to building work starting (negotiating the contracts between the employer, the contractor, sub-contractors, architects, engineers, surveyors, interior designers, etc.) and litigating when it all goes horribly wrong. Most construction practices do both contentious and non-contentious work. Some, however, are better known for one or the other. Fenwick Elliott is renowned for litigating when buildings are defective or late, while Cameron McKenna's reputation rests on its building work.

Energy

Some energy projects fall within the heading 'Project Finance' – eg, the development of the Laibin B 2x360MW power station in China – but 'energy' is a much wider field. Examples of general energy work include Cameron McKenna advising on the establishment of electricity trading arrangements in California, and Denton Hall advising the Greek Government on the creation of a gas supply industry.

Type of work

Projects vary from telecoms links in Tajikistan, oil pipelines in the Caucasus, power projects in India, toll roads in South Africa and gold mines in Indonesia, to PFI hospital projects in Ipswich and sewage plants in Scotland. The exact nature of the work depends on the type, size and location of the project. However, almost all the major infrastructure projects in which regional firms are involved will be PFI projects of one sort or another. In addition to PFI and PPP other common acronyms include BOO (Build, own and operate); BOOT (Build, own, operate, transfer) and DBFO (Design, build, finance, operate) to name but a few.

Projects work also varies depending on the type of client a firm is acting for. There are a number of parties in a project finance development. There is the *project company* – usually a special purpose company established to build, own and operate (hence BOO) the power station or whatever the project is. Often the project company is a joint venture between a number of *project sponsors* who contribute equity to part-fund the project. Project sponsors could include the manufacturer of the gas turbines to be installed in the power station, the construction company that will erect the plant, and the power company that will buy the electricity produced.

The company could also be partially owned by a government body or banks.

The *project promoter* is the organisation that commissions the project. It could be an NHS Trust that wants a new hospital built, or a host government which thinks a privately financed motorway would be a great idea. *Funders* provide the finance to build the project. Funders include banks, guarantors, export credit agencies, governments, and international funding agencies and they operate in consortiums and individually. Other categories of client are the contractors, operators, and so on. Each party requires its own legal representation.

A common feature of most major projects is the tender process. A public authority or major corporation (the procurer) will invite interested parties (bidders) to tender on the design, building, financing and operation (ie, DBFO) of a project. At the end of this tender process – which can last up to two years – the winning company or consortium will be selected to manage the project. This company will then have to secure the finance, obtain the necessary planning permission and agree construction, service and employment contracts. Lawyers advising on any of these contracts must understand the big picture. They have to see how changing one contractual term will have a knock-on effect throughout the entire transaction.

Charles Robson, a partner in Lovell White Durrant's projects department, acted for the banks in one of the PFI's flagship hospital projects, the £300m Norfolk and Norwich. "A commercial deal was struck between the project company and the NHS Trust. In the deal, the Trust promised to pay for the delivery of a new building and the services within it." says Robson. "There were two main parts to our role. We assessed how the principal parties had apportioned the risk in the project, and advised the bank on any amendments to their documents." This can sometimes include a renegotiation of the deal. The firm's other primary function was drafting the credit agreement between the project company and the banks, and the security documentation that supports it.

PFI's youth means there is still a lot of ground-breaking negotiation to be done. "It's certainly interesting, and can be pretty exhausting at times," says Robson.

The above is an example of a UK project. International transactions are generally larger, more complex and can appear more glamorous. Chris Wyman at Clifford Chance recently acted for the sponsors of a European airport. "We had to negotiate a concession with the government, sort out the contracts with the contractors and employ an airport operator. We even had to arrange for an inconvenient mountain to be lowered." Projects like these have many aspects and the legal projects team has to be master of them all.

Skills needed

Many projects lawyers have a background and specialism in another area of law such as banking, corporate, construction or property, and have broadened this specialism into an understanding of the range of issues that face projects clients. The diverse nature of projects work means that good projects lawyers need to have an all-round "commercial awareness". First they must be able to recognise when there is a deal there to be done. They then need the patience and resilience to see that deal through, without getting bogged down in details or in the mountains of paper produced by the project. Tact and diplomacy are assets, especially when negotiating risk and favourable terms for the client.

Lawyers advising on major international projects must be prepared to travel overseas several times a year, or even to live abroad for protracted periods. Before deciding to specialise in this type of work, personal circumstances should be considered. Trips abroad may sound glamorous, and there may be time to sample the local culture, but they won't be sightseeing tours. Client offices and big city hotels tend to look the same all over the world, even if they take 10 hours and a series of unpleasant inoculations to get to. For those unwilling to travel overseas, a firm that specialises in domestic PFI work would be more suitable.

Career options

Lawyers used to specialise in major projects after gaining several years' experience in a relevant discipline. Whilst a lot of people continue to enter projects work via this route, many take a more direct approach. It is now possible to specialise in projects work on qualification.

Nearly all international projects are governed (to varying degrees) by English law or New York law, so experience in this field is internationally marketable. American law firms in particular are recruiting experienced English lawyers, which has forced up salaries to make international projects work one of the highest paid specialisms in the legal world. Four year qualified assistants can expect anything up to £70k.

The Firms

International project finance is essentially a game for the largest of firms. Firms need an international presence, ideally with offices in the regions where the projects are located and in the financial markets where the funding is raised. Only a handful of English firms are significant players in the international market, however these – especially Allen & Overy, Clifford Chance, Linklaters, Freshfields and Norton Rose – are among the very best. Other well known firms are Ashurst Morris Crisp, Denton Hall and Wilde Sapte. All these firms have large teams working all over the world. (This year at Allen & Overy, for example, 30 partners and 70 assistants have worked on projects in 32 different countries from 19 overseas offices).

A number of American firms undertake projects work from London. Best known are Millbank, Tweed, Hadley & McCoy; White & Case and Shearman & Stirling.

PFI

PFI is essentially project finance in the UK. Unsurprisingly, the same firms that feature in project finance also undertake PFI. Some City firms however have a higher profile in PFI than they do in international project finance. Herbert Smith got involved in PFI when many firms were unsure whether it would work. In consequence, it is now one of the market leaders. Other firms who don't undertake international work, have reputations in PFI. Bird & Bird is well known for IT and telecoms PFIs, Berwin Leighton for property projects and Beachcroft Stanley for NHS projects.

Regional firms feature highly in PFI, usually acting for the public sector. The leading firms are Addleshaw Booth & Co in Leeds and Manchester; Eversheds (particularly for education and local authority PFIs), Pinsent Curtis, Dibb Lupton Alsop and Dickinson Dees. Masons' offices in Leeds, Manchester and Bristol are known mainly for their work for contractor led consortiums.

Construction

A large number of firms get involved in both contentious and non-contentious construction. Masons leads the field in London and has offices around the country and the world. Cameron McKenna and Rowe & Maw also have strong reputations. There are a number of niche construction practices with national, and even international, reputations. These include Fenwick Elliott (London), Shadbolt & Co (Reigate) and Neil F. Jones (Birmingham).

Energy

The City firms have a strong hold on energy work. Denton Hall is particularly good for gas work and Herbert Smith for electricity. Of the regional firms, Martineau Johnson in Birmingham acts for the National Grid on regulatory issues, Bond Pearce in Plymouth is well known in wind farms and Nabarro Nathanson in Sheffield is a leading coal practice. ▶

Leading Firms

London Firms	Projects	PFI	Construction	Energy
Allen & Overy	★★★★★★	★★★★★	★	★★★★★
Ashurst Morris Crisp	★★★★	★★★★	★★★	★★★★★
Baker & McKenzie	★★★		★	★
Barlow Lyde & Gilbert			★	
Beachcroft Stanleys		★★		★
Beale and Company			★	
Berrymans Lace Mawer			★★	
Berwin Leighton		★★★★	★★★	
Bird & Bird		★★★		
Cameron McKenna	★★★★	★★★★	★★★★	★★★★★
Clifford Chance	★★★★★★	★★★★★	★★★	★★★★★
Clyde & Co				★★★
Coudert Brothers	★★			
Davies Arnold Cooper			★★★	
Denton Hall	★★★★	★★★★★	★★	★★★★★★
Dibb Lupton Alsop			★	
Edge Ellison			★★	★
Eversheds				★★
Fenwick Elliott			★★★	
Field Fisher Waterhouse				★★
Freshfields	★★★★★	★★★★★	★★	★★★★★
Glovers			★★	
Hammond Suddards			★★★	
Herbert Smith	★★★★	★★★★★★	★★★	★★★★★★
Holman, Fenwick & Willan				★★
Ince & Co				★★
Lawrence Graham		★		★★★
Linklaters	★★★★★★	★★★★★★	★★★	★★★★★
Lovell White Durrant	★★★	★★★★★	★★★	★★★★
Macfarlanes		★		
Manches & Co			★	
Masons	★★	★★★	★★★★★★	★★
Milbank, Tweed, Hadley	★★★★★			
Nabarro Nathanson		★★	★	★★★★
Nicholson Graham & Jones			★★★	
Norton Rose	★★★★★	★★★	★★	★★★★
Richards Butler				★
Rowe & Maw		★	★★★★	
S J Berwin & Co	★★	★★	★★★	
Shearman & Sterling	★★★			
Simmons & Simmons	★★★	★★★	★	★★★
Slaughter and May	★★★★	★★★		★★★★
Speechly Bircham			★	
Taylor Joynson Garrett	★★		★★★	

Firms and their star ratings are based on Chambers' Directory 1998–1999. Six stars represent a top-ranked firm, five stars a second-ranked firm, etc. See page 3 for further details.

Leading Firms

London Firms (cont.)	Projects	PFI	Construction	Energy
Trowers & Hamlins	★★		★★	★
Warner Cranston			★★	
Watson, Farley & Williams				
Wedlake Bell				★
White & Case	★★★★		★★	
Wilde Sapte	★★★★	★★★★		
Winward Fearon			★★★	

Leading Firms

Regional Firms	Projects/PFI	Construction	Energy
Aaron & Partners, *Chester*			★
Addleshaw Booth, *Leeds*	★★★★★★	★★★★★★	
Addleshaw Booth, *Manchester*	★★★★★★	★★★★★	
Ashton Bond Gigg, *Nottingham*		★★	
Bevan Ashford, *Bristol*	★★★★	★★★★	
Birketts, *Ipswich*		★★★	
Blake Lapthorn, *Portsmouth*		★★★	
Bond Pearce, *Southampton*		★★★	★★★
Burges Salmon, *Bristol*	★★★★	★★★★	
Clarks, *Reading*		★★	
Cole & Cole, *Oxford*		★★★	
Corbett & Co, *Teddington*		★	
Crane & Walton, *Leicester*			★
Cripps Harries Hall, *Tunbridge Wells*		★★★	
Davies Arnold Cooper, *Manchester*	★★	★★★	
Deborah Mills Associates, *Marlow*			★★
Denison Till, *Leeds*		★★★	
Dibb Lupton Alsop, *Birmingham*	★★★★★★	★★★★★	
Dibb Lupton Alsop, *Sheffield*		★★★★★	
Dickinson Dees, *Newcastle*	★★★★★	★★★★★	★★
Edge Ellison, *Birmingham*	★★★★	★★★★★	★★
Edwards Geldard, *Cardiff*		★★	
Edwards Geldard, *Deeside*			★★
Elliott & Company, *Manchester*		★★	
Eversheds, *Birmingham*		★★★	★★
Eversheds, *Cardiff*		★★★	
Eversheds, *Derby*		★★	
Eversheds, *Leeds*	★★★★★★	★★★★★	★★★
Eversheds, *Manchester*	★★★★★★		
Eversheds, *Newcastle-upon-Tyne*		★★★★★★	
Eversheds, *Norwich*		★★★	
Eversheds, *Nottingham*	★★★★★	★★	
Foot & Bowden, *Plymouth*			★
Freeth Cartwright, *Nottingham*		★★	

Leading Firms

Regional Firms (cont.)	Projects/PFI	Construction	Energy
Garretts, *Birmingham*		★★	
Garretts, *Leeds*	★★		
Gateley Wareing, *Birmingham*		★★★★	
Greenwoods, *Peterborough*		★★★★★	
Hacking Ashton, *Newcastle-u-Lyme*		★★★	
Halliwell Landau, *Manchester*		★★★	
Hammond Suddards, *Leeds*		★★★★★	
Hammond Suddards, *Manchester*		★★★★★	
Hay & Kilner, *Newcastle-upon-Tyne*		★★	
Hewitson Becke, *Cambridge*		★★★★★	
Hill Dickinson, *Liverpool*		★★	
Hugh James, *Cardiff*		★★★	
Irwin Mitchell, *Sheffield*	★★★		
Kent Jones & Done, *Stoke-on-Trent*			★
Kirk Jackson, *Manchester*		★★★★	
Knight & Sons, *Newcastle-u-Lyme*		★★	★
Laytons, *Bristol*		★★★★★	
Linnells, *Oxford*		★★	
Malcolm Lynch, *Leeds*			★
Martineau Johnson, *Birmingham*			★★★
Masons, *Bristol*	★★★★★	★★★★★★	
Masons, *Leeds*	★★★★★	★★★★★★	
Masons, *Manchester*	★★★★★	★★★★★★	
Merricks, *Birmingham*		★★	
Merricks, *Ipswich*		★★★	
Mills & Reeve, *Cambridge*	★★★★★	★★★★★★	
Morgan Bruce, *Cardiff*	★★★★★	★★★	
Nabarro Nathanson, *Sheffield*		★★★	★★★
Neil F. Jones & Co, *Birmingham*		★★★★★★	
Pannone & Partners, *Manchester*		★	
Pinsent Curtis, *Birmingham*	★★★★★★	★★★★	★★
Pinsent Curtis, *Leeds*	★★★★★★		★★
Prettys, *Ipswich*		★★	
Robert Muckle, *Newcastle*		★★★★	
Shadbolt & Co, *Reigate*		★★★	
Stephens & Scown, *Exeter*			★
Stones Cann & Hallett, *Exeter*		★★	
Townsends, *Swindon*		★★	
Veale Wasbrough, *Bristol*	★★★★★	★★★★	★★
Wake Dyne Lawton, *Chester*			★
Walker Morris, *Leeds*		★★★★	
Wansbroughs, *Bristol*		★★★★	
Wansbroughs, *Sheffield*	★★★		
Ward Hadaway, *Newcastle*		★★	
Watson Burton, *Newcastle*		★★★★	
Wragge & Co, *Birmingham*	★★★★★	★★★★★★	★★★

PROPERTY

Area of law

The everyday work of a commercial property lawyer involves the sale, purchase and letting of business properties, which include retail, leisure, industrial and office premises. Property litigators are called in to negotiate the relationship between landlord and tenant as well as to resolve disputes. The basic principles of land and contract law form the backbone of property work.

During the last recession, the large City firms streamlined their property departments, and newly-qualified lawyers were reluctant to practise in this field. With the upturn in the economy leading to a mini property boom the balance was redressed and there has been a busy market for both experienced and newly-qualified property lawyers for the last few years. The current talk of another recession means property lawyers are anticipating a further turn in the commercial property market over the next year.

Property transactions are increasingly complex, and leading firms field teams of specialists in property-related tax, construction, planning, environment, PFI, development and finance. Many firms also have specialist property litigation units.

Type of work

Lawyers in other practice areas often see property as boring when set beside 'sexy' areas such as corporate finance. Geoffrey Lander, head of Nabarro Nathanson's commercial property department, does not agree. "Property lawyers are corporate lawyers whose commodity is property. It's as much about deal-making as poring over leases."

The areas of practice covered by a commercial property department are varied and offer lawyers an opportunity to make use of many different aspects of their legal knowledge, says James Harbach, senior assistant at leading London firm Linklaters. As for the complexity of property work, Geoffrey Marks at Halliwell Landau recently finished a deal concerning the

Bridgewater office development in Manchester. Five law firms were involved and meetings frequently involved up to thirty people.

Deal-making tends to be the preserve of partners. But at a lower level, the work can still be full of variety. James Harbach says that a recently qualified lawyer could expect to have primary responsibility for sales and purchases of office blocks, shopping centres and industrial parks, landlord and tenant disputes, negotiating construction warranties and providing or obtaining financing for property deals. Probably more than any other area of practice, commercial property offers newly qualified lawyers the opportunity to play a significant role in commercial transactions covering many different areas of the law such as insolvency (inevitable during a recession) and tax. "One of the main attractions of practising within a commercial property department is that lawyers tend to work closely with clients and are very 'hands on' from an early stage with a great deal of responsibility and autonomy."

Samantha Lake Coghlan, a fourth seat trainee at City firm Ashurst Morris Crisp, spent her first six months in the property department. "I went in expecting to find it boring and didn't consider it a long-term prospect. I've come out with a completely different opinion. The area was more diverse than I ever expected and included support work on corporate deals. I was amazed how many different aspects there are to buying a piece of land."

"My first sale was of industrial land. The client's agent contacted me, told me all about it and then sent me some 'Heads of Terms' covering basic points that had been agreed between the two sides. From those, I created the sale document which was then passed between the two sides for amendment. I had my client's instructions and fought his corner."

She was surprised by the amount of client contact. "I went to a lot of meetings, was continually on the 'phone and often met clients over drinks.

I'd advise trainees with no intention of ending up in property to take a seat there, if only because it's such an important part of corporate law." Samantha is now very keen to qualify into the property department when she qualifies in March 1999.

For a two-year qualified assistant in a large commercial property department the day might begin at 8.30. You'll go through the morning's correspondence and any overnight faxes before continuing work on a lease you've been drafting. It's got to be finished today and sent off to the other side for their comments. But before you can finish it, you're called in by a partner who's working on a major development. He needs some assistance – reporting on title, going through the proposed leases. In the afternoon, you're off to the development for a site visit. You've been there 20 minutes when your mobile phone rings. The corporate department is working on a big transaction which has to be completed by the end of the week. You're needed to deal with the property aspects. So you get back to the office. You want to clear your desk, but first you've got to finish that lease you've been working on. You've just started work when a client calls. He wants to know why you haven't exchanged contracts on a property he's selling. You tell him it's because the other side's still got the documents. He doesn't want to know. He just wants the deal done. So you're on the phone to the other side, telling them to get a move on. It's now 6pm and you finally turn back to your lease... .

In the property litigation department, life is just as busy. A day may be spent advising on a boundary dispute, considering a rent review, replying to a domestic nuisance enquiry and advising a major supermarket on site contamination. Like their colleagues in general commercial litigation, property litigators now do a lot of the work which used to be referred to counsel such as drafting pleadings and advocacy.

Skills needed

"The mark of a good property lawyer, as opposed to an average one, is that extra bit of business acumen," says Geoffrey Marks of Halliwell Landau. "You have to know what to fight for, what you can let go, and how to get people to agree. A lot of the time you are weighing up the opposition and deciding how best to play them. Sometimes you have to be emollient, other times you need to stick the boot in."

He also picks out stamina as a vital quality. "Major transactions are demanding and clients can be too. This isn't a nine to five job. Sometimes you'll have to sign a contract in 48 hours which means dropping everything to see it through."

Property litigators require flexibility, says Clifford Chance partner John Pickston. "You need the ability to move from advising on a complex point of property law, to negotiating a practical commercial solution to a dispute, to drafting pleadings and acting as an advocate."

Career options

Property is at the mercy of the economic cycle. In a downturn, career options are bleak – unless you have a property finance/insolvency practice which thrives on the misery of others! But during an upturn a property lawyer becomes very marketable and junior lawyers in small or provincial practices can easily find their way into City firms. Practitioners are anticipating a downturn in the market over the next year although by the time current undergraduates reach qualification the cycle will no doubt have turned again.

It is worth bearing in mind career options within private practice but outside fee-earning work. Julia Simmonds trained and qualified at Linklaters, the leading property firm in the country. After three years in the department she decided she wanted to return to academic work and took up a place on a part-time LLM (Masters in Law). She was offered a part-time job at Wilde Sapte as a property information lawyer. This is essentially a research post which entails training the property department, keeping them up-to-date on the latest developments in the law and drafting and amending in-house precedents. There is no direct client contact. When she had completed her LLM, Julia stayed on in the position working a 4-day week. Usually information, or "know-how" lawyers are highly experienced fee-earners who want to avoid the long and uncertain hours of fee-earning. It is a popular position for "maternity returners."

Other academic jobs are available with institutions such as the Law Commission, where there is opportunity to influence the drafting of future legislation.

Opportunities in-house are always hard to come by, but jobs in industry and business do crop up. Companies such as AMEC plc, ARCO British Ltd, Clyde Petroleum plc, ICL and Lasmo plc all have legal departments and lawyers with commercial, property and litigation experience are valuable to them.

Another option is a move into property development work, either going to work for an established company or setting up on your own. "I often wonder why more property lawyers don't go into development work", says Geoffrey Marks, "as they have an intimate knowledge of how the market works." The downside is the length of time and the money involved in getting development projects off the ground. Property investment is a simpler concept and may provide more openings for property lawyers with some financial knowledge.

The Firms

Commercial Property
The best property departments tend to be part of the larger commercial firms in the country. The leading national property firm is Linklaters, the second largest firm in London and one of the leading corporate City firms. It now has a pan-European presence since its alliance with firms in Belgium, the Netherlands, Sweden and Germany. Nabarro Nathanson is well-known as a strong property firm and has a huge department of 35 partners and 100 assistants. Also very well-regarded are the property departments of Ashurst Morris Crisp, Berwin Leighton and Clifford Chance. Berwin Leighton has been acting for English Partnerships, owner of the

Millennium Dome site, on the creation and development of the site and the sale of the Millennium village and superstore site.

Outside London Addleshaw Booth & Co has strong property departments in Leeds and Manchester. National firm Eversheds leads in Wales, where they do a lot of work for the Welsh Development Agency, in Manchester where they are involved with the post-bomb city centre regeneration and in Leeds, East Anglia and Birmingham.

Throughout the country there are smaller niche practices with very high quality property departments. In London, Maxwell Batley is such a firm; 40% of its workload is property and it is one of the leading small practices. Outside London, Paris Smith & Randall in Southampton acts for government departments including the Department of Transport and the Benefits Agency. Cobbetts in Manchester provides strong competition to the big guns of Addleshaws, Dibbs, Halliwell Landau and Eversheds.

Some property departments have strong links with other practices. Burges Salmon in Bristol combines its leading property and agriculture practices and handles agricultural property work for clients such as the NFU. They also handle work for commercial clients such as FirstGroup Plc's acquisition of the majority shareholding in Bristol International Airport plc.

Property finance work is strong in firms such as Allen & Overy, Clifford Chance and Wilde Sapte.

Property Litigation
A strong property litigation practice inevitably goes hand in hand with a strong commercial property practice and it is no surprise to find that Nabarro Nathanson and Linklaters lead the field in London, Burges Salmon is dominant in the south west and Addleshaw Booth & Co leads in the north east.

In the south east Donne Mileham & Haddock leads the field working from the Commercial

179

Property Services Group. Many regional practices have a less commercial bent. Hugh James in Cardiff handles primarily Housing Association work and does more tenant work than the other leading firms in Wales. McGrath & Co in Birmingham acts primarily for legally-aided clients; travellers, gypsies and others in housing need. They recently established ownership of land for two gypsies parked under a fly-over. Anthony Collins Solicitors, another Birmingham firm, are also known for work within the social housing sector.

There are other alternatives to working in a large commercial practice. Dewar Hogan, set up by an ex-Nabarros partner who also founded the Property Litigation Association, is an example of a niche property litigation practice.

Leading Firms

London Firms	Commercial Property	Property Litigation
Allen & Overy	★★★	
Ashurst Morris Crisp	★★★★★	★★★
Berwin Leighton	★★★★★	★★★★★
Boodle Hatfield	★	★★
Cameron McKenna	★★★	★★★★
Clifford Chance	★★★★★	★★★★★
Coudert Brothers	★	
D J Freeman	★★★	★★★
Denton Hall	★★★	★★★★★★
Dewar Hogan		★★
Dibb Lupton Alsop	★★	★★★
Druces & Attlee		★
Eversheds	★★	
Fenners	★	
Field Fisher Waterhouse	★★	★
Finers	★	
Fladgate Fielder	★	
Forsters	★	
Forsyte Saunders Kerman	★★	★
Freshfields	★★★	
Glovers	★	
Gouldens	★★★	
Hamlin Slowe	★	
Herbert Smith	★★★★	★★★★★
Julian Holy	★	
Lawrence Graham	★★	★★★★★
Linklaters	★★★★★	★★★★★★
Lovell White Durrant	★★★★	★★★★★
Macfarlanes	★★	★★★
Manches & Co	★★	
Maples Teesdale		★
Masons		★★★★
Maxwell Batley	★★★	★★
McGuinness Finch	★★	

Firms and their star ratings are based on Chambers' Directory 1998–1999. Six stars represent a top-ranked firm, five stars a second-ranked firm, etc. See page 3 for further details.

Leading Firms

London Firms (cont.)	Commercial Property	Property Litigation
Mishcon de Reya	★	
Nabarro Nathanson	★★★★★	★★★★★★
Nicholson Graham & Jones	★★	
Norton Rose	★★★	
Olswang	★★	★★★
Paisner & Co	★	
Park Nelson	★	
Radcliffes		★★
Richards Butler	★★	
Rowe & Maw	★★	★★★★
S J Berwin & Co	★★★★	★★★★★
Simmons & Simmons	★★★	★★★★
Slaughter and May	★★	
Speechly Bircham	★	★★★
Stephenson Harwood		★★★
Stepien Lake Gilbert & Paling	★	
Teacher Stern Selby	★	
Thomas Eggar Church Adams	★	★★
Titmuss Sainer Dechert	★★★	★★★★
Travers Smith Braithwaite	★★	
Trowers & Hamlins	★	
Wedlake Bell	★	
Wilde Sapte	★★	

Leading Firms

Regional Firms	Commercial Property	Property Litigation
Aaron & Partners, *Chester*	★★	
Addleshaw Booth & Co, *Leeds*	★★★★★★	★★★★★★
Addleshaw Booth & Co, *Manchester*	★★★★★★	★★★★★
Addleshaw Booth & Co, *Sheffield*		★★★★★★
Andrew M. Jackson, *Hull*	★★	
Anthony Collins, *Birmingham*		★★★
Archers, *Stockton-on-Tees*	★	
Attey Bower & Jones, *Doncaster*	★	
B.P. Collins, *Gerrards Cross*	★★	
Band Hatton, *Coventry*	★	
Barker, Booth & E, *Blackpool*	★★	
Beor Wilson & Lloyd, *Swansea*	★★	
Bermans, *Liverpool*	★★★★	
Berry Smith, *Cardiff*	★★★★	
Berrymans, *Liverpool*	★★	
Bevan Ashford, *Bristol*	★★★★	★★
Birketts, *Ipswich*	★★★	

Leading Firms

Regional Firms (cont.)	Commercial Property	Property Litigation
Blake Lapthorn, *Fareham*	★★★	
Bobbetts Mackan, *Bristol*		★★
Bond Pearce, *Exeter*	★★★★★	★★★
Bond Pearce, *Plymouth*	★★★★★	
Bond Pearce, *Southampton*	★★★	
Boyce Hatton, *Torquay*	★	
Brabner Holden, *Liverpool*	★★	
Brachers, *Maidstone*		★★★★
Bremner Sons, *Liverpool*	★★	
Bretherton Price, *Cheltenham*	★	
BrookStreet, *Witney*	★★	
Browne Jacobson, *Nottingham*		★★
Bullivant Jones & Co, *Liverpool*	★★★★★	
Burges Salmon, *Bristol*	★★★★★★	★★★★★★
Burstows, *Crawley*		★★
Cartwrights, *Bristol*	★★	★★★
Chaffe Street, *Manchester*	★★	
Charles Russell, *Cheltenham*	★	
Clarke Willmott, *Taunton*	★★★★	
Clarks, *Reading*	★★	
Cobbetts, *Manchester*	★★★★★★	★★★★★★
Coffin Mew, *Portsmouth*	★	★★★★★
Cole & Cole, *Oxford*	★	
Colemans, *Maidenhead*	★	
Crawford Owen, *Bristol*	★★★★	
Cripps, *Tunbridge Wells*	★★	★★★★
Cuff Roberts, *Liverpool*	★★★★	
Davies and Prtnrs, *Gloucester*	★★	
Davies Wallis Foyster, *Liverpool*	★★★★★	
Dean Wilson, *Brighton*	★	
Denison Till, *Leeds*	★	
Denton Hall, *Milton Keynes*	★★★	★★★★★
Dibb Lupton Alsop, *Birmingham*	★★	
Dibb Lupton Alsop, *Leeds*	★★★★★	★★★★★
Dibb Lupton Alsop, *Liverpool*	★★★★★★	
Dibb Lupton Alsop, *Manchester*	★★★★★★	★★★★★★
Dickinson Dees, *Newcastle*	★★★★★	★★★★
Dolmans, *Cardiff*	★	
Donne Mileham, *Brighton*	★★★	★★★★★★
Edge Ellison, *Birmingham*	★★★★	★★★★★★
Edwards Geldard, *Cardiff*	★★★★★★	★★★★★
Elliott & Company, *Manchester*	★★	
Ellison & Co, *Colchester*	★	
Eversheds, *Birmingham*	★★★★★	★★★★★
Eversheds, *Bristol*	★	★★★
Eversheds, *Cardiff*	★★★★★★	★★★★★★

Leading Firms

Regional Firms (cont.)	Commercial Property	Property Litigation
Eversheds, Derby		★★★★★
Eversheds, Ipswich		★★★★★★
Eversheds, Leeds	★★★★★	★★★★★
Eversheds, Manchester	★★★★★★	★★★★★★
Eversheds, Newcastle-upon-Tyne	★★★	★★★★★
Eversheds, Norwich	★★★★	★★★★★★
Eversheds, Nottingham		★★★★★
Few & Kester, Cambridge	★★	
Field Cunningham, Manchester	★★★★★	
Foot & Bowden, Plymouth	★	★★
Freeth Cartwright, Nottingham	★	★★★
Garretts, Leeds	★★★	
Gordons Wright, Bradford	★★	
Gorna & Co, Manchester	★★	★★★★
Gosschalks, Hull	★★★	
Gotelee & Goldsmith, Ipswich	★★	
Greenland Houchen, Norwich	★★	
Greenwoods, Peterborough	★★	
H. Montlake & Co, Ilford	★★★	
Halliwell Landau, Manchester	★★★★★★	★★★★★
Hammond Suddards, Leeds	★★★	★★★★★
Hammond Suddards, Manchester	★★★★	
Hancock & Lawrence, Truro	★	
Harold Benjamin, Harrow	★★	★★★
Harvey Ingram, Leicester	★	
Hawkins Russell Jones, Hitchin	★	
Hewitson Becke, Cambridge	★★★	★★★
Hewitson Becke, Northampton	★★	
Higgs & Sons, Brierley Hill	★★	
Hill Dickinson, Liverpool	★★★	
Hugh James, Cardiff	★★★★	★★★★★★
Irwin Mitchell, Sheffield	★★★	
Jacksons, Stockton-on-Tees	★★	
Jones Maidment, Manchester	★★★	
Kenneth Elliott, Romford	★★★	
Kitsons, Torquay	★	
Knight & Sons, Newcastle-u-Lyme	★★	
Kuit Steinart Levy, Manchester	★★	
Laceys, Bournemouth	★	
Lanyon Bowdler, Shrewsbury		★★
Lawrence Tucketts, Bristol	★★	★★
Lawrence Wood, Norwich		★★★
Laytons, Hampton Court	★	
Leathes Prior, Norwich	★★	
Lee Crowder, Birmingham	★★	
Lester Aldridge, Bournemouth	★★	

183

Leading Firms

Regional Firms (cont.)	Commercial Property	Property Litigation
Linnells, *Oxford*	**	
Lyons Davidson, *Bristol*	***	***
Manby & Steward, *Wolverhampton*	**	
Martineau Johnson, *Birmingham*	***	***
McGrath & Co, *Birmingham*		**
McGuinness Finch, *Leeds*	**	
Michelmores, *Exeter*	****	
Mills & Reeve, *Norwich*	****	******
Moore & Blatch, *Southampton*	*	
Morgan Bruce, *Cardiff*	*****	******
Morgan Bruce, *Swansea*	*****	******
Nabarro Nathanson, *Sheffield*	***	****
Napthen Houghton, *Preston*	***	
Needham & James, *Stratford*	**	
Osborne Clarke, *Bristol*	*****	*****
Oxley & Coward, *Rotherham*	*	
Palser Grossman, *Cardiff Bay*	***	
Pannone & Prtnrs, *Manchester*	**	*****
Paris Smith, *Southampton*	***	
Penningtons, *Basingstoke*	*	
Pictons, *St. Albans*	*	
Pinsent Curtis, *Birmingham*	****	***
Pinsent Curtis, *Leeds*	****	*****
Pitmans, *Reading*	**	
Porter Dodson, *Yeovil*	*	
Prettys, *Ipswich*	**	
Rawlison & Butler, *Crawley*	**	***
Read Hind Stewart, *Leeds*	***	
Rickerby Watterson, *Cheltenham*	*	
Robert Muckle, *Newcastle*	**	
Robertsons, *Cardiff*	**	
Rollit Farrell & Bladon, *Hull*	**	
Sherwin Oliver, *Portsmouth*	**	
Shoosmiths, *Northampton*	*	**
Shoosmiths, *Southampton*	**	
Slater Heelis, *Manchester*	*****	
Stamp Jackson & Procter, *Hull*	*	
Steele Raymond, *Bournemouth*	*	
Stevens & Bolton, *Guildford*	***	
Taylor Vinters, *Cambridge*	**	
Thomas Eggar, *Chichester*	***	
Thomas Eggar, *Horsham*	***	
Thomas Eggar, *Reigate*	***	
Thomas Eggar, *Worthing*	***	
Thomson Snell, *Tonbridge*		*****
Thomson Snell, *Tunbridge Wells*	**	

Leading Firms

Regional Firms (cont.)	Commercial Property	Property Litigation
Tolhurst Fisher, *Chelmsford*	★	
Tolhurst Fisher, *Southend-on-Sea*	★	
Townsends, *Swindon*	★	
Trethowan Woodford, *Salisbury*	★	
Trumps, *Bristol*	★★	
Vaudreys, *Manchester*	★★★★★	
Veale Wasbrough, *Bristol*	★★★★★	★★★★★
Walker Morris, *Leeds*	★★★★★	★★★★
Walker Smith & Way, *Chester*	★★	
Wansbroughs, *Bristol*	★★★	★★
Ward Hadaway, *Newcastle-upon-Tyne*	★★	
Watson Burton, *Newcastle-upon-Tyne*	★★	
Weightmans, *Liverpool*	★★★	★★★
Willmett & Co, Windsor	★	
Wolferstans, *Plymouth*	★	
Wollastons, *Chelmsford*	★★	
Wragge & Co, *Birmingham*	★★★★★★	★★★★★★
Wright Hassall, *Leamington Spa*	★	

Firms and their star ratings are based on Chambers' Directory 1998–1999. Six stars represent a top-ranked firm, five stars a second-ranked firm, etc. See page 3 for further details.

SHIPPING

GLOSSARY OF TERMS

P&I Club – 'Protection & Indemnity' Club: a marine insurance club run mutually by and for ship-owners

Charter-party – Commercial instrument, essentially a contract for the hire of an entire ship for the purpose of import or export of goods

Bill of Lading – a certificate of undertaking by the captain of a ship to deliver goods on payment of the named sum to a named party

Salvage – reward payable by owners of ships and goods saved at sea by 'salvors'

Underwriter – an individual who agrees to indemnify an assured person against losses under a policy of insurance

MOA – Memorandum of Agreement

Area of law

Suggest shipping law as a practice area to the majority of law students and you may well be met by a glazed look and a swift exit. At best you will call to mind images of Greek shipping magnates chewing on vast Havanas and news-coverage of dramatic disasters at sea. In fact shipping law is a complex, varied and unpredictable area of practice.

It can be defined as "the law relating to all aspects of carriage by sea and international trade" and it involves both contentious and non-contentious work.

Contentious work is divided into 'Wet' and 'Dry.' An easy, if rather simplistic, way to explain the difference is that 'Wet' (traditionally known as Admiralty) work concerns disputes arising from mishaps at sea, ie. collision, salvage, total loss etc. 'Dry'(Marine) work arises from disputes over contracts made on dry land; charterparties, bills of lading, cargo and MOAs.

Non-contentious work is often financial advice. Other niche practice areas include yachting and fishing (often regulatory advice).

Type of work

Shipping lawyers often handle litigation together with non-contentious issues, making a wide variety of work available to them. On the non-contentious side advice is given on shipbuilding contracts, sale and purchase agreements, ship finance, contracts of employment for crew members, contracts of affreightment etc. Contentious work includes ad hoc 'handholding' advice on day to day matters for regular clients, together with conduct of High Court and arbitration cases from the time of the initial dispute through issuing of pleadings and interlocutory hearings to final hearing. Clients range from owners, operators, traders and charterers to P&I Clubs, other insurers and hull underwriters.

All shipping lawyers interviewed baulked at the idea of describing a typical day; nothing about this area of law is typical – 'expect the unexpected' is the catch-phrase. Oliver Weiss from leading firm Ince & Co described how on one occasion he received an afternoon call from a client to say that a barge had capsized in the South China Sea leaving many casualties. By 10 that night he was on a flight to Singapore (with a team including trainees) to take statements from all surviving crew members. This may not be a run of the mill occurrence for trainees but it is not unusual for shipping lawyers at a senior level.

Many cases are high-profile; attracting media interest for both their factual and legal content. Consider the shipping casualties which have hit the headlines over the last 10 years; the Marchioness, Herald of Free Enterprise, the Braer and the Sea Empress – all have involved lawyers in various capacities. Consider too the case-studies we learn in contract law – many of the leading cases are complex shipping matters.

Skills needed

On the personal side, a shipping lawyer needs to be extremely flexible in terms of hours and availability to travel overseas at short notice. This may not be the job to suit the parents of young children for example; family and social life often have to take second place. On the legal side, the need for an in-depth familiarity with the laws of contract and tort goes without saying. Clients are often extremely 'clued up' on the law and lawyers need to be absolutely up to speed; if you don't enjoy learning the cases, shipping may not be for you.

Chris Hilton of Eversheds (Newcastle) says that in a trainee he looks for application and enthusiasm, flexibility with working hours, a willingness to travel if necessary and a strong personality. Tony Vlasto at Clifford Chance looks for good humour, common sense, team spirit and self-motivation - "shipping law is a more legally intensive area of law than many others - but at the same time the problems which confront us are immediate and practical and require prompt handling."

For those specialising in wet work, previous knowledge of life at sea is very useful. Many specialists are ex-mariners who have converted to the law and some have a naval background. There is a steep learning curve in the first six months of a shipping seat and a trainee who was a mariner in his/her previous incarnation will have a headstart in terms of shipping regulations and terminology. Steve Mackin of Eversheds (Newcastle) was second officer aboard a Shell supertanker until 1987 when he came ashore to take a degree in Maritime Studies. A course on Maritime Law fascinated him early on and he decided to study for the CPE on graduation. He has recently qualified into the shipping department. "People who have worked at sea tend to be categorised on the wet side" he comments, "in fact I find dry work more intellectually stimulating. My sea-faring background gives me a good feel for what is right or wrong and it means I can explain things to counsel more easily than non-mariners. It also helps you talk on the same level as your clients."

Career options

In the past shipping lawyers often developed their practice from a general litigation or international trade background. These days it is not unusual for firms to have dedicated shipping departments and for trainees to be given an opportunity to sit in the department and possibly qualify into it. Those interested in shipping law should be aware that jobs outside London are relatively few and far between. Shipping work is limited to towns with ports. After London, Liverpool and Newcastle are most important.

If private practice does not appeal, there is of course, the possibility of going in-house; shipowners, operators and marine insurers all have openings for specialist lawyers. Alternatively, for those who become seriously enthusiastic about the lifestyle, there's always a career in business as an owner-operator.

In the larger firms with overseas offices there are opportunities for assistants to gain experience of working abroad for a couple of years or permanently. Contrary to popular belief this does not kill prospects for partnership back home. In fact, according to Oliver Weiss, it enhances them since it brings the assistant into contact with clients in the same time zone. This immediacy of contact presents more of a chance to impress both clients and partners.

Because of the relatively limited opportunities in private practice, more and more shipping lawyers are choosing to go it alone as sole practitioners or are setting up niche firms. One such lawyer is Nicola Ellis (Plymouth) who set up as a sole practitioner in 1994. Her background was in general litigation, but she 'fell into' marine work on qualification after a spell at Clyde & Co in Guildford during which she handled some cargo claims. Having gained that experience she found herself handling similar work in subsequent jobs and being encouraged to specialise by one particular yacht-builder client. She is unusual in being a woman who has made a name for herself in this very male-dominated area of law. She puts the male domination down to the importance of the 'old boy network' and socialising with clients after hours. Ellis has avoided this by specialising in small claims;

mainly yachting work, representing the insured rather than the insurer in the majority of cases.

The Firms

The most well-known shipping firms in London are Clyde & Co, Holman Fenwick & Willan and Ince & Co. Holman Fenwick's workload is 50% shipping. The firm has offices in London, Paris, Rouen, Nantes, Piraeus, Hong Kong and Singapore and is particularly well-respected for its wet work. Ince & Co is an international commercial law firm with an unusual structure, being non-departmentalised. All work stems from its beginnings as a shipping and commercial firm; shipping and international trade constitute about 40% of its workload and well over half the fee earners handle shipping work. Because of its unusual structure trainees at this firm do not sit in different seats. Instead they sit with different partners and compete for work from all parts of the firm. Clyde & Co has a similar structure and is particularly rated for its dry work.

The large City firms with expertise in shipping are Clifford Chance for its contract-based dry work and Herbert Smith particularly for its contentious work. Hill Taylor Dickinson is a popular smaller firm (23 partners) with offices in London, Dubai, Greece and Hong Kong.

There are also a number of niche firms handling only or mainly shipping work. Highly rated practices include Bentleys Stokes & Lowless where all nine partners and eight assistants handle some kind of admiralty or marine insurance work; and Holmes Hardingham where 11 partners and 11 assistants handle an international workload concentrating on litigation and arbitration.

The main shipping centres outside London are Plymouth, Liverpool and Newcastle. In Plymouth, Bond Pearce and Foot & Bowden (acted for the pilot in the Sea Empress case) are the largest practices. Well respected niche practices include two partner Grant & Horton who were involved in the leading Factortame case. In Liverpool, Hill Dickinson and Dibb Lupton Alsop have reasonable-sized practices, while in Newcastle, Eversheds and niche firm Rayfield Mills are the leading practices. Other centres with a couple of practices include Felixstowe and Hull.

Leading Firms

London Firms

Barlow Lyde & Gilbert	★	Lewis Moore & Co	★
Bentleys, Stokes & Lowless	★★★	Middleton Potts	★★
Berrymans Lace Mawer	★★★★★★	More Fisher Brown	★★★
Clifford Chance	★★★★	Norton Rose	★★★★★★
Clyde & Co	★★★★★	Richards Butler	★★★
Constant & Constant	★★★	Shaw and Croft	★★★
Dibb Lupton Alsop	★★★★★	Sinclair Roche & Temperley	★★★★★
Elborne Mitchell	★★	Stephenson Harwood	★★★★★
Fishers	★	Stockler Charity	★
Herbert Smith	★	Thomas Cooper & Stibbard	★★
Hill Taylor Dickinson	★★★★	Waltons & Morse	★★★
Holman, Fenwick & Willan	★★★★★★	Waterson Hicks	★
Holmes Hardingham	★★★★★★	Watson, Farley & Williams	★★★★★★
Ince & Co	★★★★★★	Wilde Sapte	★★★★
Jackson Parton	★★★	Williamson & Horrocks	★
Lawrence Graham	★★		

Firms and their star ratings are based on Chambers' Directory 1998–1999. Six stars represent a top-ranked firm, five stars a second-ranked firm, etc. See page 3 for further details.

Leading Firms

Regional Firms

Andrew M. Jackson, *Hull*	****	Foot & Bowden, *Plymouth*	*****
Bond Pearce, *Southampton*	*****	Grant & Horton, *Plymouth*	******
Curtis Davis Garrard, *Heathrow*	*	Hill Dickinson, *Liverpool*	******
Dale & Co, *Felixstowe*	****	John Weston & Co, *Felixstowe*	****
Davies, Johnson & Co, *Plymouth*	*****	Mills & Co, *Newcastle*	****
Dibb Lupton Alsop, *Liverpool*	*****	Nicola Ellis & Co, *Plymouth*	*****
Donne Mileham, *Brighton*	*****	Rayfield Mills, *Newcastle*	******
Eversheds, *Newcastle*	******		

Firms and their star ratings are based on Chambers' Directory 1998–1999. Six stars represent a top-ranked firm, five stars a second-ranked firm, etc. See page 3 for further details.

SPORTS LAW

Area of law

"There is no such thing as sports law" was the comment from every 'sports lawyer' interviewed for this section. What these lawyers are dealing with, according to Warren Phelops, head of the sports department at Nicholson Graham & Jones, is the supply of legal services to the sports industry. This could be anything from advice to an individual on an employment contract to acquiring a new football stadium for a large company. Lawyers in this field apply their general legal and commercial skills to a particular type of client and it's the client, rather than the work itself, which makes this area fashionable. There are a few areas of law which are particularly important in sports-related work and, depending on your focus, these are intellectual property (the protection of rights); EU and competition law (looking at the structure of the sports industry to see whether it is restrictive of competition); media and entertainment law (covering broadcasting, sponsorship, advertising); commercial/corporate law; crime and personal injury.

Type of work

According to Warren Phelops there are essentially three strands to the area of law we are calling 'sport'. The first is the regulatory/disciplinary/criminal/personal injury advice given to governing bodies, teams and individuals. The second is the media/sponsorship/advertising side and the third is the large scale corporate/commercial advice. Other lawyers divide the section up more generally; for example into contentious and non-contentious work or into advice to companies and sponsors as opposed to advice to individuals or 'talent'. However you look at it, there is a whole range of work which comes under the umbrella heading 'sports law'. A week at a corporate firm advising large companies will be very different from a week at a niche media firm advising individual stars which in turn, will be different from a week at a personal injury firm advising injured players. It is worth considering early on where you want to end up – even if it is only that you feel happier at

a small firm and that your bias will be contentious rather than non-contentious work. There are firms which fall broadly into one category or another; however most firms handle a cross-section of sports-related work as required by their clients.

Denton Hall, for example, comes to sport from a strong media background and Adrian Barr-Smith is a partner in the media and technology group. Much of their work is media-related and involves advising individuals on their intellectual property rights and sponsorship. They are currently advising Tracey Edwards (skipper of the first all-woman crew attempting to sail round the world) on various trademark registrations, on a publishing deal and on setting up her own website. However, they are also involved in regulatory and disciplinary issues and even personal injury. Barr-Smith is currently acting for a football club being sued by a player who has suffered a career-ending broken leg.

Farrer & Co also have a media background, but in the sports field they are best known for their regulatory and disciplinary work. Leading sports lawyer Charles Woodhouse has advised on the formation and constitution of many governing bodies and was honorary legal adviser to the Commonwealth Games Council for England. Karena Vleck advised the British Athletics Federation in the long-running Diane Modahl case and is actively involved in the formation of the Sports Dispute Resolution Panel. She is also a director of the interim governing body for athletics and much of her work this year has been in the capacity of a business person rather than strictly as a lawyer. As well as dealing with constitutional issues she has been negotiating TV rights and sponsorship, agency and event agreements.

Firms such as Russell Jones & Walker and Davies Arnold Cooper enter the sector from an insurance/personal injury background. The former firm represents plaintiffs in personal injury actions (generally rugby and football players) and they acted for rugby player Victor Ubogu when he was alleged to have bitten the ear of fellow player Simon Fenn. The latter firm acts for defendants in the same cases, generally for the insurer of a rugby or football club.

On the corporate side, Nicholson Graham & Jones handle sports-related work for clients such as Wasps, Richmond and London Welsh RFCs. They were recently involved in the joint venture between the RFU and the English First Division professional rugby clubs. Freshfields have been advising the FA in disciplinary proceedings against Bruce Grobbelaar and Hans Segers following their acquittal on criminal charges. Another sports law firm, Epstein Grower & Michael Freeman advised them on the criminal proceedings

When asked to describe a typical day the lawyers interviewed were adamant that there is no such thing. But they all agreed that what sets this field apart from other areas is the high profile nature of much of the work and the consequent press attention. If commenting on your cases for television or fending off newspaper reporters interests you, then you'll enjoy this discipline. As Karena Vleck says: "I like the fact that my work is reported in the paper and that people are interested in my work." She also likes the other perks to the job and admits that she has "only ever watched football from a director's box!"

Skills needed

"Make sure your legal grounding is rock-solid", says Adrian Barr-Smith, "because you never know what to expect." For example you're advising a footballer who has been playing abroad for a season and is negotiating a deal to come back and play in England. He returns to the UK after 363 days, signs the contract and lands himself with a huge tax bill. Had he remained outside the country for 365 days this bill would have been avoided. "I'm not saying you have to be a tax expert", says Barr-Smith, "you just have to know what the issues are."

This need for an awareness of the whole legal spectrum was emphasised by all the sports lawyers interviewed. Particularly important is a "good commercial grounding", a knowledge of contract and intellectual property law and increasingly, an awareness of EU and competition law. Obviously if you're thinking of sports law from the personal injury/criminal proceedings angle then these areas of law and the ability to litigate will be paramount.

Personal qualities are as important as legal skills in this people-driven industry. Warren Phelops looks for excellent "people skills as well as paper skills" – vibrant team players with energy and a determination to succeed. He also emphasises the need for people with a desire to protect client confidentiality. "Much of the work we do is very high profile and we must resist the temptation to talk about it."

Karena Vleck indicates that the most successful sports lawyers are generally outgoing, sociable individuals with big personalities. It is quite an individual-led field, so although being a team player is essential, it is important to have the confidence to go it alone if necessary. It is not an industry for shrinking violets. However, neither is it an industry for people who are star-struck and in it for the glamour – "we don't want prima donnas," says Phelops.

A passion for sport is obviously a major requirement in this highly competitive field. But as Karena Vleck points out, it's not enough just to say you enjoy sport and have played for your university team. Unfortunately for the majority of people, this is an area where good contacts can really sway a job interview. A sports department will be much more likely to look at you if you've played rugby for Harlequins and England, or if your father runs the English cricket board. Jonny Searle, lawyer with Ashurst Morris Crisp and olympic oarsman, also suggests that clients tend to treat you with less suspicion when they know you are a sports player yourself. Many sportsmen and women have an inherent distrust of lawyers and the business of making money out of sport – "it helps if they feel you can empathise with them and understand their problems because you've been there," says Searle.

However as Warren Phelops and Adrian Barr-Smith are keen to point out – contacts are not everything. You've got to be able to do the job and bright, determined candidates should not be discouraged from trying to enter this field. Barr-Smith has just taken on a junior litigator from a City firm who had 'fallen out of love with shipping law' and displayed the ability and enthusiasm to apply his skills to the sports world.

Career options

In private practice, sports specialists move into this area both by accident and by design. Sports lovers often try to steer their careers in this direction, while corporate, litigation, intellectual property or personal injury lawyers who have acquired a sporting clientele suddenly find themselves referred to as sports lawyers. "Getting your first client – that's the hard thing", says Karena Vleck, "when you've got one it can just snowball from there."

Some firms offer a seat in their sports unit during training, but an alternative route is to gain as much general commercial and perhaps, media experience as possible and try to pick up sports clients later.

There are various in-house opportunities in the sports world. You could work for a governing body such as the FA or the RFU; for a sports broadcaster negotiating TV rights; or, in conjunction with agents for individual sports personalities or teams. Lawyer Mel Stein has made a name for himself in this respect with his work for Paul Gascoigne.

The Firms

Townleys in London remains the only specialist sports law firm in the country. Over the past year the practice has expanded and now boasts 5 partners and 15 assistants. Much of their work concerns the commercial exploitation of sporting and cultural events. During 1997/1998 they worked on events such as the Five Nations Championship, the Rugby World Cup 1999, the Commonwealth Games 2002 and Formula One motor racing. Much of their work is international

and foreign language skills are useful. Some of the staff are former professional sports people.

Denton Hall is an example of a large commercial firm with a well-developed sports practice. Four partners and three assistants handle sports-related work. There are overlaps with the firm's entertainment practice and with the planning department whose clients include Chelsea Football Club.

Medium-sized firms such as Farrer & Co, Bird & Bird and Edward Lewis all have respected sports departments. Bird & Bird advise Greg Rusedski and Stefan Edberg on matters ranging from sponsorship to tax planning. Edward Lewis advised on Damon Hill's new contract with Jordan Grand Prix and count former England rugby player, Brian Moore, among their lawyers.

Large city firms are increasingly advising on sports-related work. Herbert Smith maintains a strong reputation for commercial, broadcasting, litigation and disciplinary matters. They acted for West Ham United on their recent reorganisation and also work for the FA and the IAAF. Freshfields are also advising the FA on the improper use of agents in football transfers and in the disciplinary proceedings against Bruce Grobbelaar and Hans Segers. Ashurst Morris Crisp advise the Professional Cricketers Association on matters ranging from sponsorship to employment and have former Derbyshire cricketer Tim O'Gorman and Olympic oarsman Jonny Searle among their lawyers. At Lovell White Durrant sports work is handled in conjunction with the intellectual property department. Recent work includes advising Mars on their sponsorship of English and Scottish football teams at World Cup 1998. Nicholson Graham & Jones have a corporate bias to their work. They recently acted on behalf of Mohammed Al Fayed in his investment in Fulham FC.

Outside London a variety of firms handle sports-related work. In Bristol, Osborne Clark is involved in restructuring the PGA's disciplinary procedure and Alsters continues to advise all first division players in the EPRUC and RFU negotiations. In St Albans, Pickworths was involved in the Ayrton Senna manslaughter trial. In Exeter, Stones Cann & Hallett have a niche practice handling ski-ing injuries. In the midlands, Edge Ellison advised on the flotations of Aston Villa and Leicester City. James Chapman & Co in Manchester and McCormicks in Leeds are two of the best known sports firms in the north, while larger firms like Walker Morris and Addleshaw Booth & Co also handle sports work. The former acts for ASICS and David Batty; the latter is advising Adidas re Prince Naseem's sponsorship contract.

Leading Firms

London Firms

Ashurst Morris Crisp	*	Keene Marsland	*
Bird & Bird	*****	Lawrence Graham	**
Charles Russell	****	Lovell White Durrant	*
Clintons	***	Max Bitel, Greene	****
Collyer-Bristow	***	Memery Crystal	**
Davies Arnold Cooper	*	Mishcon de Reya	*
Denton Hall	******	Moorhead James	**
Edward Lewis	****	Nicholson Graham & Jones	****
Epstein Grower & Michael Freeman	**	Payne Hicks Beach	*
Farrer & Co	******	Russell Jones & Walker	***
Field Fisher Waterhouse	*	Simmons & Simmons	*
Freshfields	****	The Simkins Partnership	*
Hammond Suddards	*	Theodore Goddard	*
Harbottle & Lewis	**	Townleys	******
Herbert Smith	*****	Wedlake Bell	**
John Bowden Trainer & Co	*		

Leading Firms

Regional Firms

Addleshaw Booth & Co, *Manchester*	***	Matthew McCloy & Prtnrs, *Newbury*	**
Alsters, *Bristol*	**	McCormicks, *Leeds*	******
David Jeacock, *Swindon*	**	Osborne Clarke, *Bristol*	**
Edge Ellison, *Birmingham*	***	Pickworths, *St. Albans*	**
George Davies & Co, *Manchester*	*****	Stones Cann & Hallett, *Exeter*	**
German & Soar, *Nottingham*	*	Trethowan Woodford, *Salisbury*	***
Gorna & Co, *Manchester*	****	Trethowan Woodford, *Southampton*	***
Greenland Houchen, *Norwich*	**	Walker Morris, *Leeds*	****
James Chapman & Co, *Manchester*	******	Zermansky & Partners, *Leeds*	***

Firms and their star ratings are based on Chambers' Directory 1998–1999. Six stars represent a top-ranked firm, five stars a second-ranked firm, etc. See page 3 for further details.

TAX

(including Corporate Tax and VAT. For personal tax see Private Client section)

Area of law

"Tax," says Greg Sinfield, partner at Lovell White Durrant "is that rather mysterious and ever-changing process by which government extorts money from individuals and companies."

In this section we are solely concerned with taxes paid by companies, such as corporation tax, capital gains, VAT, stamp duty, etc. Taxes paid by individuals and private trusts – inheritance tax, income tax, etc. – are dealt with under Private Client.

Type of work

Contrary to popular belief, tax is a very general subject.

As far as companies are concerned, tax is just another financial expense, like their electricity bill or insurance, albeit a rather large one. In order to maximise profits, companies want to pay as little tax as possible. The greater part of a tax lawyer's work is advising on the tax consequences of transactions and how they can be structured to reduce the amount of tax payable. "But before you can understand the financial consequences of a transaction," says Linklaters' tax partner, Yash Rupal, "you have to understand the transaction itself and the commercial issues involved."

Tax lawyers therefore have to be familiar with a wide number of areas. "You need a good grounding in the basic concepts of other practice areas – banking, property, corporate finance, etc," says Kay Butler, head of tax at Olswangs. "You can only apply tax law if you have a good grasp of those basics." Yash Rupal explains why: "There's no point coming up with a tax-efficient structure for a banking deal if that structure is outside the way banks operate."

While transactional advice forms the majority of their work, tax lawyers get involved in two other activities – disputes between tax payers and the tax authorities (the Inland Revenue and Customs

& Excise), and pure tax consultancy. The latter might involve reviewing a bank's proposal for a new financial product and analysing it to see what the tax consequences are. Or it may involve being given the germ of an idea and developing a financial product from scratch which achieves a desired objective as tax-efficiently as possible.

A tax lawyer's day starts on the train. Tax law changes constantly and keeping up-to-date involves a lot of reading, at least an hour every day, possibly two, and usually in your own time. However, while each day may start the same, once at work you will rarely, if ever, be working on the same project for weeks on end. Most deals involve some element of tax. Even if they are not tax led, they will require the input of the tax department. Yash Rupal works on three or four different projects each day. Greg Sinfield typically works on two or three but could have up to 50 projects going at any one time.

As a trainee and assistant, you will spend much of your time in the library researching 'black letter' law – reading legislation and law reports - and making notes. It might be on the tax consequences of a particular employee share scheme, or devising a tax-efficient structure for a multinational joint venture, or how the making of a film can be structured to take advantage of tax reliefs. Whatever it is, research skills are key. "You need to be interested in reading cases and finding out what the law is," says Rupal. "If you have the attitude that after law school you're done with the legal stuff, then tax will not be your forte."

Lunch is often spent in a departmental meeting discussing topical issues, or catching up on some reading. The afternoon belongs to boiling down your twenty page analysis of the highly complex situation that you researched in the morning, into a four or five paragraph letter of advice. This is interspersed with attending meetings on corporate and property deals which require your input. In addition to this there are a multitude of 20 minute queries. People calling up and requiring an immediate answer can often disrupt your plan for the day.

Skills needed

Tax lawyers have a reputation for being highly intelligent "anoraks". If this was ever true, it certainly isn't now. Tax lawyers can no longer get away with poring over statutes in back rooms. If a deal is tax-driven or a transaction has a large tax element, the tax lawyer needs to be out in front calling the shots.

"Communication skills are essential," according to Kay Butler. People don't like to talk to tax lawyers. Tax involves far too much law for most solicitors let alone clients. The art of the tax lawyer is to take the complicated and from it distil a simple, readily understood explanation, both orally and in writing.

Obviously, presentation skills are not enough in themselves. Academic rigour is essential. "Tax is not intuitive," says Greg Sinfield. "It involves a huge reading-in period. As a rule of thumb, you need to have been practising for five years to be really useful." Yash Rupal admits to being daunted initially by the complexity of the subject. "It was like a foreign language," he says. Clearly patience and resilience are necessary attributes to succeed in this field.

According to Butler, a tax lawyer needs to be "a bit of a terrier – someone with a thirst for knowledge, who won't stop until they know the answer." To succeed "you need a great eye for detail," says Rupal, "you can't have a broad brush approach." Sinfield agrees – "if you miss the smallest detail it can mess up the whole result."

As the tax department could be called upon to advise on any deal that their firm is involved with, tax lawyers must be adaptable and versatile. "You have to be able to turn your hand to whatever is thrown at you," says Rupal. Confidence in your own judgement is also essential. There is a fine line between tax avoidance (legal) and tax evasion (illegal). The situations brought before tax lawyers are often on the cusp.

On the up side, there are skills that tax lawyers don't require. "You don't need to be any good at maths," according to Kay Butler, "in fact, you don't even need to know how to switch on a calculator." If there are sums to be done they're done by the accountants. Lawyers advise on the law not the figures. Paper management, the curse of most solicitors, is similarly not a problem. Tax lawyers spend far more time reviewing documents than they do producing them. "Even when you're driving a transaction, you don't have to do the dull paperwork," says Rupal.

Career options

Good tax lawyers have extremely bankable – and recession proof – skills. Alternatives to private practice include the Bar or joining a firm of accountants. Every year a few 'big names' leave private practice heading in those directions. Tax barristers are amongst the highest paid at the Bar.

Other options include an in-house position as a tax manager. Most tax managers currently come from an accounting background but lawyers are making inroads. Banks are also keen to recruit tax lawyers, not just as in-house tax advisers but as front line bankers. "Banks have recognised that tax is a vital part of their business. Four or five of my bank clients are actively recruiting at the moment," according to Rupal. An alternative path would be to join the Inland Revenue to focus on the policy issues behind tax legislation.

The Firms

To a significant degree, tax departments are service departments. While they do generate their own work, their main 'clients' are often other departments within the firm – banking, project finance, employment, property, etc., but particularly corporate. The top five firms in London – Allen & Overy, Clifford Chance, Freshfields, Linklaters and Slaughter and May – have the largest corporate departments. Consequently they also have the largest, and best, tax departments. The average size of the tax department at these firms is in the region of 10 partners and 25 assistants; and there are specialist areas such as capital markets or employee benefits. In the leading medium-sized firms, tax departments are considerably smaller (Macfarlanes has a department of 3 partners and 4 assistants and Travers Smith Braithwaite has 4 partners and 7 assistants) and in general, each lawyer handles a wider practice area. Freshfields and Slaughter and May both advised on tax aspects of the Guinness/Grand Met merger, while Clifford Chance advised the Burton Group on its demerger from Debenhams. Macfarlanes advised on the demerger of Saatchi & Saatchi and Travers on the private equity film finance for 'The Professionals' film.

Tax is less well developed outside London. Regional firms rely more on referral work from accountants and are reluctant to compete with them head on. It is, however, a growing area. Pinsent Curtis is leading the way in Birmingham and Leeds, while Hammond Suddards, Addleshaws, Wragges and the other big regional firms are now muscling in on the action – often by poaching each others teams.

Leading Firms

London Firms

Firm	Rating	Firm	Rating
Allen & Overy	★★★★★	Lovell White Durrant	★★★
Ashurst Morris Crisp	★★★	Macfarlanes	★★★
Berwin Leighton	★	Nabarro Nathanson	★
Cameron McKenna	★★	Norton Rose	★★★
Clifford Chance	★★★★★	Olswang	★
Clyde & Co	★	S J Berwin & Co	★★
Denton Hall	★	Simmons & Simmons	★★★
Dibb Lupton Alsop	★	Slaughter and May	★★★★★★
Field Fisher Waterhouse	★	Theodore Goddard	★★
Freshfields	★★★★★★	Travers Smith Braithwaite	★★
Hammond Suddards	★	Watson, Farley & Williams	★★
Herbert Smith	★★★	Wilde Sapte	★★
Linklaters	★★★★★★		

Leading Firms

Regional Firms

Firm	Rating	Firm	Rating
Addleshaw Booth & Co, *Leeds*	★★★★	Hammond Suddards, *Leeds*	★★★★
Addleshaw Booth & Co, *Manchester*	★★★★	Hammond Suddards, *Manchester*	★★★★
Blake Lapthorn, *Fareham*	★★	Mills & Reeve, *Cambridge*	★★★
Burges Salmon, *Bristol*	★★★	Mills & Reeve, *Norwich*	★★★
Clarke Willmott & Clarke, *Taunton*	★★	Osborne Clarke, *Bristol*	★★★
Dibb Lupton Alsop, *Birmingham*	★★★	Pinsent Curtis, *Birmingham*	★★★★★
Dickinson Dees, *Newcastle*	★★★	Pinsent Curtis, *Leeds*	★★★★★★
Eversheds, *Ipswich*	★★★	Thomas Eggar, *Chichester*	★★
Eversheds, *Leeds*	★★★	Walker Morris, *Leeds*	★★★
Eversheds, *Manchester*	★★★	Wiggin and Co, *Cheltenham*	★★★
Eversheds, *Norwich*	★★★	Wragge & Co, *Birmingham*	★★★★
Eversheds, *Nottingham*	★★★		

a-z of
Law Firms

- *Index to firms*
- *Full entries*
- *Short entries*

INDEX TO FIRMS

Firms which have chosen to take a full entry appear first, on page 206. These are followed, on page 335, by the shorter entries.

ADDLESHAW BOOTH & CO

Sovereign House PO Box 8 Sovereign Street Leeds LS1 1HQ
Tel: (0113) 209 2000 Fax: (0113) 209 2060
101 Barbirolli Square Manchester M2 3AB
Tel :(0161) 934 6000 Fax: (0161) 934 6060
Email: jru@addleshaw-booth.co.uk
Website: www.addleshaw-booth.co.uk

Partners	90
Assistant Solicitors	330
Total Trainees	55

Contact
Joanna Rue, Graduate Manager

Firm Profile
Addleshaw Booth & Co, formed by a 1997 merger, is recognised as one of the leading commercial law firms in the UK with a wide range of clients in the corporate, financial, public and private sectors.

Method of Application
Application form

Selection Procedure
Interview, assessment day

Main Areas of Work
Banking and Financial Services; Commercial; Commercial Property; Corporate Finance; Litigation and Dispute Resolution; Private Client; Recoveries Management

Closing date for 2001
16 July 1999

Application

Training contracts p.a.	20–25
Applications p.a.	2,000
% interviewed p.a.	6%
Required degree grade	2:1

Trainee Profile
Graduates of all disciplines who are capable of achieving a 2:1, can demonstrate commercial awareness, a flexible attitude and a willingness to learn. Non-academic interests and achievements will also be taken into account and applications from mature applicants are welcomed.

Training

Salary: 1st year(1999)	£15,000–£15,500
Salary: 2nd Year(1999)	£16,500–£17,000
Holiday entitlement	25 days
% of trainees with a non-law degree p.a.	40%
No. of seats available abroad p.a.	0

Training Environment
During each six-month seat, there will be regular two-way performance reviews with the supervising partner or solicitor. Trainees are given the opportunity to spend a seat in the other office and there are also a number of secondments to the in-house legal departments of various clients such as Zeneca and Airtours. The on-the-job training received within teams is complemented by a programme of lectures and residential courses, many designed specifically for trainees. The firm has a reputation of being a friendly and pleasant place to work and particular emphasis is placed upon building relationships and valuing everybody's contribution towards the success of the business.

Post-Qualification

Salary (1999)	£25,000
% of trainees offered job on qualification (1998)	90%

Benefits
Corporate membership of gyms, profit related pay, season ticket loan.

Vacation Placements
Places for 1999: 24; Duration: 2 weeks; Remuneration: £125 p.w.; Closing Date: 28 February 1999.

Sponsorship & Awards
CPE and LPC fees paid and £3,500 maintenance for both years where applicable.

ALLEN & OVERY

One New Change London EC4M 9QQ
Tel: (0171) 330 3000 Fax: (0171) 330 9999
Website: www.allenovery.com

Firm Profile
One of the UK's leading international firms, with major strengths in banking, international capital markets and corporate work. All departments work closely together to meet the needs of clients which include governments, financial institutions, businesses and private individuals.

Main Areas of Work
Banking; International Capital Markets; Corporate; Litigation; Property; Private Client; Tax; Employment and related areas

Trainee Profile
Intellectual ability is a prerequisite but, as Allen & Overy is a commercial firm, highly academic candidates with a lack of business understanding, are unlikely to fit in. The firm looks for creative, problem solving people who can quickly identify salient points without losing sight of detail. You will need to be highly motivated, demonstrate initiative and the ability to alternate between leading and being part of a team. Assertive rather than aggressive people tend to succeed.

Training Environment
Within a highly pressurised environment, trainees obtain a balance of practical and formal tuition. You will experience at least four different areas of work, but will spend a significant amount of time in at least two of the following departments: banking, corporate and international capital markets. Your preferences will be balanced with the firm's needs. Seminars provide practical advice and an introduction to each area of law. Placements abroad are available. A positive, open and co-operative culture is encouraged both professionally and socially. A range of sporting activities are available.

Benefits
PPP scheme, private medical insurance, season ticket loans, gym membership, subsidised restaurant, 6 weeks unpaid leave on qualification.

Vacation Placements
Places for 1999: 70; Duration: 3 weeks; Remuneration: £200 p.w.; Closing Date: 18 February 1999.

Sponsorship & Awards
CPE and LPC fees and £4,000 maintenance p.a. (£3,750 outside London and Guildford).

Partners	200*
Assistant Solicitors	677*
Total Trainees	152

* denotes world-wide figures

Contact
Sarah Bate

Method of Application
Application form

Selection Procedure
Assessment centre

Closing date for 2001
CPE candidates: December 1998; Law students: July 1999

Application
Training contracts p.a.	100
Applications p.a.	3,000
% interviewed p.a.	12%
Required degree grade	2:1

Training
Salary: 1st year(1999) £21,000
Salary: 2nd Year(1999) £24,000
Holiday entitlement 22 days
% of trainees with
a non-law degree p.a. 30%
No. of seats available
abroad p.a. 22

Post-Qualification
Salary (1999) £30,500
% of trainees offered job
on qualification (1998) 100%
% of partners (as at 1/9/98)
who joined as trainees 70%

Overseas Offices
Beijing, Brussels, Budapest, Dubai, Frankfurt, Hong Kong, Madrid, Milan, Moscow, New York, Rome, Paris, Prague, Singapore, Tokyo, Turin, Warsaw

ANTHONY GOLD, LERMAN & MUIRHEAD

New London Bridge House 25 London Bridge Street
London SE1 9TW
Tel: (0171) 940 4000 Fax: (0171) 378 8025
Email: agold@agold.law.co.uk

Partners	11
Assistant Solicitors	11
Total Trainees	9

Firm Profile
A progressive and expanding practice founded in 1963, with a commitment to working for the whole community. It offers affordable services to both business and individuals. It prides itself on its intellectual calibre and its client service.

Main Areas of Work
Family 25%; Personal Injury/Medical Negligence 25%; Conveyancing/Probate 10%; Corporate/Commercial 20%; Housing/Public Law 20%.

Trainee Profile
Trainees must possess a strong academic background, common sense and a commitment to the firm's work. They should display excellent written and oral communication skills and an ability to form effective interpersonal relationships.

Training Environment
Trainees will spend six months in each of the four departments (public law and property litigation, personal injury and medical negligence, a mix of contentious and non-contentious and family law). You will be expected to deal professionally with clients, and will often be in charge of delegating tasks and supervising where appropriate. There is a strong commitment to achieving the best possible result for the client. The practice embraces advanced technology, as well as the need to keep abreast of recent developments in the law. Outside courses are encouraged and there are also internal lectures. The firm is currently working towards obtaining accreditation under the quality standard "Investors In People".

Benefits
Subsidised gym, LVs, STL.

Sponsorship & Awards
£1,000 paid for LPC fees and interest free loan.

Contact
Kim Beatson

Method of Application
Handwritten letter and/or application form

Selection Procedure
One interview

Application
Training contracts p.a.	3
Applications p.a.	400
% interviewed p.a.	7.5%
Required degree grade	2:1

Training
Salary: 1st year(1999)	£13,750
Salary: 2nd Year(1999)	£15,400
Holiday entitlement	20 days

Post-Qualification
Salary (1999)	£23,350
% of trainees offered job on qualification (1998)	100%
% of assistants (as at 1/9/98) who joined as trainees	63%
% of partners (as at 1/9/98) who joined as trainees	42%

ASHURST MORRIS CRISP

Broadwalk House 5 Appold St London EC2A 2HA
Tel: (0171) 638 1111 Fax: (0171) 972 7990
Email: jane.ahern@ashursts.com
Website: www.ashursts.co.uk

Partners	90*
Assistant Solicitors	285*
Total Trainees	76

* denotes world-wide figures

Firm Profile

An international City practice, smaller than its principal competitors yet consistently ranked amongst the top few firms in the country in terms of the work in which it is involved and clients for whom it acts.

Main Areas of Work

Company 45%; Property 25%; Litigation 15%; Banking 10%; Tax 5%.

Trainee Profile

Candidates should want to be involved in the highest quality work that a City firm can offer. The firm wants high achievers academically as the work is intellectually demanding. Candidates should show common sense, good judgement, a willingness to take on responsibility, a sense of humour and an outgoing nature. Language skills and an international perspective on life will impress.

Training Environment

The training contract comprises four or five seats including company/commercial, property/planning and litigation. Opportunities exist to work in Brussels, Paris, Frankfurt, Milan, Singapore and Tokyo, or on secondment to a client. The firm runs the LPC and PSC in partnership with the College of Law. A fast-track two week course covers the examinable modules of the PSC and there is an extensive in-house training programme. The firm gives trainees as much responsibility as they can manage, and a full role in servicing clients' needs. Trainees are encouraged to take on pro bono work.

Benefits

Season ticket loan, medical cover, life cover, membership of a gym/squash club, subsidised annual health check.

Vacation Placements

Places for 1999: 45–50; Duration: 3 weeks; Remuneration: £200 p.w.(1998); Closing Date: 1 January–28 February 1999.

Sponsorship & Awards

CPE and LPC funding and maintenance allowance.

Contact
Jane Ahern

Method of Application
Handwritten or typed letter and CV

Selection Procedure
Interview with 2 partners

Closing date for 2001
31 August 1999

Application

Training contracts p.a.	45–50
Applications p.a.	3,000
% interviewed p.a.	13%
Required degree grade	n/a

Training

Salary: 1st year(1998)	£21,000
Salary: 2nd Year(1998)	£23,500
Holiday entitlement	22 days
% of trainees with a non-law degree p.a.	50%
No. of seats available abroad p.a.	14

Post-Qualification

Salary (1998)	£32,000
% of trainees offered job on qualification (1998)	95%
% of assistants (as at 1/9/98) who joined as trainees	45%
% of partners (as at 1/9/98) who joined as trainees	35%

Overseas Offices
Brussels, Delhi, Frankfurt, Paris, Singapore, Tokyo; associated offices in Milan, Rome and Verona.

BAKER & MCKENZIE

100 New Bridge Street London EC4V 6JA
Tel: (0171) 919 1000 Fax: (0171) 919 1999
Email: jo.darby@bakernet.com
Website: http://www.bakerinfo.com

Partners	63
Assistant Solicitors	111
Total Trainees	39

Firm Profile

Baker & McKenzie is the world's largest law firm. The London office is a leading City practice with a domestic and foreign client base. It provides business and financial legal services to corporations, financial institutions, governments and entrepreneurs.

Main Areas of Work

Corporate/Finance/EC/Tax/Commercial 47%; Litigation/ Construction 23%; Employment/Pensions/Immigration 13%; Intellectual Property 10%; Commercial Property 7%.

Trainee Profile

Baker & McKenzie are looking for trainees who are stimulated by intellectual challenge and want to be 'the best' at what they do. Effective communication together with the ability to be creative but practical problem solvers, team players and to have a sense of humour are qualities which will help them stand out from the crowd. Language and IT skills are also valued. The firm encourages their trainees to take time out before commencing their training contract whether just to travel or undertake further studies.

Training Environment

Four six-month seats which include corporate and litigation together with the possibility of a secondment abroad or with a client. During each seat you will have formal and informal reviews to discuss your progress as well as subsequent seat preferences. Your training contract commences with a highly interactive and practical induction programme which focuses on key skills including practical problem solving, interviewing, presenting and the application of information technology. The firm's training programmes include important components on management and other business skills, as well as seminars and workshops on key legal topics for each practice area. They run the Professional Skills Course in-house – two modules of which are undertaken at the start of your training contract. There is a Trainee Solicitor Liaison Committee which acts as a forum for any new ideas or problems which may occur during the training contract. Trainees are actively encouraged to participate in a variety of pro bono issues and outside of office hours there is a varied sporting and social life.

Contact
Joanna Darby

Method of Application
Letter and application form

Selection Procedure
Candidates to give short presentation, interview with 2 partners, meeting with a trainee

Closing date for 2001
Non-law: 12/3/99; Law: 13/8/99

Application

Training contracts p.a.	22
Applications p.a.	2,000
% interviewed p.a.	6%
Required degree grade	2:1

Training

Salary: 1st year(1999)	£21,000
Salary: 2nd Year(1999)	£23,500
Holiday entitlement	22 days
% of trainees with a non-law degree p.a.	26%
No. of seats available abroad p.a.	Variable

Post-Qualification

Salary (1999)	£34,000
% of trainees offered job on qualification (1998)	80%
% of partners (as at 1/9/98) who joined as trainees	40%

Benefits

Permanent health insurance, life insurance, private medical insurance, group personal pension plan, gym membership, luncheon vouchers, interest-free season ticket loan.

Vacation Placements

Places for 1999: 30; Duration: Easter (2 weeks), Summer (3 weeks); Remuneration: £200 p.w.; Closing Date: 12 February 1999.

Sponsorship & Awards

CPE Funding: Fees paid + £4,000 maintenance.
LPC Funding: Fees paid + £4,000 maintenance.

Additional Information

As mentioned, trainees have the opportunity to spend three months working in one of our overseas offices. Trainees have already been seconded to our offices in Sydney, Palo Alto and Riyadh. In addition they also operate an Associate Training Programme which enables lawyers with 18–24 months pqe to spend between 6–24 months working in an overseas office. In recent years the firm has had associates spend time in Palo Alto, Chicago, Moscow, Hong Kong and Sydney. Baker & McKenzie have a very extensive know-how practice both in London and globally which is ably assisted by BakerWeb, the Firm's intranet.

Trainee Comments

"I have really enjoyed the amount of responsibility I have been given at Baker & McKenzie. The nature of the work has been diverse and challenging right from the start. The fact that transactions often have an international angle makes the work even more interesting." (Nadia Darwazeh, first year trainee, read Law at Warwick University).

"I have been very impressed by the training. Right from the start the partners are involved in presenting our seminars. This is evidence of their genuine interest in our professional development and provides the perfect opportunity for us to get to know them as well." (Charlotte Hutchinson, second year trainee, read Russian at Bristol University).

"Right from day one you notice the friendly atmosphere; everyone from the secretaries through to the partners is keen to help you find your feet and settle in. This attitude to trainees makes you feel instantly part of a team and brings out the best in you." (James Thomson, first year trainee, read Classics at Liverpool University).

"What really drew me to Baker & McKenzie was not just its name or international nature: it seemed to have interesting work and clients and a diverse range of people." (Kate Hope, second year trainee, read Law at Cambridge University).

Overseas Offices

Almaty, Amsterdam, Bangkok, Barcelona, Beijing, Berlin, Bogota, Brasilia, Brussels, Budapest, Buenos Aires, Cairo, Caracas, Chicago, Dallas, Frankfurt, Geneva, Hanoi, Ho Chi Minh City, Hong Kong, Houston, Juarez, Kiev, Lausanne, Madrid, Manila, Melbourne, Mexico City, Miami, Milan, Monterrey, Moscow, Munich, New York, Palo Alto, Paris, Prague, Rio de Janeiro, Riyadh, Rome, St Petersburg, San Diego, San Francisco, Santiago, Sao Paulo, Singapore, Stockholm, Sydney, Taipei, Tijuana, Tokyo, Toronto, Valencia, Warsaw, Washington DC, Zurich

BARLOW LYDE & GILBERT

Beaufort House 15 St. Botolph Street London EC3A 7NJ
Tel: (0171) 247 2277 Fax: (0171) 782 8500
Email: grad.recruit@blg.co.uk
Website: www.blg.co.uk

Partners	68
Assistant Solicitors	110
Total Trainees	32

Firm Profile
Barlow Lyde & Gilbert is a major commercial City practice and is a leader in commercial litigation and insurance and reinsurance law. The Corporate & Finance Division is the fastest growing area of the firm.

Main Areas of Work
Commercial litigation; Corporate and Commercial; Banking; Tax; Property; Insurance and Reinsurance; Professional Indemnity; Aviation; Shipping; Construction; Environmental; Employment; Information Technology; Personal Injury and Medical Negligence.

Trainee Profile
Barlow Lyde & Gilbert recruit 16 trainees each year and we look for intelligent and motivated graduates with good academic qualifications and with the social skills that will enable them to communicate effectively and get along with their colleagues and clients. Trainees must be able to work independently or in a team and are expected to display common sense and initiative. An appreciation of the client's commercial interest is essential.

Training Environment
Four six-month seats are divided between the litigation, corporate/commercial and property divisions. Every effort is made to accommodate a trainee's preference for a particular type of work and there may be opportunities to spend time in the Hong Kong office or on secondment with clients. A capable trainee will be given responsibility from an early stage in his or her training, subject of course to supervision, and will have to deal regularly with clients. All trainees are expected to undertake and assist in practice development and client care. Social activities play an important role for BLG and successful candidates can look forward to a variety of sporting and social events which ensure that people in different parts of the firm have a chance to meet and stay in contact with each other.

Vacation Placements
Places for 1999: Vacation schemes are run over Easter and in the summer. The closing date for the Easter scheme is 31 December and for the summer schemes is 28 February

Sponsorship & Awards
Financial assistance is available for both the CPE and LPC.

Contact
Caroline Walsh

Method of Application
Standard application form

Closing date for 2001
31 July 1999

Training
Salary: 1st year(1999) £21,000
Salary: 2nd Year(1999) £23,000
Holiday entitlement 4 weeks

Post-Qualification
Salary (1999) £33,000

Overseas Offices
Hong Kong

BERRYMANS LACE MAWER

Salisbury House London Wall London EC2M 5QN
Tel: (0171) 638 2811 Fax: (0171) 920 0361
Email: gbblmall@ibmmail.com

Partners	84
Assistant Solicitors	118
Total Trainees	31

Firm Profile
Berrymans Lace Mawer is a nationwide commercial and litigation practice serving the insurance market and commercial, professional and private clients in the UK and overseas.

Main Areas of Work
Personal Injury (incl Medical law) 24%; Commercial Litigation: (Gen Prod Liab/Educ/Debt Coll/Insur Rec) 15%; Comp/Comm (incl Empl, Corp Fin & Banking/EU & Competition) 14%; Construction 11%; Professional Indemnity 10%; Insurance/Reinsurance 7%; Marine/Shipping 5%; Commercial Property 5%; Environmental 3%; Employment 3%; Private Client (incl Family) 2%.

Trainee Profile
Trainees will need an impressive academic record, drive and enthusiasm.

Training Environment
Four seats of six months are spent in the firm's main departments and will include a non-contentious seat where possible. You will be supervised under Law Society guidelines in each department. Levels of responsibility and direct client contact will increase in line with your capabilities. You may also be involved in department meetings if appropriate. The PSC is taught externally at a college of law.

Vacation Placements
Places for 2000: yes; Duration: 2 weeks; Remuneration: depends on office; Closing Date: 31 March 1999.

Contact
London, Southampton, Birmingham (Claire Douglas); Manchester, Liverpool, Leeds (Kate Whitmore)

Method of Application
CV with covering letter

Selection Procedure
First interview, assessment day, second interview.

Closing date for 2001
31 July 1999

Application
Training contracts p.a.	14
Applications p.a.	1,000+
% interviewed p.a.	5–10%
Required degree grade	2:1

Training
Salary: 1st year(1999) £13,000–£19,500 (depending on area)
Salary: 2nd Year(1999) £14,000–£20,500+ (depending on area)

Holiday entitlement	20 days
% of trainees with a non-law degree p.a.	50%
No. of seats available abroad p.a.	0

Post-Qualification
Salary (1999) £22,000–£30,000 (depending on office)

% of trainees offered job on qualification (1998)	87.5%
% of assistants (as at 1/9/98) who joined as trainees	50%
% of partners (as at 1/9/98) who joined as trainees	10%

Overseas Offices
Dubai

213

S J BERWIN & CO

222 Grays Inn Road London WC1X 8HB
Tel: +44(0)171 533 2222 Fax: +44(0)171 533 2000
Email: info@sjberwin.com

Partners	72
Assistant Solicitors	155
Total Trainees	54

Firm Profile
Since its formation in 1982, S J Berwin & Co has established a strong reputation in corporate finance. It also has a number of niche specialisms in areas such as film finance and private equity. Much work is international and clients range from major multi-national business corporations and financial institutions to high net worth individuals.

Main Areas of Work
Company/Commercial 50%; Commercial Property 20%; Litigation 17%; EU/Competition 10%; Tax 3%.

Trainee Profile
The firm wants ambitious, commercially-minded individuals who seek a high level of involvement from day one. Candidates must be bright and determined to succeed. They should be likely to achieve a 2:1 or first.

Training Environment
Four seats of six months each will be completed. Most trainees do a corporate seat, a litigation or employment seat and a commercial property seat. There is also usually a European Union, general commercial or tax seat. One seat may be spent in Brussels. The firm has a dedicated training department and the PSC is run in-house. Study leave is granted prior to the examinations. Business language tuition is available to those with a European language.

Benefits
PRP, corporate sports membership, free lunch.

Vacation Placements
Places for 2000: 60; Duration: 3 weeks; Remuneration: £200 p.w.; Closing Date: 14 February 1999.

Sponsorship & Awards
CPE and LPC Fees paid and £3,750 maintenance p.a.

Contact
Helen Turnbull

Method of Application
Handwritten letter and CV

Selection Procedure
Interview (early September)

Closing date for 2001
10 August 1999

Application
Training contracts p.a.	28
Applications p.a.	3,000
% interviewed p.a.	10%
Required degree grade	2:1

Training
Salary: 1st year(1999)	£21,500
Salary: 2nd Year(1999)	£24,500
Holiday entitlement	20 days
% of trainees with	
a non-law degree p.a.	40
No. of seats available	
abroad p.a.	1

Post-Qualification
Salary (1999)	£31,000
% of trainees offered job	
on qualification (1998)	82%
% of assistants (as at 1/9/98)	
who joined as trainees	25%
% of partners (as at 1/9/98)	
who joined as trainees	16%

Overseas Offices
Brussels, Frankfurt

214

BIDDLE

1 Gresham St London EC2V 7BU
Tel: (0171) 606 9301 Fax: (0171) 606 3305
Email: gradrecruit@Biddle.co.uk
Website: www.Biddle.co.uk

Partners	34
Assistant Solicitors	36
Total Trainees	12

Firm Profile
A progressive, medium-sized business law practice based in the City. Clients range from institutional investors, pension funds and insolvency practitioners, to newspapers, publishers and major casinos. They are a member of LOGOS, a group of law firms with offices throughout the European Union.

Main Areas of Work
Corporate/Commercial 33%; Litigation 20%; Pensions 14%; Media & IT 14%; Property 8%; Insolvency 7%; Employment 4%.

Trainee Profile
The firm values, above all, first-class intelligence, common-sense, willingness to learn and commercial awareness. They are not looking for specific character traits. Their aim is to build a team of varied yet complementary personalities where, for example, the more bookish are balanced by the charismatic. A second language is an asset but not essential.

Training Environment
On-the-job training is supplemented with in-house seminars and courses. Coaching in IT is also given. Trainees spend three to four six-month placements in varying departments: corporate, commercial, litigation, media and entertainment, pensions, property, taxation, private client, insolvency, and employment law. The final seat is likely to be in the area in which you wish to specialise. Trainees sit with partners and progress during each seat is closely monitored by the relevant partner. The company culture is open-door and informal.

Benefits
BUPA, life assurance, season ticket loan.

Sponsorship & Awards
CPE and LPC fees paid.

Additional Information
The firm's website has a special Graduate Section developed by current trainees. Find it at www.Biddle.co.uk.

Contact
Martin Webster

Method of Application
2 page CV and covering letter

Selection Procedure
1 interview

Closing date for 2001
31 August 1999

Application
Training contracts p.a.	8
Applications p.a.	1,500
% interviewed p.a.	2.5%
Required degree grade	2:1

Training
Salary: 1st year(1997) £20,000
Salary: 2nd year(1997) £22,000
Holiday entitlement 4 weeks
% of trainees with
a non-law degree p.a. 50%
No. of seats available
abroad p.a. 0

Post-Qualification
Salary (1997) £30,000
% of trainees offered job
on qualification (1998) 100%
% of assistants (as at 1/9/98)
who joined as trainees 54%
% of partners (as at 1/9/98)
who joined as trainees 36%

BIRD & BIRD

90 Fetter Lane London EC4A 1JP
Tel: (0171) 415 6000 Fax: (0171) 415 6111
Website: www.twobirds.com

Partners	42*
Assistant Solicitors	72*
Total Trainees	17

denotes world-wide figures

Firm Profile
Bird & Bird is an international medium-sized commercial law firm offering a full range of legal services. The firm, which has broadened its practice by building on established specialist areas such as IT and telecommunications law, aims to be pre-eminent in the fields in which it practises and has a highly regarded technology capability. Teams of lawyers are drawn from each department to service clients' commercial objectives.

Main Areas of Work
Company 46%; Intellectual Property 30%; Property 11%; Litigation 11%; Private Client 2%.

Trainee Profile
The firm looks for high calibre recruits – confident individuals capable of developing expert legal skills and commercial sense.

Training Environment
Following an introduction course, you will undertake four seats of six months, three of which are spent in company, litigation and property. The choice of final seat is yours. You will share an office with a partner or senior assistant who will guide and advise you. You will hone drafting and legal research skills and gain familiarity with legal procedures. The firm encourages you to make an early contribution to case work and to meet clients immediately. Internal seminars and external lectures are arranged to cover the PSC. Trainees are welcome to join the number of sports teams at the firm and to attend various social events and outings.

Benefits
BUPA, season ticket loan, subsidised sports club membership, life cover, PHI.

Vacation Placements
Places for 1999: 12; Duration: 3 weeks; Remuneration: £145 p.w.; Closing Date: March 1999.

Sponsorship & Awards
LPC and CPE fees paid and a yearly maintenance grant of £3,500.

Contact
Lynne Walters

Method of Application
CV and letter

Selection Procedure
First Interview and Second Interview

Closing date for 2001
August 1999

Application
Training contracts p.a.	7
Applications p.a.	2,000
% interviewed p.a.	10%
Required degree grade	2:1

Training
Salary: 1st year(1999)	£21,000
Salary: 2nd Year(1999)	£22,500
Holiday entitlement	20 days
% of trainees with a non-law degree p.a.	varies
No. of seats available abroad p.a.	0

Post-Qualification
Salary (1999)	£33,000
% of trainees offered job on qualification (1998)	100%
% of assistants (as at 1/9/98) who joined as trainees	25%
% of partners (as at 1/9/98) who joined as trainees	28%

Overseas Offices
Brussels, Hong Kong

BLAKE LAPTHORN

Harbour Court Compass Road North Harbour
Portsmouth PO6 4ST

Tel: (01705) 221122 Fax: (01705) 221123

Firm Profile

Founded in 1869 and one of the largest and most progressive
regional law firms in the south of England, the firm's main
activities are centred in two large purpose built out of town
offices on the M27 – one providing commercial and litigation
services and the other private client services. In addition there
are offices in Southampton and London and all the offices are
equipped with state of the art information technology. The size
of the firm means that it is able to offer clients the same range
and level of service expected from the best London firms.
There are 43 partners, many of whom were trainees with the
firm and a total staff approaching 400.

Main Areas of Work

Company/Commercial 24%; Commercial Property 17%;
Litigation 26%; Private Client (PI, Property, Family, Crime,
Probate, Finance) 33%.

Trainee Profile

In addition to excellent academic achievements, the firm
values previous experience, which has developed maturity and
a wider perspective. Commercial awareness, teamworking and
well-developed communication skills are also an advantage as
well as familiarity with the use of IT.

Training Environment

Ten trainees are recruited each year and have a minimum of
four placements lasting three or six months. Trainees'
preferences are taken into account as far as possible, but the
firm believes in providing well-rounded training supplemented
with in-house education and regular appraisals and reviews
with the Training Principal.

Benefits

Trainee accommodation.

Sponsorship & Awards

LPC: loan of £4,000 repayable from salary.

Partners	43
Assistant Solicitors	87
Total Trainees	20

Contact
Ruth Kalinowicz
Director of Personnel & Training

Method of Application
Firm's Application form plus c.v.

Selection Procedure
Interview with Partners,
including giving a presentation

Closing date for 2001
31st July 1999

Application

Training contracts p.a.	10
Applications p.a.	750
% interviewed p.a.	8/10%
Required degree grade	2.1

Training

Salary: 1st year(1998)	£13,000
Salary: 2nd Year(1998)	£14,000
Holiday entitlement	22 days

Post-Qualification

Salary (1998)	£20,000
% of trainees offered job on qualification (1998)	80%

BOND PEARCE

Ballard House West Hoe Road Plymouth PL1 3AE
Tel: (01752) 266 633 Fax: (01752) 225 350
Email: jl@bondpearce.com
Website: www.bondpearce.com

Partners	53
Assistant Solicitors	99
Total Trainees	36

Firm Profile
Major commercial law firm. With offices in Bristol, Exeter, Plymouth and Southampton they are one of the largest commercial legal practices in southern England. One of 10 law firms nationally to be shortlisted for Chambers' Law Firm of the Year Award.

Main Areas of Work
The size of Bond Pearce and the full range of legal services provided ensures trainee solicitors gain unrivalled experience with training in four separate specialist seats. Specialist groups within Bond Pearce, backed up by effective support services, provide the highest quality of services to a broad range of clients: Commercial Group; (Corporate, Banking & Insolvency, Commercial Litigation); Insurance Group; Property Group (Commercial Property, Planning & Environment, Private Client); Personal Injury and Family Group.

Trainee Profile
Experience has shown that successful candidates usually have a 2:1 in their chosen subject, not necessarily law, together with a wide range of interests and an enthusiastic and energetic approach to work. Personal qualities are paramount – they look for individuals who can demonstrate initiative, commercial acumen, enthusiasm, team working skills and a sense of humour.

Training Environment
Trainee solicitors have their own desks in the same office as the partner, associate or senior solicitor with whom they are working. They become an integral part of each team, closely involved in the diversity of their work and whilst fully supervised, trainees are encouraged to take on as much responsibility as possible. Training enhances existing legal skills and teaches trainees to apply those skills in a practical and effective manner. Technology plays a vital role in Bond Pearce. Their offices are linked by a networked computer system, the accounts and time recording systems are fully computerised and all staff, including trainee solicitors, are equipped with a fully networked PC on their desks. There are close links between the firm's offices and trainee solicitors join together in all training and many social activities. Bond Pearce has a thriving sports and social club.

Sponsorship & Awards
CPE and LPC financial assistance.

Contact
Jenny Litton

Method of Application
Application form, handwritten letter, CV and photograph

Selection Procedure
Interviews and selection day

Closing date for 2001
31 July 1999

Application
Training contracts p.a.	20
Applications p.a.	750
% interviewed p.a.	10%
Required degree grade	2:1

Training
Salary: 1st year(1999)	£13,500
Salary: 2nd Year(1999)	£14,500
Holiday entitlement	20 days
% of trainees with a non-law degree p.a.	25%
No. of seats available abroad p.a.	0

Post-Qualification
Salary (1999)	£21,000
% of trainees offered job on qualification (1998)	75%
% of assistants (as at 1/9/98) who joined as trainees	12%
% of partners (as at 1/9/98) who joined as trainees	27%

218

BOYES TURNER & BURROWS

10 Duke St Reading RG1 4RX
Tel: (0118) 959 7711 Fax: (0118) 957 3257
Email: ssales@b-t-b.co.uk
Website: www.btb-solicitors.co.uk

Partners	13
Assistant Solicitors	15
Total Trainees	4

Firm Profile
Boyes Turner & Burrows is a leading Thames Valley practice, renowned for its Insolvency and Medical Negligence work and well respected for Corporate and Commercial, Commercial Property, Intellectual Property, Employment, Personal Injury, Family law and Private Client. While the focus for growth has been commercial work, the firm retains a commitment to acting for individuals and also to civil legal aid.

Main Areas of Work
Company / Commercial (including Employment) 20%; Commercial Property 20%; Medical Negligence / Personal Injury 20%; Litigation 15%; Insolvency 10%; Family 5%; Private Client 10%.

Trainee Profile
BTB regards its trainees of today as its assistant solicitors and beyond of tomorrow and expects a high level of commitment, hard work and resourcefulness. Trainees must be responsive to the Firm's mission to provide an excellent quality of service to both commercial and individual clients and also contribute to the team-working philosophy.

Training Environment
The programme is structured so that trainees spend six months in each of four areas: property, litigation, private client and commercial. Work covers both individual and commercial clients, with as much client contact as possible, supervised by a partner or a senior solicitor. A training partner oversees all aspects of the programme, while each trainee is assigned a director (one of the partners) who reviews their progress monthly. This is on two levels – first in assessing how the trainee is developing as a lawyer and secondly how the trainee is developing as an individual, including communication and negotiating skills.

Benefits
Free medical insurance.

Sponsorship & Awards
CPE and LPC loan of £3,000 and only one loan per applicant. Interest free and re-paid over training contract.

Contact
Susan Sales

Method of Application
Letter and CV

Selection Procedure
2 interviews

Closing date for 2001
31 August 1999

Application
Training contracts p.a.	2/3
Applications p.a.	750
% interviewed p.a.	1%+
Required degree grade	2:2

Training
Salary: 1st year(1998)	£15,000
Salary: 2nd Year(1998)	£16,000
Holiday entitlement	4 weeks
% of trainees with a non-law degree p.a.	Varies

Post-Qualification
Salary (1998)	£23,500
% of trainees offered job on qualification (1998)	100%
% of assistants (as at 1/9/98) who joined as trainees	33%
% of partners (as at 1/9/98) who joined as trainees	20%

219

B.P. COLLINS & CO

Collins House 32-38 Station Rd Gerrards Cross SL9 8EL
Tel: (01753) 889995 Fax: (01753) 889851
Email: JJS@bpcollins.co.uk

Partners	15
Assistant Solicitors	15
Total Trainees	4

Firm Profile
B P Collins & Co was established in 1965, and has expanded significantly to become one of the largest and best known legal practices at the London end of the M4/M40 corridors. At its main office in Gerrards Cross, the emphasis is on commercial work, with particular strengths being company/commercial work of all types, commercial conveyancing and general commercial litigation. Alongside this there is a highly respected private client department specialising in tax planning, trusts, charities, wills and probates.

Main Areas of Work
Company/Commercial, Employment, IT/IP, Civil Litigation, Commercial Conveyancing, Property Development, Personal Injury, Private Client.

Trainee Profile
Most of the partners and other fee earners have worked in London at one time or another but, tired of commuting, have opted to work in more congenial surroundings and enjoy a higher quality lifestyle. Gerrards Cross is not only a very pleasant town with a large number of high net worth private clients but it is also a convenient location for serving the extremely active business community at the eastern end of the Thames Valley including West London, Heathrow, Uxbridge, Slough and Windsor. The firm therefore looks for trainees who are likely to respond to this challenging environment.

Training Environment
The firm aims to have five trainee solicitors at different stages of their training contracts at all times. Trainees serve five months in four separate departments of their choice. The final four months is spent in the department handling the sort of work in which the trainee intends specialising. The firm has a training partner with overall responsibility for all trainees and each department has its own training principal who is responsible for day to day supervision. There are regular meetings between the training principal and the trainee to monitor progress and a review meeting with the training partner at the end of each departmental session. The firm also likes to involve their trainees in social and marketing events including golf and cricket matches, they have their own six a side football team, go karting and other sporting and non sporting activities.

Sponsorship & Awards
50% LPC costs payable once trainee starts contract.

Contact
Mrs JJ Symons

Method of Application
Handwritten covering letter and CV

Selection Procedure
Screening interview and selection half day

Closing date for 2001
31 August 1999

Application
Training contracts p.a. 4

Training
Salary: 1st year(1999) £13,500
Salary: 2nd Year(1999) £14,500

BRISTOWS

3 Lincoln's Inn Fields London WC2A 3AA
Tel: (0171) 400 8000 Fax: (0171) 400 8050
Email: info@bristows.co.uk
Website: www.bristows.com

Partners	19
Assistant Solicitors	45
Total Trainees	12

Firm Profile
Bristows is a leading commercial practice in Central London, pre-eminent in intellectual property law including IT, multimedia, brands and biotechnology. It has a substantial practice in company and commercial law with strong complementary practices in competition, environmental and property law.

Main Areas of Work
Intellectual Property 50%; Company/Corporate Finance/Commercial 15%; Computer and IT 10%; Commercial Litigation 10%; Commercial Property 10%; Charities/Professional Institutions/Partnership/Environmental 5%.

Trainee Profile
They recruit graduates of all disciplines. As well as academic ability, they look for practical intelligence, the capacity to communicate well and the ability to assimilate complex materials while still seeing the wood for the trees.

Training Environment
Trainees receive a high level of individual attention, spending each of their four seats with either a partner or senior fee-earner. This, plus the opportunity of secondments to leading clients, gives trainees closer involvement in cases and greater contact with partners and clients alike. Continuous and formal assessment by seat holders, regular counselling sessions with the training partner and a comprehensive in-house training programme all provide additional support for trainees to develop the skills gained from this excellent hands on experience. Working in small teams, with each team headed by a partner, trainees play an active role from very early on in their training, seeing assignments through from start to finish.

Benefits
Excellent career prospects, a competitive City package, firm pension scheme, life assurance and health insurance.

Vacation Placements
Places for 1999: 45; Duration: Summer – 2 weeks, Christmas/Easter – 1 week; Remuneration: £175 p.w.; Closing Date: Christmas – 15/11; Easter/Summer – 28/2.

Sponsorship & Awards
CPE and LPC funding, £4,000 p.a. plus fees.

Contact
Graduate Recruitment Officer

Method of Application
Application form

Selection Procedure
2 individual interviews

Closing date for 2001
31 January 1999 for February interviews, 31 August for September interviews

Application
Training contracts p.a.	8
Applications p.a.	1,000
% interviewed p.a.	6%
Required degree grade	2.1
	(Preferred)

Training
Salary: 1st year(1999)	£18,500
Salary: 2nd Year(1999)	£20,500
Holiday entitlement	4 weeks
% of trainees with a non-law degree p.a.	75%

Post-Qualification
Salary (1999)	£30,000
% of trainees offered job on qualification (1998)	72%
% of assistants (as at 1/9/98) who joined as trainees	50%
% of partners (as at 1/9/98) who joined as trainees	47%

BROWNE JACOBSON

44 Castle Gate Nottingham NG1 7BJ
Tel: (0115) 950 0055 Fax: (0115) 947 5246
Email: info@brownej.co.uk

Partners	36
Assistant Solicitors	40
Total Trainees	16

Firm Profile
A Nottingham-based firm with an office in the City and an associated office in Paris. Its strengths are in corporate/commercial work and litigation. Clients include businesses and professional institutions.

Main Areas of Work
Corporate/Commercial 27%; Commercial & Other Litigation 25%; Insurance & Personal Injury Litigation 23%; Professional Indemnity 17%; Taxation/Trusts 5%; Other 3%.

Trainee Profile
The firm requires academic ability, enthusiasm and commitment. A sense of humour and a common-sense approach are essential.

Training Environment
Trainees will spend six months in four of the following five departments: corporate/ commercial, property, litigation, insurance, and private client. You will be allocated a second year trainee as a personal mentor, and will have regular appraisals. In addition to the PSC, the firm provides a comprehensive induction programme and structured skills training. All trainees have PCs and the atmosphere is friendly and supportive. Early responsibility is encouraged. Teamwork is an important factor in this practice. There are opportunities to move between offices. An active sports and social calendar operates.

Sponsorship & Awards
CPE and LPC fees paid.

Contact
Carol King
Training Officer

Method of Application
Letter and CV

Selection Procedure
Assessment Centre

Closing date for 2001
31 July 1999

Application

Training contracts p.a.	8
Applications p.a.	1,000
% interviewed p.a.	8%
Required degree grade	2:1

Training

Salary: 1st year(1999)	£14,000
Salary: 2nd Year(1999)	£15,500
Holiday entitlement	20 days
% of trainees with a non-law degree p.a.	20%

Post-Qualification

Salary (1998)	£21,500
% of trainees offered job on qualification (1998)	100%

Overseas Offices
Paris

BURGES SALMON

Narrow Quay House Narrow Quay Bristol BS1 4AH
Tel: (0117) 902 2725 Fax: (0117) 902 4400
Email: lisa.head@burges-salmon.com
Website: www.burges-salmon.co.uk

Partners	40
Assistant Solicitors	56
Total Trainees	27

Firm Profile
Burges Salmon is one of the country's leading firms of solicitors outside London. All of the firm's 400 staff are located in modern waterfront offices situated in the heart of Bristol's thriving commercial centre, currently undergoing a multi-million pound regeneration scheme. Burges Salmon is a name recognised and respected internationally and synonymous with quality, professionalism and corporate success, the firm is enjoying sustained growth.

Main Areas of Work
Working for both commercial and private clients, Burges Salmon provide specialist advice across a broad range of subjects including Company, Commercial & Corporate Finance, Property, Commercial & Property Litigation and Private Client.

Trainee Profile
To be successful, candidates will have to demonstrate high levels of analytical ability, communication skills, resilience and a clear understanding of client service.

Training Environment
Training at Burges Salmon is a partnership between the trainee and the firm. Trainees provide talent and commitment, the firm provides resources and support. The firm's record for retaining trainees is excellent and this success is, in part, due to an unusual placement system consisting of five periods of four months in the main practice areas, followed by a final four months in a specific area chosen by the trainee in consultation with the Recruitment Partners. Trainees are not kept in the background on mundane tasks and are actively involved in setting the tempo and direction of their training, taking on responsibility and gaining expertise at a pace appropriate for them.

Benefits
Rates of pay are substantially in excess of the Law Society recommendations and reviewed on 1 November each year.

Vacation Placements
Places for 1999: 24; Duration: 2 weeks; Remuneration: £100 p.w.; Closing Date: 5 March 1999.

Sponsorship & Awards
CPE and LPC fees paid + £2,000 maintenance p.a.

Contact
Lisa Head
Graduate Recruitment
Co-Ordinator

Method of Application
Employer's Application Form

Selection Procedure
Penultimate year of law degree or final year of non-law degree, apply for open days and work experience by 5 March 1999 and year 2001 training contracts by 18 August 1999.

Closing date for 2001
13 August 1999

Application
Training contracts p.a.	15
Applications p.a.	1,000
% interviewed p.a.	5%
Required degree grade	2:1 or higher

Training
Salary: 1st year(1998)	£15,500
Salary: 2nd Year(1998)	£16,500
Holiday entitlement	23 days
% of trainees with a non-law degree p.a.	40%

Post-Qualification
Salary (1999)	£25,000
% of trainees offered job on qualification (1998)	89%
% of assistants (as at 1/9/98) who joined as trainees	45%
% of partners (as at 1/9/98) who joined as trainees	13%

CAMERON McKENNA

Mitre House 160 Aldersgate Street London EC1A 4DD
Tel: (0845) 3000 491 Fax: (01753) 608 005
Email: cameronmckenna@barkers-response.co.uk
Website: www.cmck.com

Partners	180
Assistant Solicitors	400
Total Trainees	104

Firm Profile

Winner of 'The Best Large Law Firm of the year' (The Lawyer/ HIFAL Awards, 1998), Cameron McKenna is a major full service UK and international commercial firm advising businesses and governments on transactions and projects particularly in the UK, continental Europe, the Asia Pacific region, North America and Southern Africa. They have particular strengths in a number of industry sectors such as banking and finance, corporate, construction, projects, energy, healthcare, bioscience, insurance and property. The firm is modern, entrepreneurial and innovative and are strong on achievement. They believe the key to success is clear communication.

Main Areas of Work

Banking and International Finance; Commercial; Commercial Litigation/Dispute Resolution; Corporate; Energy, Projects & Construction; Property; Taxation & Employee Benefits; Insurance/Reinsurance

Trainee Profile

The firm looks for high-achieving team players with good communication, analytical and organisational skills. You will need to show initiative and be able to accept personal responsibility, not only for your own work, but also for your career development. You will need to be resilient and focused on achieving results.

Training Environment

The firm is friendly and supportive and puts no limits on a trainee's progress. It offers four six month seats, three of which will be in the firm's main area of practice. In addition you may gain experience of a specialist area or opt for a secondment to national or international clients. In each seat you will be allocated high quality work on substantial transactions for a range of government and blue-chip clients. Regular appraisals will be held with your seat supervisor to assess your progress, skills and development needs. The three compulsory modules of the PSC will be completed before joining, allowing trainees to become effective and participate on a practical level as soon as possible. The Professional Skills Course is complemented by a comprehensive in-house training programme that continues up to qualification and beyond.

Contact
Graduate Recruitment Team
0845 3000 491

Method of Application
Employer's application form

Selection Procedure
Two-stage selection procedure. Initial interview followed by assessment centre

Closing date for 2001
By September 1999

Application

Training contracts p.a.	80
Applications p.a.	1,500
% interviewed p.a.	27%
Required degree grade	2:1

Training

Salary: 1st year(1999) £21,000
Salary: 2nd Year(1999) £23,100
Holiday entitlement 22 days increasing to 24 days in second year
% of trainees with a non-law degree p.a. 40%
No. of seats available abroad p.a. (currently) 8

Post-Qualification

Salary (1999) £34,000
% of trainees offered job on qualification (1998) 87%

Benefits

Private medical insurance, Corporate gym membership, Season ticket loan, Personal Health Insurance, Life assurance, 22 days holiday, Travel bursaries.

Vacation Placements

Places for 1999: 55; Duration: 2 weeks; Remuneration: £200 p.w.; Closing Date: 12 February 1999.

Sponsorship & Awards

CPE and LPC Funding: Fees paid and a maintenance grant of £4,000 (London and Guildford), £3,750 (elsewhere).

Additional Information

Every trainee has a PC on their desk with email connection and access to legal and business databases. The firm financially supports trainees who wish to learn or improve a foreign language. There will be the opportunity to become involved in a number of sporting and social events.

Trainee Comments

"The firm is incredibly focused on what it wants to achieve. It is aware of its strengths and training is certainly one of them. It's an element you should focus on in your career choice. You need to have a real idea of what you want to do, where you want to do it and how you can achieve your ambitions. Be disciplined. Focus on the positives. Play to your own strengths." (Tom Ince, final seat trainee).

"Life at Cameron McKenna is what you make it. Do what you do best. Capitalise on opportunities as and when they arise, or take the initiative and make things happen. Everyone is supported and encouraged to fulful their potential. You see a little bit of yourself in every other trainee. There is the opportunity for us all to succeed." (Simon Massey, third seat trainee).

"You have to be creative, to think on your feet, to look around a problem to find the best way of approaching it. Some seats are notoriously difficult, but as you gain experience, you gain confidence. You have to work hard, no question about it, whether you're from a law or non-law discipline, but if you have an enterprising nature, you will get results." (Neel Malviya, final seat trainee).

Branch Offices

Aberdeen, Almaty, Beijing, Bristol, Brussels, Budapest, Hong Kong, Moscow, Prague, San Francisco, Stockholm, Tashkent, Warsaw, Washington D.C. and associated offices in Copenhagen, Stuttgart

cameron mcKenna

CAPSTICKS

77-83 Upper Richmond Road London SW15 2TT
Tel: (0181) 780 2211 Fax: (0181) 780 1141

Partners	15
Assistant Solicitors	47
Total Trainees	9

Firm Profile
One of the leading legal advisers to the National Health Service, the firm handles litigation, administrative law, commercial and property work for NHS Trusts and health authorities, as well as other public sector bodies and their insurers. Voted Lawyer/HIFAL 'Law Firm of the Year' (Best Medium size firm) 1997.

Main Areas of Work
Clinical Negligence/Personal Injury 40%; Commercial and Property Transactions 25%; Commercial and Property Litigation 15%; Employment Law 10% Administrative Law 10%.

Trainee Profile
Successful candidates possess intellectual agility, good interpersonal skills and are capable of taking initiative.

Training Environment
Four six-month seats, which may include clinical negligence/personal injury; commercial property; contract and commercial; employment law and commercial/property litigation. Trainees take responsibility for their own caseload and are involved in client meetings from an early stage. There are also opportunities to contribute to the firm's marketing and management processes. There are numerous in-house lectures for all fee earners, and trainees also attend an Open University-accredited Diploma in clinical negligence and risk management which the firm runs for its clients. There is an open door policy, and trainees receive informal feedback and supervision as well as regular appraisals. Despite the firm's rapid expansion, it has retained a friendly atmosphere and a relaxed working environment. There are numerous informal social and sporting activities which occur on a team and departmental basis.

Benefits
Bonus scheme, PRP, PHI, death in service cover.

Vacation Placements
Places for 1999: yes; Duration: 2 weeks; Closing Date: 31 March 1999.

Sponsorship & Awards
Scholarship contributions to CPE and LPC courses.

Contact
Sue Laundy

Method of Application
Application by CV and covering letter

Selection Procedure
Candidates are encouraged to participate in the firm's summer placement scheme. Final selection is by interview with the Training Principal and other partners

Closing date for 2001
31 March 1999

Application
Training contracts p.a.	6–8
Applications p.a.	1000+
% interviewed p.a.	2.5%
Required degree grade	2:1 or above

Training
Salary: 1st year(1999) c. £20,500
Salary: 2nd year(1999) c. £22,500
Holiday entitlement 20 days p.a.
(increased by 1 day p.a.)
% of trainees with
a non-law degree p.a. c. 50%

Post-Qualification
Salary (1999) £28,000 + bonus scheme
% of trainees offered job
on qualification (1998) 100%
% of assistants (as at 1/9/98)
who joined as trainees 15%
% of partners (as at 1/9/98)
who joined as trainees 6%

CARTWRIGHTS

Marsh House 11 Marsh Street Bristol BS99 7BB
Tel: (0117) 929 3601 Fax: (0117) 926 2403
Email: info@cartwrights.com

Partners	16
Assistant Solicitors	32
Total Trainees	10

Firm Profile

This leading Bristol firm has a national reputation for leisure and licensing, insurance litigation, employment and transport law. Its clients range from major PLCs (including more than 20 of the FTSE 100) to sole traders and private individuals. Cartwrights offers a broad training with a quality of work normally associated with the City. The firm's hallmark is its detailed understanding of its clients' market sectors and their business needs.

Main Areas of Work

Commercial (including corporate, litigation, property, employment and transport) 34%; Insurance Litigation 33%; Licensing and Leisure 24%; Private Client 9%.

Trainee Profile

Good academic performance (2:1 degree, law or non-law), enthusiasm, motivation, commercial understanding and teamworking skills. Relevant work experience, language and IT skills an advantage. Non-academic achievement is also valued.

Training Environment

On arrival, trainees take part in a comprehensive induction programme and are then assigned to a six-month seat in company commercial, commercial litigation, commercial property, insurance or private client. Thereafter, trainees are consulted on the allocation of their remaining three seats. You will share an office with other trainees, working under the supervision of a partner or senior fee-earner whom you will actively assist. In some departments you will conduct your own files, in others you will work as part of a team. Initiative and responsibility are encouraged. Progress is reviewed regularly. Social and sporting life is varied and the Bristol Trainee Solicitors Group is active.

Benefits

Grant and interest free loan for LPC, life assurance.

Vacation Placements

Places for 1999: 18; Duration: 1 week; Remuneration: £125 p.w.; Closing Date: 28 February 1999.

Sponsorship & Awards

Up to £5,000 paid towards LPC fees and £2,400 interest free loan.

Contact
Christopher Eskell

Method of Application
Application form

Selection Procedure
Interviews and aptitude tests

Closing date for 2001
1 August 1999

Application

Training contracts p.a.	5
Applications p.a.	750
% interviewed p.a.	5%
Required degree grade	2:1

Training
Salary: 1st year(1999) £14,000–£14,600
Salary: 2nd Year(1999) £15,200–£15,800

Holiday entitlement	20 days

Post-Qualification

Salary (1999)	£22,500
% of trainees offered job on qualification (1998)	80%
% of assistants (as at 1/9/98) who joined as trainees	31%
% of partners (as at 1/9/98) who joined as trainees	31%

CHARLES RUSSELL

8–10 New Fetter Lane London EC4A 1RS
Tel: (0171) 203 5000 Fax: (0171) 203 0200
Website: www.cr-law.com

Partners	69
Assistant Solicitors	197
Total Trainees	20

Firm Profile

Charles Russell is a progressive City law firm with regional offices in Cheltenham and Guildford and a network of close professional contacts throughout the world. The fifth fastest growing law firm in the UK, they offer a wide range of legal services for both corporate and private clients. The firm recruits a small number of trainees for a firm of their size as they believe it enables them to provide the best possible training. The firm is committed to their clients and their demands. It also respects the fact that its staff need to have a life of their own.

Main Areas of Work

Whilst our commercial division offers the opportunity for involvement in major corporate transactions, the firm's commitment to private clients and charities remains unshaken. Charles Russell is particularly well known for media and communications, commercial property, charities, insurance and reinsurance and offer clients specialist expertise in employment and pensions, corporate finance, tax, intellectual property, family, computer law, sports regulation, planning and environmental law.

Trainee Profile

Trainees should be balanced, rounded achievers with a solid academic background. Outside interests are fundamental.

Training Environment

Trainees spend six months in four of the following training seats – litigation, insurance & reinsurance, company/commercial, property, private client, family, employment and intellectual property. Wherever possible the firm will accommodate an individual preference. You will be seated with a partner/senior solicitor. Regular appraisals are held to discuss progress and direction. Trainees are encouraged to attend the extensive in-house training courses. The PSC is taught both internally and externally. All trainees are expected to fully immerse themselves, taking on as much responsibility as possible. A social committee organises a range of activities from quiz nights through to sporting events.

Benefits

PPP immediately, PHI and Life Assurance after 1 year's service.

Sponsorship & Awards

CPE and LPC fees paid and £3,000 maintenance p.a. (currently under review).

Contact
Elaine Emmington
Graduate Recruitment Line:
0171 203 5353

Method of Application
Hand written letter and
application form

Selection Procedure
Assessment days to include:
interview, fact finding exercise
and group exercises designed
to assess identified performance
criteria

Closing date for 2001
31 July 1999

Application
Training contracts p.a.	10–12
Applications p.a.	1,500
% interviewed p.a.	3%
Required degree grade	2:1

Training
Salary: 1st year(1998) £20,000
Holiday entitlement 22 days

Post-Qualification
Salary (1998) £32,000

Regional Offices
Also offer training contracts in
our Cheltenham and Guildford
offices. For further details,
please telephone the graduate
recruitment line

CLIFFORD CHANCE

200 Aldersgate Street London EC1A 4JJ
Tel: (0171) 600 1000 Fax: (0171) 600 5555
Website: http://www.cliffordchance.com

Firm Profile

Clifford Chance is a leading international law firm offering a comprehensive range of domestic and international legal service to businesses, financiers and governments from 25 offices worldwide. The firm maintains a friendly working atmosphere. Our working style is characterised by a real sense of energy, enthusiasm and determination to provide the best possible service to our clients. The work requires individuals with a combination of legal knowledge and a broad understanding of the issues which face our clients, coupled with a practical and creative approach.

Main Areas of Work

International Banking and Finance; Corporate/Commercial including Competition law, Intellectual Property, Communications, Computers, Entertainment and Media; Contentious Business including Insurance, Shipping, Insolvency and International Arbitration; Property; Tax, Pensions and Employment.

Trainee Profile

A consistently strong academic profile, with a broad range of interpersonal skills and extra-curricular activities and interests.

Training Environment

Four six month periods or 'seats'. Training seats are available in all areas of the firm's practice and about 50% of trainees will spend a seat on secondment to an international office or a client. Trainees share an office and work with a senior lawyer, and practical experience is supplemented by formal training and courses to develop personal and business skills. Trainees are encouraged to use initiative to make the most of the expertise and resources available in the firm. Three monthly appraisals and monitoring in each seat ensure trainees gain a range of work and experience.

Benefits

Prize for first class degree and distinction in LPC, interest free loan, private health insurance, subsidised restaurant, fitness centre (swimming pool, squash courts, gym), life assurance, confidential assistance, occupational health service, and permanent health assurance.

Partners	273*
Assistant Solicitors	1200*
Total Trainees	249*

* denotes world-wide figures

Contact
Anne Niblock
Recruitment and
Development Manager

Method of Application
Application form

Selection Procedure
First interview with partner and senior assistant, followed by assessment day and interview

Closing date for 2001
N/A

Application

Training contracts p.a.	130
Applications p.a.	2,000
% interviewed p.a.	33%
Required degree grade	2:1

Training
Salary: 1st year(1999) £21,000
Salary: 2nd Year(1999) £24,000
Holiday entitlement
11 days per seat
% of trainees with
a non-law degree p.a.   40%
No. of seats available
abroad p.a.   82

Post-Qualification
Salary (1999)   £32,000
% of trainees offered job
on qualification (1998)   95%

▶

229

CLIFFORD CHANCE *continued*

Vacation Placements

Places for 1999: A total of 80 placements are available during the Easter and Summer vacations 1999; Duration: The two-week placement provides an insight into the practical side of law and a structured programme for lectures, case studies and visits to City institutions provide an idea of the scope of our work and of the friendly, stimulating environment; Remuneration: not less than £200 per week; Closing Date: 26 February 1999.

Sponsorship & Awards

CPE and LPC fees paid and £4,000 maintenance p.a. (£3,400 outside London and Guildford).

Trainee Comments

"I chose Clifford Chance because, having done a summer placement, I knew that I would be involved in quality work alongside highly motivated, 'down-to-earth' people." (Katherine Webster, 2nd seat trainee, read Law & French at East Anglia).

"I wanted to work for Clifford Chance because I knew that its unrivalled breadth and depth – both in the UK and abroad – would provide the international opportunities that I sought". (Rob Crothers, 1st seat trainee, read PPE at Merton College, Oxford).

Overseas Offices

Amsterdam, Bangkok, Barcelona, Brussels, Budapest, Dubai, Düsseldorf, Frankfurt, Hanoi, Ho Chi Minh City, Hong Kong, Madrid, Milan, Moscow, New York, Padua, Paris, Prague, Rome, Sao Paulo, Shanghai, Singapore, Tokyo, Warsaw

CLIFFORD CHANCE

CLYDE & CO

51 Eastcheap London EC3M 1JP
Tel: (0171) 623 1244 Fax: (0171) 623 5427
Email: careers@clyde.co.uk
Website: www.clydeco.com

Partners	96
Assistant Solicitors	104
Total Trainees	36

Firm Profile
A major international firm with over 600 staff world-wide and a client base spanning more than 100 countries. It has particular strengths in international trade, insurance, reinsurance, shipping, energy, corporate and finance matters. It has UK offices in London, Guildford and Cardiff, with trainee solicitors recruited for London and Guildford.

Main Areas of Work
Marine 30%; Insurance/Reinsurance 30%; Company, Commercial, Banking, Property 20%; International Trade 10%; Other Commercial Litigation 10%.

Trainee Profile
The firm has no stereotypical trainee. Non-law graduates are welcome, especially those with modern languages or science degrees. The firm places as much importance on finding candidates with an outgoing, interesting personality as it does on academic credentials.

Training Environment
Trainees become immediate 'casehandlers' and usually have their own office. They are encouraged to take on as much responsibility and client contact as possible, and are involved in developing business relationships. The PSC is run in-house and there is a full programme of lectures, seminars, courses, workshops and educational visits.

Benefits
Subsidised sports club, interest free ticket loan, staff restaurant and weekly free bar (London); monthly staff lunch and monthly free bar (Guildford).

Legal Training Days
Legal training days: 64; Duration: 1 day; Remuneration: travel expenses; Closing Date: 28 February 1998. Call our hotline for further details.

Sponsorship & Awards
CPE and LPC Fees paid and maintenance grant. Sponsorship provided where no LEA funding available.

Contact
Sharon Lithgow
Recruitment Officer

Method of Application
Application form and covering letter

Selection Procedure
Individual interview with recruitment officer, followed by interview with two partners

Closing date for 2001
31 August 1999

Application
Training contracts p.a.	16
Applications p.a.	2,000
% interviewed p.a.	varies
Required degree grade	2:1

Training
Salary: 1st year (1998) £20,000–
£20,500
Salary: 2nd Year (1998) £21,000–
£22,000
Holiday entitlement	22 days
% of trainees with a non-law degree p.a.	varies
No. of seats available abroad p.a.	varies

Post-Qualification
Salary (1998) £31,500
% of trainees offered job on qualification (1998) 94%

Overseas Offices
Hong Kong, Singapore, Dubai, Caracas, Paris, Piraeus
Associate office – St Petersburg

CRIPPS HARRIES HALL

Seymour House 11–13 Mount Ephraim Road Tunbridge Wells, Kent TN1 1EN
Tel: (01892) 515121 Fax: (01892) 506069
Email: aol@crippslaw.com

Partners	28
Assistant Solicitors	43
Total Trainees	12

Firm Profile
Established almost 150 years ago, Cripps Harries Hall has grown steadily to become the largest firm in Kent and East Sussex. The firm is progressing steadily towards being regarded as the leading law firm in the South East outside London. It is an innovative and young firm; most of the partners are in their thirties or forties and the atmosphere is friendly and outgoing. Their headquarters are in Tunbridge Wells. In addition, they have an office in London and two offices in East Sussex.

Main Areas of Work
Commercial Litigation: 25% Corporate & Commercial Property: 24%; Finance and Investment Services: 20% Private Client: 14%; Residential conveyancing and agriculture: 12%; General Litigation: 5%.

Trainee Profile
Cripps Harries Hall are looking for talented, confident, capable people who want to make a contribution during their period of training and who will want to stay with us as assistant solicitors and potential partners. You will be expected to integrate expert legal advice with a highly developed use of information technology.

Training Environment
The two year training contract is divided into six periods, each spent in a different department or division where you will receive a thorough grounding in the relevant practice. You will usually share a room with a partner, and work as an integral member of a small team. At the end of each period in a department, monitored monthly by the partner, there is a more formal review with the Managing Partner and the Personnel Manager. The Director of Education will arrange your continuing education. In addition to the Professional Skills Course, you will attend seminars and courses and receive training in business, presentation, IT and marketing skills.

Benefits
PPP, DIS, PHI.

Sponsorship & Awards
Discretionary LPC Funding: Fees – 50% interest free loan, 50% bursary.

Contact
Annabelle Lawrence
Personnel Manager

Method of Application
Handwritten letter and firm's application form.

Selection Procedure
1 interview with Managing Partner and Personnel Manager

Closing date for 2001
31 July 1999

Application
Training contracts p.a.   8
Applications p.a.   Up to 1,000
% interviewed p.a.   5%
Required degree grade   2.1

Training
Salary: 1st year(1998)   £13,000
Salary: 2nd Year(1998)   £15,000
Holiday entitlement   20 days
% of trainees with
a non-law degree p.a.   25%

Post-Qualification
Salary (1998)   £21,500
% of trainees offered job
on qualification (1998)   100%
% of assistants (as at 1/9/98)
who joined as trainees   42%
% of partners (as at 1/9/98)
who joined as trainees   30%

Associated Firms
Berlin, Frankfurt, Madrid, Munich, Paris, Rotterdam

DAVENPORT LYONS

1 Old Burlington Street London W1X 2NL
Tel: (0171) 468 2600 Fax: (0171) 437 8216
Email: dl@davenport-lyons.co.uk

Firm Profile
Davenport Lyons is a leading entertainment and media law practice and combines this work with strong company/commercial, litigation, property and private client departments. The firm adopts a keen commercial and practical partner-led approach and builds on long-term partnerships with its clients.

Main Areas of Work
Litigation 23%; Company Commercial 25%; Entertainment/ Media 22%; Commercial Property 18%; Private Client 12%

Trainee Profile
Upper Second plus; interesting background; business acumen; sociability; knowledge of foreign languages an advantage. Scope for being the extra piece in the jigsaw.

Training Environment
Four seats of six months each. Six monthly assessments. Supervision from within departments. Ongoing programme of in-house lectures and professional skills training. Contributions to gym membership and the firm has softball, cricket and football teams. Davenport Lyons offers interesting hands-on training. Trainees are treated as junior fee earners and are encouraged to develop their own client relationships and to handle their own matters under appropriate supervision.

Benefits
Season ticket loans, bonuses in summer and Christmas. Client introduction bonuses.

Vacation Placements
Places for 1999: 10; Duration: 2–3 weeks; Remuneration: £130 p.w.; Closing Date: none fixed.

Sponsorship & Awards
The firm will consider financial assistance when appropriate.

Partners	15
Assistant Solicitors	15
Total Trainees	6

Contact
Michael Hatchwell

Method of Application
Letter and cv

Selection Procedure
Interviews

Closing date for 2001
Easter 1999

Application

Training contracts p.a.	3
Applications p.a.	1,500
% interviewed p.a.	20%
Required degree grade	2:1

Training
Salary: 1st year(1999) £19,000+
Salary: 2nd Year(1999) £20,000+

Holiday entitlement	4 weeks
% of trainees with a non-law degree p.a.	60–70%

Post-Qualification

Salary (1999)	£26,000
% of trainees offered job on qualification (1998)	50%
% of assistants (as at 1/9/98) who joined as trainees	27%
% of partners (as at 1/9/98) who joined as trainees	21%

DAVIES ARNOLD COOPER

6–8 Bouverie Street London EC4Y 8DD
Tel: (0171) 936 2222 Fax: (0171) 936 2020
Email: daclon@dac.co.uk

Partners	63*
Assistant Solicitors	259*
Total Trainees	40

* denotes world-wide figures

Contact
Ruth Elliot

Method of Application
DAC application form

Selection Procedure
Open days and individual interviews

Closing date for 2001
31 July 1999

Required degree grade
2:1 capability

Firm Profile

Davies Arnold Cooper is one of the UK's leading insurance and reinsurance practices. They have offices in London, Manchester, Newcastle and Madrid. Well known for a practical and commercial approach which, combined with a campaigning and pioneering style and our involvement in most of the UK's highest profile litigation cases in the last 10 years, has meant that the firm is one of the most written about law firms in Europe.

Main Areas of Work

Insurance, reinsurance, corporate and commercial litigation, construction and property, healthcare and technology.

Trainee Profile

Davies Arnold Cooper look for people who can demonstrate a strong intellect combined with analytical and problem solving skills. Well organised, flexible and self motivated you must be a strong communicator and able to work effectively with a variety of different people. You will thrive in a fast moving, commercial environment with plenty of opportunity for early responsibility. The firm welcomes applications from all age groups and backgrounds, from people who want to make a positive difference.

Training Environment

One of the only two law firms listed in the 'Britain's Best Employers' Directory. Their induction and training schemes are widely admired and trainees receive a comprehensive grounding in core legal skills. As a medium sized firm they offer a flexible training programme with the opportunity for early responsibility within a supportive environment. Their aim is to recruit for the future of the firm and they select a maximum of 20 trainees each year to ensure positions will be available on qualification.

Vacation Placements

Places for 1999: 35; Method of Application: Comprehensive CV and covering letter; Duration: 3 weeks; Remuneration: under review; Closing Date: 31 January 1999.

Sponsorship & Awards

CPE and LPC: grants covering course and examination fees. Discretionary interest-free loans for maintenance up to £4,000.

DENTON HALL

5 Chancery Lane Clifford's Inn London EC4A 1BU
Tel: (0171) 242 1212 Fax: (0171) 404 0087
Email: info@dentonhall.com
Website: http://www.dentonhall.com

Firm Profile

Following merger and lateral growth, Denton Hall is one of the largest firms in the City, with particular strengths in the media/entertainment/telecommuncations industries and in the energy/ infrastructure sectors as well as in corporate, project finance, banking/financial services, property and planning, litigation arbitration IP and IT. It has an international outlook, including an extensive Asian network, offices in the Middle East and a European network of associated offices.

Main Areas of Work

Company and commercial 38%; Litigation and arbitration 26%; Property and planning 22%; Media and technology 14%.

Trainee Profile

The firm looks for candidates with high academic ability and ambition. They should be commercially aware, self-motivated, determined and should show flair and precision. Languages are an advantage, but not essential.

Training Environment

Four six-month seats. Three of the seats are likely to be spent in company/commercial or media/technology and in the property and litigation departments. In the fourth seat, you may decide to specialise within a main seat. For example, company/commercial includes energy and infrastructure, corporate finance, tax, competition, banking & financial markets and insolvency. Trainees sit with a partner/senior solicitor who supervises their work. Seats abroad or client secondments are sometimes available. A range of sporting and social activities are available.

Benefits

Holiday entitlements rise by 1 day after each year served, luncheon vouchers, private health cover, season ticket loan, gym membership.

Sponsorship & Awards

CPE funding: fees and £3,500 maintenance; LPC funding: fees and £3,500 maintenance (less any Local Authority contribution in both respects).

Partners	115*
Assistant Solicitors	205*
Total Trainees	66

denotes world-wide figures

Contact
Virginia Glastonbury
Partner

Method of Application
Application form and
handwritten letter

Selection Procedure
Interview

Closing date for 2001
6 August 1999 (from 1 June 1999)

Application

Training contracts p.a.	25–30
Applications p.a.	2,500
% interviewed p.a.	8%
Required degree grade	2:1

Training

Salary: 1st year(1998)	£20,500–£21,500
Salary: 2nd Year(1998)	£22,500–£23,500
Holiday entitlement	21 days
% of trainees with a non-law degree p.a.	50% max.
No. of seats available abroad p.a.	Sometimes available

Post-Qualification

Salary (1998)	£32,500
% of trainees offered job on qualification (1998)	80% approx.

Overseas Offices
Beijing, Brussels, Cairo, Gibraltor,
Hong Kong, Istanbul, Moscow,
New York, Singapore, Tokyo,
and associated offices at
Barcelona, Berlin, Chemnitz,
Cologne, Copenhagen,
Düsseldorf, Frankfurt, Hamburg,
Madrid, Munich, Oslo, Paris,
Vienna

DIBB LUPTON ALSOP

125 London Wall London EC2Y 5AE
Tel: (0345) 262 728 Fax: (0121) 212 5792

Firm Profile
This ambitious firm thinks of itself as a business as much as a law firm. Its expansion has been meteoric. In 1989, it was below the top 35 UK firms in terms of size – it is now the seventh largest. It has offices in six major cities in the UK, but still operates as one partnership. The full range of corporate and commercial services are offered.

Main Areas of Work
Corporate 18%, Insurance 18%, Property & Construction 18%, Litigation 16%, Corporate Recovery & Insolvency 8%, Human Resources 7%, Communications & Technology 6%, Business Services 5%, Banking 4%

Trainee Profile
The firm only wants exceptional people. Good academic ability is no longer sufficient. It wants people with different backgrounds and skills. The successful candidates will believe in themselves, relate well to other people, have an appetite for life and a desire to succeed in business.

Training Environment
The firm deliberately takes on a relatively small number of trainees for its size. This enables it to offer in-depth experience and excellent prospects. Trainees will be assigned a mentor to guide them through their contract. They will spend four six month seats in different commercial areas, and may spend time in more than one office. They will sit with a partner or assistant and learn through practice and observation. There is an ongoing commercial skills training programme and the PSC is run in-house. Good sports and social facilities.

Benefits
PRP, pension, health insurance, life assurance, 25 holiday days after two years

Vacation Placements
Places for 1999: 100; Duration: 2 weeks; Remuneration: £175 p.w. London, £125 p.w. regions; Closing Date: 28 February 1999.

Sponsorship & Awards
CPE and LPC fees paid and £3,500 maintenance for LPC.

Partners	210*
Assistant Solicitors	250*
Total Trainees	97

denotes world-wide figures

Contact
Sally Carthy

Method of Application
Application form

Selection Procedure
First interview, assessment afternoon, second interview with 2 partners

Closing date for 2001
31 July 1999

Application

Training contracts p.a.	50
Applications p.a.	2,200
% interviewed p.a.	10%
Required degree grade	2:1

Training
Salary: 1st year(1999) £21,000
(London) £15,500 (regions)
Salary: 2nd Year(1999) £22,000
(London) £16,500 (regions)
Holiday entitlement   23 days
% of trainees with
a non-law degree p.a.   40%

Post-Qualification
Salary (1999) £32,000 (London)
£25,000 (regions)
% of trainees offered job
on qualification (1998)   90%

Trainee Comments

"Growing up in Liverpool and having spent all my academic life here, it was not a question of where I wanted to start my professional career but who I wanted to start it with. I applied to a number of firms in Liverpool but it was Dibb Lupton Alsop which impressed me the most. Dibb Lupton Alsop provided an opportunity to do high quality commercial work in my home town and showed commitment and dedication to my training and future career which was second to none." (Clare Tickle, first year trainee in the Liverpool office, read law at Liverpool University).

"I had lived in London for three years on and off before starting work and I had long wanted to work in a City firm. I chose Dibb Lupton Alsop for their obvious ambition - particularly evidenced around the time I applied for a training contract by the well documented merger and their expansionist ideas. I was influenced greatly by the unstuffy attitude I perceived at interview. This was a marked difference from some other firms who interviewed me." (Guy Sheppard, first year trainee in the London office, read Latin at Exeter University).

"As a truly national firm Dibb Lupton Alsop offers me a City reputation, excellent quality of work and a commitment to training without being in London. As a trainee with a past 'non legal life' Dibb Lupton Alsop is a firm with a modern culture that recognises the added value that alternative disciplines can offer. As business lawyers with a reputation for being pro-active, ambitious and competitive in the market, Dibb Lupton Alsop are always looking to be better and committed to be the best." (Joely Richardson, second year trainee in the Birmingham office, studied Business Studies at Leeds Business School).

"I chose Dibb Lupton Alsop for my training contract because it is a truly national firm. This offered me the opportunity to receive the same quality of training as a trainee in a City firm, whilst having the quality of life gained through living in the provinces. I was also influenced by the fact that the firm recruits fewer trainees than other firms of similar size and retains the majority of its trainees on qualification. For me this demonstrates that the firm is committed to the longer term careers of the people it recruits." (Wayne Smith, second year trainee in the Sheffield office, studied law at Nottingham Trent University).

Overseas Offices
Brussels, Hong Kong, New York

DICKINSON DEES

St. Ann's Wharf 112 Quayside
Newcastle-upon-Tyne NE99 1SB
Tel: (0191) 279 9000 Fax: (0191) 279 9100
Email: law@dickinson-dees.co.uk
Website: www.dickinson-dees.com

Partners	45
Assistant Solicitors	38
Total Trainees	14

Firm Profile
The largest firm in the north east, Dickinson Dees offers both commercial and private client services. The firm has new premises on the Quayside in Newcastle. The firm has an associated office in Brussels with opportunities for trainees to spend time on secondment there.

Main Areas of Work
Corporate 30%; Property 30%; Private Client 20%; Litigation 20%.

Trainee Profile
Good academic and analytical ability. Good commercial and business sense. Confident, personable and adaptable with good communication skills. Able to fit into a team.

Training Environment
Trainees are relatively few for the size of the practice. You are fully integrated into the firm and involved in all aspects of firm business. The training contract consists of four seats. One seat is spent in each of the commercial property, company/commercial and litigation departments. You are able to specialise for the fourth seat. This is encouraged so that personnel rise through the firm rather than being recruited from outside. Trainees sit with partners or associates and training is reviewed every three months. The firm has its own Training & Development Manager. There are in-house induction courses on each move of department and opportunities for trainees to get involved in the in-house training programme. The professional skills course is run in conjunction with Northumbria University and the firm has played a key role in the development and implementation of this course. The working environment at Dickinson Dees is supportive and friendly. You will lead a busy life with sporting and social events organised by the office.

Vacation Placements
Places for 1999: 20; Duration: 1 week; Remuneration: £50 p.w.; Closing Date: 28 February 1999. Application forms are available.

Open Days
Open days will be held in the summer of 1999. Application forms are available on request. Closing date: 30 April 1999.

Contact
Jen Smurthwaite

Method of Application
Application form and handwritten letter

Selection Procedure
Interview

Closing date for 2001
31 July 1999

Application

Training contracts p.a.	8
Applications p.a.	700
% interviewed p.a.	10%
Required degree grade	2:1

Training

Salary: 1st year(1999)	£14,750
Salary: 2nd Year(1999)	£15,750
Holiday entitlement	4 weeks
% of trainees with a non-law degree p.a.	50%
No. of seats available abroad p.a.	2

Sponsorship & Awards

LPC fees paid and £1,000 interest free loan.

Trainee Comments

"Dickinson Dees, as well as being a firm with an impressive range of clients and work, immediately struck me as being a friendly employer – a heady mix!"
(Oliver Bennett, first year trainee, read Law at Durham University).

"I wanted to work for a leading commercial firm with a progressive outlook and an excellent training record; Dickinson Dees is the law firm that fulfils all their criteria."
(Elizabeth Allen, first year trainee, read English at University of London and LLB at Northumbria University).

"I wanted to work for an expanding and developing commercial firm that invested time and effort in its trainees. Dickinson Dees offers all of the above with an enthusiastic and friendly approach."
(Edward Meikle, second year trainee read Art History at University of East Anglia).

"After completing a week of work experience at Dickinson Dees I felt that I would get a thorough training at a leading commercial firm and great future prospects."
(Sara Brody, first year trainee, read law at Hull University).

"Dickinson Dees offered exposure to a wide range of work and clients and a positive approach to trainees. What stood out was a keenness to involve and develop trainees: the firm's culture is certainly progressive, but also supportive and friendly. You never feel the 'typical' trainee solicitor; your work is valued."
(Kevin Mercer, second year trainee read Geography at Nottingham University).

"Dickinson Dees offers trainees the highest level of training. Trainees are involved at all levels and have a high degree of client contact. Overall a great place to work in a friendly and relaxed environment."
(Ian Hornby, first year trainee, read Law at Newcastle Univesity).

Post-Qualification

Salary (1999)	£22,250
% of trainees offered job on qualification (1998)	66%
% of assistants (as at 1/9/98) who joined as trainees	60%
% of partners (as at 1/9/98) who joined as trainees	29%

Branch Office

Rond Point Schuman 9 - Box 13
B-1040 Brussels
Tel: 0032 2 233 3747
Fax: 0032 2 233 3740

D J FREEMAN

43 Fetter Lane London EC4A 1JU
Tel: (0171) 583 4055 Fax: (0171) 353 7377
Email: aem@djfreeman.co.uk
Website: djfreeman.co.uk

Partners	47
Assistant Solicitors	62
Total Trainees	27

Firm Profile
An innovative firm whose lawyers work in multi-disciplinary teams concentrating on specific business sectors. It is one of the leading firms in the property, insurance and media/communications industries, and has a strong commercial litigation department. It also has more women partners than any other City law firm.

Main Areas of Work
Property Services 41%; Insurance Services 25%; Commercial Litigation 22%; Media & Communications 12%.

Trainee Profile
Clear and creative thinkers who work well under pressure and as part of a team.

Training Environment
Trainees spend six months in the firm's major practice areas, and once a month are able to discuss their progress in each seat with a partner. Believing supervised experience to be the best training, the firm soon gives trainees the chance to meet clients, be responsible for their own work and join in marketing and client development activities. Regular workshops in each seat help develop basic skills in the different departments. Any suggestions or concerns can be voiced at a trainee solicitors' committee. The firm has an active social committee which organises events from quiz evenings to wine tasting, as well as a theatre club.

Benefits
Subsidised meals in staff restaurant; BUPA after three months; a variety of social and sporting events.

Vacation Placements
Places for 1999: 16; Duration: 3 weeks; Remuneration: £150 p.w.; Closing Date: 14 March 1999.

Sponsorship & Awards
CPE or LPC Funding.

Contact
Anne Mellars

Method of Application
Application form

Selection Procedure
Interview

Closing date for 2001
16 July 1999

Application
Training contracts p.a.	12–15
Applications p.a.	1,000
% interviewed p.a.	8%
Required degree grade	2:1

Training
Salary: 1st year(1999)	£19,000
Salary: 2nd Year(1999)	£21,500
Holiday entitlement	20 days

Post-Qualification
Salary (1999)	£31,000

DONNE MILEHAM & HADDOCK

100 Queens Road Brighton BN1 3YB
Tel: (01273) 744 340 Fax:(01273) 744 404

Firm Profile
Donne Mileham & Haddock aims to offer expertise and
service comparable to City firms. Its main commercial offices
are at Brighton and Crawley where the firm continues its rapid
expansion. The firm also undertakes international work at all
six of its offices.

Main Areas of Work
Corporate/Commercial; Commercial Property; Employment;
Commercial Litigation; Transport; Private Client.

Trainee Profile
The firm looks for trainees with a sound academic background,
experience/interest in law, and external interests. Local
connections are also of value.

Training Environment
Usually four six-month seats taken from the following areas:
Employment, Commercial Litigation, Company, Planning,
Commercial Property, Construction Litigation, Personal Injury,
Civil Litigation and Private Client work. Trainees are closely
supervised by the partner to whom they are attached. The
majority of seats are in Brighton and Crawley, but there are
also seats at the East Grinstead, Lewes and Worthing offices.

Vacation Placements
Places for 1999: limited number, priority given to trainee
interviewees and Sussex University; Duration: 1–2 weeks;
Remuneration: £75.00 p.w. expenses; Closing Date: 31 March
1999.

Partners	32
Assistant Solicitors	24
Total Trainees	9

Contact
Jean Clack

Method of Application
CV and letter

Closing date for 2001
December 1999

Application
Training contracts p.a.	4–5
Applications p.a.	350–450
% interviewed p.a.	3%
Required degree grade	2:1

Training
Salary: 1st year(1998)	£12,500
Salary: 2nd Year(1998)	£15,000
Holiday entitlement	20 days
% of trainees with a non-law degree p.a.	50%

Post-Qualification
Salary (1998)	£19,500
% of trainees offered job on qualification (1998)	100%
% of assistants (as at 1/9/98) who joined as trainees	33%
% of partners (as at 1/9/98) who joined as trainees	52%

EDGE ELLISON

Rutland House 148 Edmund St Birmingham B3 2JR
Tel: (0121) 200 2001 Fax: (0121) 200 1991
Email: Helen.Thomas@edge.co.uk
Website: www.edge.co.uk

Partners	80
Assistant Solicitors	145
Total Trainees	41

Firm Profile

One of the best established UK commercial law practices headquartered outside the City of London with offices in Birmingham, London and Leicester. Included within its three-year business plan is the Firm's commitment to become pre-eminent in the Midlands, to double the size of the London Office and treble the volume of transatlantic business.

Main Areas of Work

Commercial/Corporate 24%; Litigation 34%; Property 21%; Banking/Insolvency 7%; Construction 4%; Pensions & Tax/ Employment 10%.

Trainee Profile

Trainees are recruited to retain and, provided a satisfactory training contract is completed, there are excellent propects. The firm is acknowledged to be one of the most innovative and progressive firms in the country. They seek to recruit motivated, ambitious, creative people who crave a training environment that will let them use their skills and intelligence to solve problems, exploit opportunities and help develop leading edge legal solutions for a high profile national and international client list. Along the way, you will attain job satisfaction, fantastic earning potential and a considerable degree of personal fulfilment. Trainees are given their own level of responsibility.

Training Environment

Six months is spent in each of the four main departments (litigation, commercial, corporate and property) with the fourth seat in an area of your choice. In each department you will be fully involved in the work of your supervisor: attending client interviews and meetings from an early stage. In certain seats, you will soon be responsible for your own files but guidance will always be on hand. The PSC is integrated into a structured programme which includes seminars, workshops and skills development. Feedback will be given midway and at the end of each seat. A full social and sports programme is on offer.

Benefits

Private health cover, pension (post qualification/25 years of age).

Vacation Placements

Places for 1999: 80; Duration: 1 week; Remuneration: £100 p.w.; Closing Date: 15 February 1999.

Contact
Helen Thomas, Recruitment & Coaching Manager

Method of Application
Application form

Selection Procedure
Selection day, including group exercises and interview

Closing date for 2001
30 July 1999

Application
Training contracts p.a.	30
Applications p.a.	1,600
% interviewed p.a.	9–10%
Required degree grade	2:1

Training
Salary: 1st year (2000)
London	£19,500;
Midlands	£15,500

Salary: 2nd Year (2000)
London	£20,500;
Midlands	£16,500
Holiday entitlement	20 days
% of trainees with a non-law degree p.a.	35%

Post-Qualification
Salary (1999) London £30,000
Midlands £25,000
% of trainees offered job
on qualification (1998) 90%
% of assistants (as at 1/9/98)
who joined as trainees 35%
% of partners (as at 1/9/98)
who joined as trainees 40%

Sponsorship & Awards

CPE Funding: Fees paid LPC Funding: Fees paid & £3,500 maintenance.

Additional Information

edge ellison offers its trainees one to one coaching facilities that sharpen up mind mapping, brainstorming, photo reading and lateral thinking abilities. They'll also instruct you in the art of techniques like self management and delegation. Led by a core group of Coaching Pioneers, our dynamic approach is helping individuals and teams alike to realise their full potential. At the same time it creates the capacity within the organisation to design, develop and deliver outstanding services for the future.

Trainee Comments

"I saw genuine teamwork within the offices. The Firm has the dynamism, resource and commitment to expand, providing a wide variety of legal and commmercial challenges working for 'household name' clients." (Craig Armstrong, first year trainee, read Law at Cardiff University).

"It was obvious that trainees' contributions were really valued and responsibility was given. I liked the well structured training programme encompassing a broad range of good quality work; both of these created an atmosphere which encourage legal skills to develop. I also liked the opportunities to get to know colleagues through activities as diverse as women's football to legal advice work at the CAB!" (Claire Mortimer, first year trainee, read Law at Nottingham University).

"edge ellison attracted me for two reasons. Its size means it attracts major clients and offers 'real work' for trainees. Secondly, the biggest attraction is the people. Everyone seems willing to help from trainees to partners and two months into my training contract, my opinion hasn't changed." (Stuart James, first year trainee, read Politics, Philosophy & Economics at Oxford University).

"I knew I would receive excellent training and work with edge ellison but for me, what made edges stand apart from other firms was the friendly atmosphere and warm welcome extended to me when visiting the firm. I realise this sounds like an old cliché, but it really was the deciding factor in making the choice." (Oliver Stacey, second year trainee, read Law/French at Cardiff University).

"I joined edges because to me, I felt it had the perfect balance. Yes the quality of work and training is fantastic but there's more to life at edges than work, work, work. They were interested in me as a person as well as me as a lawyer. That made a real difference!" (Jan Lucas, second year, Head Trainee, read European Law at Warwick University).

EDWARD LEWIS

Verulam Gardens 70 Gray's Inn Road London WC1X 8NF
Tel: (0171) 404 5566 Fax: (0171) 404 2244
Email: mail@edlewis.mhs.compuserve.com
Website: http://www.edwardlewis.co.uk

Partners	26
Assistant Solicitors	40
Total Trainees	10

Firm Profile
Edward Lewis has strong European connections and provides services to UK and foreign clients. It operates in the private and public business sectors.

Main Areas of Work
Insurance Litigation; Commercial Litigation; Corporate; Commercial Property; Private Client.

Trainee Profile
Aside from academic excellence, you will need to be commercially and practically minded with good self-motivation.

Training Environment
It is a young and friendly firm with a hard-working attitude which you will experience immediately. As soon as you have completed the trainee induction programme, you will be expected to attend and participate in department and client meetings, attend court and draft documents. Responsibility is encouraged, but all work will be monitored in each of your four pre-selected seats. These will be chosen from property, corporate/commercial, insurance litigation, commercial litigation and private client. Your formal training will be a combination of external courses and in-house lectures and seminars. The social life is always lively and includes a number of seasonal parties.

Benefits
Permanent Health Insurance; Death in Service Benefit Payment; Private Medical Healthcare (after 12 months); Discretionary Christmas Bonus; 22 days holiday; Season Ticket Loan (after 6 months); Pension (on qualification).

Vacation Placements
Places for 1999: 15; Duration: 2 weeks; Remuneration: £160 p.w.; Closing Date: Apply 1 February 1999 to 30 May 1999 only.

Sponsorship & Awards
LPC funding.

Contact
Howard Lupton

Method of Application
Letter and CV

Selection Procedure
Interview

Closing date for 2001
Apply 1 May 1998 to 31 July 1999 only

Application
Training contracts p.a.	5
Applications p.a.	1000+
% interviewed p.a.	5%
Required degree grade	2:1

Training
Salary: 1st year(1999)	£19,000
Salary: 2nd Year(1999)	£21,000
Holiday entitlement	22
% of trainees with a non-law degree p.a.	50%

Post-Qualification
Salary (1999)	£29,500
% of trainees offered job on qualification (1998)	100%
% of assistants (as at 1/9/98) who joined as trainees	26%
% of partners (as at 1/9/98) who joined as trainees	5%

EVERSHEDS

Senator House 85 Queen Victoria Street London EC4V 4JL
Tel: (0171) 919 4500 Fax: (0171) 919 4919
Email: gradrec@eversheds.com
Website: www.eversheds.com

Partners	324
Assistant Solicitors	588
Total Trainees	188

Firm Profile

Eversheds has offices in the City of London and 18 other commercial centres in the UK and Europe. The practice has a complement of over 3,000 staff including 324 partners. The merger in August 1998 between Frere Cholmeley Bischoff and the London office further strengthened our international presence. Our offices are strategically located to support our clients operating internationally and offers the breadth and depth of legal advice you would expect from one of Europe's largest firms.

Main Areas of Work

Company, Commercial, Employment, Litigation, Dispute Management, Property plus specialist groups and in addition to these core areas there are a further 30 business and industry sectors.

Trainee Profile

You must be commercially aware with an analytical mind and an ability to identify problems and come up with solutions. You should be able to communicate in a friendly and professional way with clients and colleagues and be self motivated.

Training Environment

A steep learning curve begins with a month of basic training followed by four seats. These cover the firm's main practice areas of litigation, property, company and commercial. You may return to one of these areas or specialise in another of your choice. You will be encouraged to play a major part in the direction your training and development takes, with advice and supervision always available from training supervisors. In each department you will sit with a partner or senior assistant and participate from an early stage in varied, complex and high value work. Eversheds aims to retain as many of its trainees as possible on qualifying and many of the partners were trainees with the firm.

Benefits

Regional variations.

Vacation Placements

Places for 1999: 120; Duration: 2 weeks; Remuneration: regional variation; Closing Date: 28 February 1999.

Sponsorship & Awards

CPE/LPC fees and maintenance grant.

Contact
Mr Andrew M. Looney

Method of Application
Application form and handwritten covering letter to be returned to London address

Selection Procedure
Selection days include group and written exercises, plus interview.

Closing date for 2001
31 July 1999

Application
Training contracts p.a.	100 –120
Applications p.a.	3,000
% interviewed p.a.	15%
Required degree grade	2:1

Training
Salary: 1st year(1999) Regional variations
Salary: 2nd Year(1999) Regional variations
Holiday entitlement	21 days
% of trainees with a non-law degree p.a.	45%
No. of seats available abroad p.a.	Up to 10

Post-Qualification
Salary (1999) Regional variations
% of trainees offered job on qualification (1998)   80%

Overseas Offices
Brussels, Monaco, Moscow, Paris

Associated Offices
Copenhagen, Sofia

FARRER & CO

66 Lincoln's Inn Fields London WC2A 3LH
Tel: (0171) 242 2022 Fax: (0171) 831 9748

Partners	39
Assistant Solicitors	48
Total Trainees	13

Firm Profile
Farrer & Co is one of the UK's leading law practices. It provides a range of specialist advice to private, institutional and corporate clients.

Main Areas of Work
The firm's breadth of expertise is reflected by the fact that it has an outstanding reputation in fields as diverse as matrimonial law, offshore tax planning, employment, heritage work, charity law and defamation.

Trainee Profile
Trainees are expected to be highly motivated individuals with keen intellects and interesting and engaging personalities. Those applicants who appear to break the mould – as shown by their initiative for organisation, leadership, exploration, or enterprise – are far more likely to get an interview than the erudite, but otherwise unimpressive, student.

Training Environment
The training programme involves each trainee in the widest range of cases, clients and issues possible in a single law firm. This provides a broad foundation of knowledge and experience and the opportunity to make an informed choice about the area of law in which to specialise. A high degree of involvement is encouraged under the direct supervision of solicitors and partners. Trainees attend an induction programme and regular internal lectures. The training principal reviews trainees' progress at the end of each seat and extensive feedback is given. The firm has a very friendly atmosphere and regular sporting and social events.

Benefits
Health and life insurance, subsidised gym membership, season ticket loan.

Vacation Placements
Places for 1999: 18; Duration: 2 weeks at Easter, 3 weeks in summer; Remuneration: £180 p.w.; Closing Date: 28 February 1999.

Sponsorship & Awards
CPE Funding: Fees paid + £4,000 maintenance.
LPC Funding: Fees paid + £4,000 maintenance.

Contact
Personnel Manager

Method of Application
CV or firm's application form and covering letter

Selection Procedure
Interviews with Personnel Manager and Partners

Closing date for 2001
31 July 1999

Application
Training contracts p.a.	6
Applications p.a.	1,500
% interviewed p.a.	1%
Required degree grade	2:1

Training
Salary: 1st year(1998)	£20,000
Salary: 2nd Year(1998)	£22,000
Holiday entitlement	20 days
% of trainees with non-law degrees p.a.	46%

Post-Qualification
Salary (1999)	£32,000
trainees offered job on qualification (1998)	5 out of 6
% of assistants (as at 1/9/98) who joined as trainees	62%
% of partners (as at 1/9/98) who joined as trainees	70%

FENNERS

180 Fleet Street London EC4A 2HD
Tel: (0171) 430 2200 Fax: (0171) 430 2218
Email: info@fenners.co.uk

Partners	4
Assistant Solicitors	4
Total Trainees	1

Firm Profile
Fenners is a City based firm specialising in company/commercial law, corporate finance, commercial property, town planning and residential property development. The firm has a broad client base, including listed and unquoted companies, financial advisers, brokers, banks and other institutions.

Main Areas of Work
Commercial Property 50%; Corporate/Commercial 40%; Residential Property Development 10%.

Trainee Profile
Candidates will demonstrate academic exellence combined with commitment and motivation to pursuing a career in a niche City firm. In addition, extra curricular activities and interests are highly regarded as evidence of a balanced and well rounded candidate.

Training Environment
Training consists of seats within the firm's commercial property and corporate/commercial departments, with an option for a further contentious seat. You will sit with a Partner or an experienced solicitor who will provide you with daily tasks and support. In addition, you will have an opportunity to receive feedback and discuss your progress with your training principal every three months. Fenners' trainees are highly valued and their development within the firm is encouraged by providing a challenging, supportive and enjoyable environment in which to work.

Benefits
Health insurance, season ticket loan.

Vacation Placements
Places for 1999: 10; Duration: 2 weeks; Remuneration: competitive rates; Closing Date: 30 April 1999.

Sponsorship & Awards
CPE and LPC funding to be discussed with candidates.

Contact
Robert Fenner

Method of Application
Handwritten letter and CV.
Brochures available on request

Selection Procedure
2 interviews with partners. The firm does not require completion of an application form.
Candidates should submit CVs

Closing date for 2001
Applications should preferably be received by November 1999.

Application

Training contracts p.a.	3
Applications p.a.	400
% interviewed p.a.	10%
Required degree grade	2:1

Training

Salary: 1st year(1999)	Market for city
Salary: 2nd Year(1999)	Market for city
Holiday entitlement	22 days
% of trainees with a non-law degree p.a.	0%

Post-Qualification

Salary	Market for city

FIELD FISHER WATERHOUSE

41 Vine Street London EC3N 2AA
Tel: (0171) 481 4841 Fax: (0171) 488 0084
Email: Neil.Palmer@FFW.sprint.com
Website: http://www.ffwlaw.com

Partners	58
Assistant Solicitors	86
Total Trainees	25

Firm Profile
Field Fisher Waterhouse is a City-based firm with a substantial UK and international corporate practice. It has a reputation of providing an excellent all-round service to an impressive list of clients drawn from a variety of sectors. In January 1998 the firm merged with Allison & Humphreys to create a one-stop service to clients in the communications and media sector. The merger has also increased the firm's corporate finance, pensions and litigation practices. The firm prides itself on its collegiate atmosphere, its constructive approach to career development and its creative and commercial approach to law.

Contact
Mr T.J. Davies

Method of Application
CV and handwritten letter and application form

Selection Procedure
Interview

Closing date for 2001
31 July 1999

Main Areas of Work
Company/Commercial/Tax 25%; Commercial Property 22%; IP/IT 14%; Litigation 13%; Banking and Finance 11%; Professional Regulation 9%; Employment 6%.

Application

Training contracts p.a.	10
Applications p.a.	3,000
Required degree grade	2:1

Trainee Profile
There is no stereotypical recruit. Both academic and personal qualities are highly valued, and the firm seeks to recruit trainees with ability, enthusiasm, common sense and determination. The firm regards trainees as an investment for its future: a substantial number of its current partners trained there.

Training

Salary: 1st year(1998)	£20,000
Salary: 2nd Year(1998)	£21,000
Holiday entitlement	21 days
% of trainees with a non-law degree p.a.	40%

Training Environment
Three five month seats in the three principal departments: company and commercial, property and litigation, and a department of your choice. In each seat, trainees are directly responsible to a partner, and will assist with his or her transactions. The firm aims not only to develop your grasp of legal principles but also to foster a commercial awareness and a practical ability to deal with problems. Trainees receive a formal written assessment at the end of each seat to assess their professional, practical and personal qualities. The firm has a comprehensive training programme of in-house lectures given by partners and outside speakers and a thriving social committee.

Post-Qualification

Salary (1998)	£27,500
% of trainees offered job on qualification (1998)	100%
% of assistants (as at 1/9/98) who joined as trainees	40%
% of partners (as at 1/9/98) who joined as trainees	40%

Overseas Offices
Brussels

Benefits
Season ticket loans, PHI cover, death in service benefit.

Vacation Placements
Places for 1999: Limited places available.

Sponsorship & Awards
CPE and LPC fees paid.

FISHBURN BOXER

60 Strand London WC2N 5LR
Tel: (0171) 925 2884 Fax: (0171) 486 3256

Firm Profile
Fishburn Boxer is a close-knit, medium-sized firm with two London offices. It is a commercial practice acting for corporate, institutional and private clients. The firm's strengths lie in insurance, reinsurance and professional indemnity litigation.

Main Areas of Work
Litigation 95%; Corporate and Commercial 5%.

Trainee Profile
Usually a 2:1 degree is required, not necessarily in law. The firm looks for a willingness to take on responsibility and be directly involved. Ambition and thoroughness are also prized qualities. Commitment is essential as the firm expects to have a first option to employ its trainees for at least a further two years.

Training Environment
Save for six months in the non-contentious department, training is not divided on a six month seat basis. Eighteen months spent undertaking contentious work in areas such as building and construction disputes, most areas of professional negligence and insurance and reinsurance matters. Six months may be spent at the St. Mary's Axe office. Trainees can expect early responsibility for their own case-load, under a partner's supervision. All trainees take part in and attend regular in-house seminars.

Benefits
Private health insurance, season ticket loan, subsidised gym membership, group personal pension.

Vacation Placements
Places for 1999: 8; Duration: 2 weeks; Remuneration: expenses; Closing Date: 31 March 1999.

Sponsorship & Awards
Discretionary.

Partners	13
Assistant Solicitors	18
Total Trainees	4

Contact
Philip Heartfield

Method of Application
CV and covering letter

Selection Procedure
Informal first and formal second interview

Closing date for 2001
31 August 1999

Application

Training contracts p.a.	2
Applications p.a.	800
% interviewed p.a.	4%
Required degree grade	2:2

Training
Salary: 1st year(1999) City rates
Salary: 2nd Year(1999) City rates
Holiday entitlement 23 days
% of trainees with
a non-law degree p.a. 80%

Post-Qualification
Salary (1999) City rates
% of trainees offered job
on qualification (1998) 100%
% of assistants (as at 1/9/98)
who joined as trainees 44%
% of partners (as at 1/9/98)
who joined as trainees 85%

FOOT & BOWDEN

Foot & Bowden Building 21 Derry's Cross
Plymouth PL1 2SW
Tel: (01752) 675000 Fax: (01752) 671802
Email: E-MAIL@foot-bowden.co.uk

Partners	20
Assistant Solicitors	16
Total Trainees	7

Firm Profile
Established in 1908, with main office in Plymouth (moved premises 1995) and smaller commercial office in Exeter (opened 1997); associated with other independent firms; offering a wide range of commerical and private client services (specified below) together with niche specialisations in media/defamation and shipping; aiming to expand particularly in commercial sectors.

Main Areas of Work
Commercial 60%; Private Client 40%.

Trainee Profile
Strong academic background and communciation skills, practical approach and well-reasoned wish to develop a career in the south west.

Training Environment
Trainees are guided by the firm into an initial six-month seat (from banking litigation, commercial litigation, commercial property, employment, childcare, company/commercial, personal injury, property litigation, civil agency, wills & trusts and criminal litigation). The next three six-month seats are negotiated with the training partner. Guidance is offered and effort is made to try to accommodate the wishes of trainees, subject to the evolving needs of each team. Trainees shadow their supervisors and sit near them, but are also an integral part of the team. Levels of responsibility vary from team to team, and according to trust. Trainees are encouraged to grow into taking responsibility for their own conduct. Following an induction course, trainees attend an in-house seminar programme. The PSC is taught externally. Monthly meetings are held with supervisors (individually) and the training partner (together). Appraisals are conducted quarterly by supervisors. A non-partner acts as confidential and objective counsellor. The atmosphere is open and friendly, encouraging trainees to learn as much as possible. A variety of social/ sporting functions are organised.

Benefits
Use of first-come first-served staff parking area. Life assurance for over 30s after 12 months.

Vacation Placements
Occasional opportunities for early applicants.

Contact
Robin Brown

Method of Application
Handwritten letter and CV

Selection Procedure
Interview and competitive assessment day including oral presentation, written test and individual interview followed by psychometric test

Selection for 2000
Apply a.s.a.p.

Selection for 2001
First selection after
31 August 1999

Application

Training contracts p.a.	4
Applications p.a.	300
% interviewed p.a.	varies
Required degree grade	
Usually 2:1	

Training
Salary: 1st year(1998) £12,500
Salary: 2nd Year(1998) £14,000
Holiday entitlement 25 days
% of trainees with
a non-law degree p.a. no limit

Post-Qualification
Salary (1998) £23,000
% of trainees offered job
on qualification (1998) varies
% of assistants (as at 1/9/98)
who joined as trainees 31%
% of partners (as at 1/9/98)
who joined as trainees 35%

FOX WILLIAMS

City Gate House 39–45 Finsbury Square
London EC2A 1UU
Tel: (0171) 628 2000 Fax: (0171) 628 2100
Email: mail@foxwilliams.co.uk

Partners	13
Assistant Solicitors	19
Total Trainees	6

Firm Profile
Fox Williams is one of the most highly regarded City firms undertaking top quality work. It provides a comprehensive service for the business client but is best known for its mergers and acquisitions, employment and partnership work. It acts for leading companies in the healthcare and food industries. The practice also has considerable experience in advising on legal issues arising from the use of the Internet.

Main Areas of Work
Corporate 32%; Employment 28%; Litigation 18%; Commercial 11%; Property 11%.

Trainee Profile
The firm welcomes approaches from high academic achievers who are confident and outgoing, committed to the law and who have a genuine interest in business.

Training Environment
You spend six months in each of the corporate, commercial, employment, litigation and property departments. Client contact and the acceptance of responsibility are encouraged from the first day of training. You receive a thorough grounding in all aspects of commercial work, with both practical and academic training. The hope is that trainees make their mark and stay on to become assistant solicitors and partners in the firm. The young and dynamic partners of Fox Williams treat you as individuals, and are keen to create a happy working environment for all their team members.

Benefits
Health care, life assurance, season ticket loans.

Vacation Placements
Places for 1999: 4; Duration: 1 week; Remuneration: £100; Closing Date: 31 January 1999.

Sponsorship & Awards
£5,000 grant.

Contact
Tina Williams

Method of Application
Application form

Selection Procedure
1 interview

Closing date for 2001
31 August 1999

Application

Training contracts p.a.	3
Applications p.a.	1,000
% interviewed p.a.	2%
Required degree grade	2:1

Training

Salary: 1st year(1998)	£20,000
Salary: 2nd Year(1998)	£22,000
Holiday entitlement	20 days
% of trainees with a non-law degree p.a.	50%

Post-Qualification

Salary (1999)	£31,000
% of trainees offered job on qualification (1998)	100%
% of assistants (as at 1/9/98) who joined as trainees	35%
% of partners (as at 1/9/98) who joined as trainees	0%

FRESHFIELDS

65 Fleet Street London EC4Y 1HS
Tel: (0171) 936 4000 Fax: (0171) 832 7001
Email: email@freshfields.com
Website: http://www.freshfields.com

Partners	211*
Assistant Solicitors	625*
Total Trainees	115

denotes world-wide figures

Firm Profile
A major international law firm providing a comprehensive worldwide service to corporations, financial institutions and governments. This service has been strengthened in 1998 by a strategic alliance with the leading German law firm Deringer Tessin Herrmann & Sedemund. Together the firms offer clients a network of over 1,100 lawyers operating out of 20 offices in 14 countries.

Main Areas of Work
Corporate; Mergers and Acquisitions; Banking; Litigation; Arbitration; Jt Ventures; Employment, Pensions and Benefits; Asset Finance; Comm Property; Tax; Capital Mrkts; Intellectual Property; Project Finance; US securities; EU/Competition; Communications and Media; Construction and Engineering; Energy; Environment; Financial Services; Insolvency; Insurance; International Tax; Investment Funds.

Trainee Profile
Good academic qualifications, good record of achievement in other areas, common sense and creative thinking. Linguistic and computer skills also an advantage.

Training Environment
12-15 months will be spent in the corporate, finance and litigation departments. Thereafter, seats in property, intellectual property, employment or tax are offered. Trainees may also have the option of spending 6 months in another office or in the legal department of a client. High priority is given to trainees' preferences. A comprehensive programme of technical legal training and skills training, as well as the PSC, is provided.

Benefits
Life Ass, permanent health ins, group personal pension, after 3 mths an interest-free loan for a season travel ticket, after six mths free m'ship to the firm's private medical ins scheme, subsidised staff restaurant, gym.

Vacation Placements
Places for 1999: 100; Duration: 2 weeks; Remuneration: £200 p.w.; Closing Date: 14 February 1999 but apply early.

Sponsorship & Awards
CPE and LPC fees paid and £4,500 maintenance p.a. (£4,000 outside London and Guildford).

Contact
Tom Head

Method of Application
Application form

Selection Procedure
1 interview with 2 partners

Closing date for 2001
31 August 1999

Application
Training contracts p.a.	90
Applications p.a.	3,000
% interviewed p.a.	10%
Required degree grade	2:1

Training
Salary: 1st year(1999)	£21,000
Salary: 2nd Year(1999)	£24,000
Holiday entitlement	22 days
% of trainees with a non-law degree p.a.	36%
No. of seats available abroad p.a.	30

Post-Qualification
Salary (1999)	£32,000
% of trainees offered job on qualification (1998)	98%

Overseas Offices
Bangkok, Barcelona, Beijing, Brussels, Hanoi, Ho Chi Minh City, Hong Kong, Madrid, Milan, Moscow, New York, Paris, Rome, Singapore, Tokyo, Washington

GARRETTS

180 Strand London WC2R 2NN
Tel: (0171) 344 0344 Fax: (0171) 438 2518

Firm Profile
Garretts is a nationwide practice, with an office in London and five further offices around the country. It is also a member of the Andersen Legal international network of law firms which has branches in 72 countries. Its strengths lie in corporate and IT work.

Main Areas of Work
Corporate 48%; Intellectual Property/Info Technology 19%; Property 13%; Employment & Benefits 13%; Litigation 5%; Pensions & Tax 2%.

Trainee Profile
Successful candidates will have a strong academic background, outgoing personality, relevant work experience and an interest in extra-curricular activities.

Training Environment
Trainees spend six months in four different seats, in a variety of departments. You will have the opportunity to choose your fourth seat. Formal training consists of a residential induction course, two day courses at the start of each new placement and professional in-house lectures. Social and sporting activities are encouraged.

Benefits
BUPA.

Vacation Placements
Places for 1999: 70 throughout the UK; Duration: 2 weeks; Remuneration: £100–£175 p.w. (1998); Closing Date: n/a.

Sponsorship & Awards
CPE + LPC fees paid and £3,750–£4,000 grant p.a.

Partners	108
Assistant Solicitors	329
Total Trainees	39

Contact
Kate Henry

Method of Application
Application form or covering letter and CV

Selection Procedure
1 hour interview in London, second interview held in regional office of choice

Closing date for 2001
N/A

Application
Training contracts p.a.	50
Applications p.a.	2,000
% interviewed p.a.	c.30%
Required degree grade	2:1

Training
Salary: 1st year(1998) £20,000 (London)
Holiday entitlement 20 days

GOODMAN DERRICK

90 Fetter Lane London EC4A 1EQ

Tel: (0171) 404 0606 Fax: (0171) 831 6407

Firm Profile

Founded in 1954 by Lord Goodman, the firm now has a broad commercial practice and is well known for its media and defamation work, particularly relating to television.

Main Areas of Work

Media 35%; Commercial and General Litigation 25%; Corporate 20%; Property 15%; Charities/Private Client 5%.

Trainee Profile

Candidates must show that they will quickly be able to handle responsibility and deal directly with clients. They must be suited to the firm's work environment, present themselves confidently and be quick thinking and practically-minded.

Training Environment

Training at the firm is based on direct and active involvement with the work of the practice. The PSC is partly carried out at the start of the training contract, with some courses taking place over the following two years, coupled with the firm's general training programme. Trainees are in addition expected to initiate personal research if specialist knowledge needs to be gained for a particular piece of work. Four periods of six months are spent in litigation, property, media (contentious and non-contentious) and company/commercial law. Work groups within these main departments allow you to experience further specialist fields. For example, litigation includes employment work. Your own preferences and aptitude will be monitored by your supervising partner and discussed at monthly meetings and at three-monthly appraisals. The firm has a very friendly and informal environment.

Benefits

Medical Health Insurance, season ticket loan.

Sponsorship & Awards

LPC fees plus maintenance grant.

Partners	14
Assistant Solicitors	13
Total Trainees	5

Contact
Nicholas Armstrong

Method of Application
CV and covering letter

Selection Procedure
2 interviews

Closing date for 2001
27 August 1999

Application
Training contracts p.a.	3
Applications p.a.	800–900
% interviewed p.a.	4%
Required degree grade min.	2:1

Training
Salary: 1st year(1998)	£18,000
Holiday entitlement	20 days
% of trainees with a non-law degree p.a.	20%

Post-Qualification
% of trainees offered job on qualification (1998)	33%
% of assistants (as at 1/9/98) who joined as trainees	40%
% of partners (as at 1/9/98) who joined as trainees	40%

GOULDENS

22 Tudor Street London EC4Y 0JJ
Tel: (0171) 583 7777 Fax: (0171) 583 3051
Email: recruit@gouldens.com
Website: http://www.gouldens.com

Partners	34
Assistant Solicitors	66
Total Trainees	21

Firm Profile
Gouldens is a leading commercial firm based in the City of London with a high quality client base in the UK and abroad. It provides a full range of legal services to major commercial clients from the UK and overseas.

Main Areas of Work
Company/Commercial (incl Corporate Tax) 42%; Property (inc. Planning) 23%; Litigation (incl IP) 20%; Banking/Capital Markets 12%; Personal/International Tax Planning 3%.

Trainee Profile
Candidates should have obtained or are predicted a 2:1 degree in any discipline. They should be willing to accept the challenge of responsibility in an atmosphere where not only technical expertise but flair, originality and enthusiasm are rewarded.

Training Environment
The firm operates a non-rotational system of training which is unique in the City. Trainees receive work simultaneously from all departments in the firm and see matters through from start to finish. They are encouraged to assume their own workload which allows for early responsibility and development of potential at a faster rate than might otherwise be the case, and more extensive client contact. Work will vary from small cases which you may handle alone (with appropriate supervision) to larger matters where you will assist a partner or an assistant solicitor. Practical experience is supported by a full training programme, including twice-weekly seminars as well as regular sessions. Provided performance during training has been good, the firm aims to offer jobs to all trainees on qualification.

Benefits
BUPA, season ticket loan, subsidised sports club membership, group life cover.

Vacation Placements
Places for 1999: 30; Duration: 2 or 3 weeks; Remuneration: £225; Closing Date: 28 February 1999.

Sponsorship & Awards
CPE and LPC fees paid and £4,500 maintenance p.a.

Contact
Jeanette Ryan

Method of Application
Letter and CV

Selection Procedure
2 interviews with partners

Closing date for 2001
30 October 1999

Application

Training contracts p.a.	20
Applications p.a.	2,500
% interviewed p.a.	10%
Required degree grade	2.1

Training

Salary: 1st year(1999)	£24,000
Salary: 2nd Year(1999)	£26,000
Holiday entitlement	4 weeks
% of trainees with a non-law degree p.a.	25%

Post-Qualification

Salary (1999)	£36,750
% of trainees offered job on qualification (1998)	90%
% of assistants (as at 1/9/98) who joined as trainees	55%
% of partners (as at 1/9/98) who joined as trainees	52%

HALLIWELL LANDAU

St. James's Court Brown St Manchester M2 2JF
Tel: (0161) 835 3003 Fax: (0161) 835 2994
Email: info@halliwells.com

Partners	41
Assistant Solicitors	60
Total Trainees	12

Firm Profile

Halliwell Landau is one of Manchester's largest commercial law firms. Over the last few years the firm has increased substantially in both size and turnover and now has in excess of 120 fee earners. This development leads to a continuing requirement for solicitors and has given rise to more internal promotions to partnerships.

Main Areas of Work

Corporate/Banking 24%; Commercial Litigation 20%; Commercial Property 17%; Insolvency 12%; Insurance Litigation 12%; Planning/Environmental law 4%; Trust and Estate Planning 4%; Intellectual Property 4%; Employment 3%

Trainee Profile

Candidates need to show a good academic ability but do not necessarily need to have studied law at University. They should demonstrate an ability to fit into a hardworking team. In particular we are looking for candidates who will develop with the firm after their initial training.

Training Environment

Each trainee will spend six months in at least three separate departments. These will usually include commercial litigation, corporate and property. So far as possible if an individual trainee has a particular request for experience in one of the more specialist departments then that will be accommodated. In each department the trainee will work as a member of one of the teams within that department as well as being able to assist other teams. Specific training appropriate to each department will be given and in addition trainees are strongly encouraged to attend the firm's regular seminars on legal and related subjects. There is also a specific training programme for trainees. Each trainee will be assessed both mid-seat and at the end of each seat.

Benefits

A subsidised gym membership is available.

Vacation Placements

Places for 1999: 25; Duration: 2 weeks; Remuneration: £100 p.w.; Closing Date: 31 March 1999.

Sponsorship & Awards

A contribution will be made to either CPE or LPC fees.

Contact
Paul Rose

Method of Application
CV and application form

Selection Procedure
Open days or summer placements

Closing date for 2001
31 July 1999

Application

Training contracts p.a.	6
Applications p.a.	600
% interviewed p.a.	5%
Required degree grade	2:1

Training
Salary: 1st year(1999) £15,000
Salary: 2nd Year(1999) £16,000

Post-Qualification

Salary (1999)	£23,000
% of trainees offered job on qualification (1998)	100%
% of assistants (as at 1/9/98) who joined as trainees	12%
% of partners (as at 1/9/98) who joined as trainees	9%

HAMMOND SUDDARDS

7 Devonshire Square Cutlers Gardens London EC2M 4YH
2 Park Lane Leeds LS3 1ES
Trinity Court 16 Dalton Street Manchester M6O 8HS
Tel: (0171) 655 1000 Fax: (0171) 655 1001
Website: www.hammondsuddards.co.uk

Partners	88
Assistant Solicitors	229
Total Trainees	40

Firm Profile

Hammond Suddards is a leading commercial law firm with offices in London, Leeds, Manchester and Brussels. They have over 1,200 staff, including 88 partners, 229 solicitors and 40 trainees, and are regarded as innovative, opportunistic and highly successful in the markets in which they operate. The firm's rapid growth has meant they have doubled in size during the last four years.

Contact
Ben Reeves
Head of Recruitment
(London office)

Method of Application
CV and covering letter

Selection Procedure
Interview

Closing date for 2001
31 July 1999

Main Areas of Work

Banking; Corporate Finance; Commercial Dispute Resolution; Construction; Employment; Financial Services & Corporate Tax; Insolvency; Intellectual Property; Insurance; Pensions; Property.

Application
Training contracts p.a.	20
Applications p.a.	2,000
% interviewed p.a.	3%
Required degree grade	2:1

Trainee Profile

Hammond Suddards seek applications from all disciplines for both vacation work and training contracts. They look for three characteristics: strong academic performance, work experience in the legal sector and significant achievement in non-academic pursuits.

Training
Salary: 1st year(1999) £16,000 + accommodation
Salary: 2nd Year(1999) £18,000+ accommodation
Holiday entitlement   23 days
% of trainees with
a non-law degree p.a.   25%
No. of seats available
abroad p.a.   3

Training Environment

Around 20 trainee solicitors are recruited each year who each carry out six four-month seats during their training contract. All trainees are encouraged to move around the offices during their training and subsidised trainee accommodation is provided in all our locations to facilitate this process. Trainees can choose their seats as they progress through the training contract.

Post-Qualification
Salary (1998)   £31,000
% of trainees accepting job
on qualification (1998)   95%

Benefits

Subsidised accommodation in all locations. Flexible benefits scheme which allows trainees to choose their own benefits from a range of options.

Overseas Offices
Brussels

Vacation Placements

Places for 1999: 30; Duration: 4 weeks; Remuneration: £200 p.w. (London), £150 pw (Leeds and Manchester); Closing Date: 26 February 1999.

Sponsorship & Awards

CPE and LPC fees paid and maintenance grant of £4,100 p.a.

HARBOTTLE & LEWIS

Hanover House 14 Hanover Square London W1R 0BE
Tel: (0171) 667 5000 Fax: (0171) 667 5100
Email: hal@harbottle.co.uk
Website: www.harbottle.co.uk

Partners	15
Assistant Solicitors	50
Total Trainees	9

Firm Profile
Harbottle & Lewis is recognised for the unique breadth of its practice in the entertainment, media, travel (including aviation) and leisure industries. It undertakes significant corporate commercial and contentious work for clients within these industries including newer industries such as digital mixed media.

Main Areas of Work
Music, film and television production, theatre, broadcasting, computer games and publishing, sport, sponsorship and advertising, aviation and leisure.

Trainee Profile
Trainees will have demonstrated the high academic abilities, commercial awareness, and initiative necessary to become part of a team advising clients in dynamic and demanding industries.

Training Environment
The two year training contract is divided into four six months seats where trainees will be given experience in a variety of legal skills including company commercial, litigation, intellectual property and real property working within teams focused on the firm's core industries. The firm has a policy of accepting a small number of trainees to ensure they are given relevant and challenging work and are exposed to and have responsibility for a full range of legal tasks. The firm has its own lecture and seminars programme in both legal topics and industry know-how. An open door policy and a pragmatic entrepreneurial approach to legal practice provides a stimulating working environment.

Sponsorship & Awards
LPC fees paid and interest free loans towards maintenance.

Contact
Kathy Beilby

Method of Application
CV and letter

Selection Procedure
Interview

Closing date for 2001
31 July 1999

Application
Training contracts p.a.	5
Applications p.a.	800
% interviewed p.a.	5%
Required degree grade	2:1

Training
Salary: 1st year(1998)	£19,500
Salary: 2nd Year(1998)	£20,500
Holiday entitlement	20 days
% of trainees with a non-law degree p.a.	40%

Post-Qualification
Salary (1998)	£30,500
% of trainees offered job on qualification (1998)	50%

HARVEY INGRAM OWSTON

20 New Walk Leicester LE1 6TX
Tel: (0116) 254 5454 Fax: (0116) 255 4559
Email: cvf@hio.co.uk

Partners	26
Assistant Solicitors	80
Total Trainees	6

Firm Profile
Located in Leicester, Harvey Ingram Owston is one of the East Midlands' leading commercial law firms. We are ambitious and forward-looking in our approach and committed to providing all our clients with an efficient and friendly service.

Contact
Mr Chris Findlay

Method of Application
CV followed by application form

Main Areas of Work
The firm is divided into four main departments – Company and Commercial, Property, Litigation and Probate and Trust.

Closing date for 2001
31 August 1999

Trainee Profile
Harvey Ingram Owston looks for applicants with a good academic record. Successsful applicants have a practical and disciplined approach to their work together with the virtues of common sense, flexibility, strong communication skills and a sense of humour.

Training Environment
Harvey Ingram Owston places great emphasis on training and career development. Trainee Solicitors usually spend at least five months in each of the firm's main departments and thus gain a broad experience in all the different aspects of legal work. Trainees are encourageed to take on responsibility at an early stage but support and supervision is always on hand. Trainee Solicitors have regular individual meetings with the training partner to discuss the progress of the trainee. Salaries are competitive and are generally increased during the training contract. The long term prospects are very good for successful applicants for training contracts.

Sponsorship & Awards
Assistance with LPC funding is considered on application.

HEMPSONS

33 Henrietta Street Covent Garden London WC2E 8NH

Tel: (0171) 836 0011 Fax: (0171) 836 2783

Email: london-hempsons@btinternet.com

Partners	30
Assistant Solicitors	70
Total Trainees	10

Firm Profile

With offices in London's Covent Garden, central Manchester and Harrogate, Hempsons is recognised as a leading practice in the provision of legal services to the NHS, hospital trusts and healthcare professionals. The firm also provides specialist legal services to a range of charity clients. The practice has expanded considerably in the recent past and now totals more than 300 members.

Main Areas of Work

Medical Litigation 38%; Healthcare 15%; Partnership 15%; Commercial Property 12%; Commercial Litigation/ Defamation 10%; Charity 10%.

Trainee Profile

The firm looks for intellectual rigour and a sound academic record together with emotional maturity and evidence of an ability to empathise with clients' needs. Genuinely open-minded about a candidate's age and degree discipline, we are not searching for one particular type of personality as we recognise the importance of a varied team. Relevant work experience is useful and preference may be given to candidates seeking to become dually qualified in law and a medical discipline.

Training Environment

The trainee usually undertakes four six-month seats. Depending on the office in which the trainee is based, these will be drawn from a combination of some of the following: healthcare litigation; employment; partnership; PFI; defamation; commercial property; commercial litigation; crime, probate and trusts; charities. The trainee is allocated to a team and sits with a partner or senior solicitor in each seat. A local partner has reponsibility for the trainees in that office (typically four) and meets monthly with each trainee to review progress and deal with any problems arising. A senior partner monitors consistency, progress and development across the three offices. An open door policy applies and trainees are regarded very much as an integral part of the team to which they have been allocated. The atmosphere is friendly and forward thinking due both to the firm's origin as a small, traditional practice as well as to its recent expansion.

Benefits

Non-contributory pension. Season ticket loan for London based trainees. Holiday entitlement: 20 Days.

Contact
Trainee Solicitor Co-ordinator, London office

Method of Application
Application form and covering letter.

Selection Procedure
2 interviews. Second interviews held in London.

Closing date for 2001
To be decided

Application
Training contracts p.a.   6

HERBERT SMITH

Exchange House Primrose Street London EC2A 2HS
Tel: (0171) 374 8000 Fax: (0171) 374 0888
Email: herbertsmith@dial.pipex.com
Website: http://www.herbertsmith.com

Partners	145*
Assistant Solicitors	370*
Total Trainees	130

denotes world-wide figures

Firm Profile
A major City firm with an international dimension, Herbert Smith has particular strengths in international M & A, corporate finance and international projects with a strong profile in litigation and arbitration. The working environment is strongly team-orientated, friendly and informal, probably as a result of the diverse backgrounds of the firm's partners and staff.

Main Areas of Work
International M & A; Corporate Finance and Banking (including Capital Markets); Energy; Projects and Project Finance; Competition; Property; International Litigation; Arbitration.

Trainee Profile
Trainees need common sense, self-confidence and intelligence to make their own way in a large firm. They are typically high-achieving and intelligent, numerate and literate with general and legal work experience.

Training Environment
Structured training and supervision are designed to allow trainees to experience a unique range of both contentious and non-contentious work and take on responsibilities as soon as they can. You will work within partner-led teams and have your own role. Individual strengths will be monitored, developed and utilised. On-the-job training is divided into four six-month seats: three in the firm's major areas of practice and one abroad or in a specialist area. Lectures and case studies will take up 30 days of the contract and the firm runs its own legal development programme. There are good social and sporting activities and a life outside work is positively encouraged.

Benefits
PRP, gym, private health insurance, season ticket loan, life assurance.

Vacation Placements
Places for 1999: 80; Duration: 1x2 weeks; 3x3 weeks; Remuneration: £200 p.w.; Closing Date: Mid-February.

Sponsorship & Awards
CPE and LPC fees paid and £4,000 maintenance p.a. (£3,600 outside London).

Contact
Stephanie Hartshorn

Method of Application
Application form

Selection Procedure
Interview

Closing date for 2001
31 October 1999

Application
Training contracts p.a.	80
Applications p.a.	2,000
% interviewed p.a.	10%
Required degree grade	2:2

Training
Salary: 1st year(1999)	£21,000
Salary: 2nd Year(1999)	£24,000
Holiday entitlement	23 days
% of trainees with a non-law degree p.a.	c. 40%

Post-Qualification
Salary (1999)	£30,000
% of trainees offered job on qualification (1998)	95%

Overseas Offices
Brussels, Hong Kong, Paris, Singapore, Indonesia

HEWITSON BECKE + SHAW

42 Newmarket Road Cambridge CB5 8EP
Tel: 01604 233 233 Fax: (01223) 316511
Email: mail@hewitsons.com (for all offices)
Website: www.hbslaw.co.uk (for all offices)

Partners	51
Assistant Solicitors	40
Total Trainees	18

Firm Profile
Established in 1865, the firm handles mostly company and commercial work, but has a growing body of public sector clients. The firm has four offices: Cambridge, Northampton, Peterborough and Saffron Walden.

Main Areas of Work
Litigation 36%; Commercial Property 26%; Company/Commercial 22%; Private Client 16%.

Trainee Profile
The firm is interested in applications from candidates who have achieved a high degree of success in academic studies and who are bright, personable and able to take the initiative.

Training Environment
The firm offers seats in private client work, property, company commercial and litigation.

Benefits
The PSC is provided by the College of Law during the first year of the Training Contract. This is coupled with an extensive programme of Trainee Solicitor Seminars provided by specialist in-house lawyers.

Vacation Placements
Places for 1999: a few placements are available, application is by way of letter and CV to Caroline Lewis; Duration: 1–2 weeks.

Sponsorship & Awards
Funding for the CPE and/or LPC is not provided.

Contact
Caroline Lewis
7 Spencer Parade,
Northampton, NN1 5AB

Method of Application
Letter and CV

Selection Procedure
Interview

Closing date for 2001
End of August 1999

Application

Training contracts p.a.	15
Applications p.a.	2,000
% interviewed p.a.	10%
Required degree grade 2:1 min	

Training

Salary: 1st year(1999)	£12,500
Salary: 2nd Year(1999)	£14,500
Holiday entitlement	22 days
% of trainees with a non-law degree p.a.	50%

Post-Qualification

Salary (1999)	Under review
% of trainees offered job on qualification (1998)	57%
% of assistants (as at 1/9/98) who joined as trainees	31%
% of partners (as at 1/9/98) who joined as trainees	13%

HILL DICKINSON

Pearl Assurance House 2 Derby Square Liverpool L2 9XL
Tel: (0151) 236 5400 Fax: (0151) 236 2175
Email: Law@HillDicks.com

Partners	65
Assistant Solicitors	53
Total Trainees	21

Firm Profile
The firm is one of the largest in the North West, with offices in Manchester, Liverpool Chester and also London. It adopts a pragmatic and personal approach with clients on a local, national and international level.

Main Areas of Work
Litigation (Insurance/Construction/Professional Negligence) 50%; Commercial Property, Planning and Environmental 15%; Shipping: 15%; Health/Medical Negligence 10%; Company, Commercial, Pensions, Tax, Intellectual Property, PFI 10%.

Trainee Profile
Consistent achievers of a high intellectual calibre, possessing team skills, commercial acumen, resilience and a sense of humour. The firm recruits people who vary greatly in terms of personality and values outside interests.

Training Environment
Trainees spend six months in each of the four departments (insurance litigation, mercantile health, and commercial) and will be given the chance to specialise in specific areas. You will be given the opportunity to learn and develop communication and presentation skills, legal research, drafting, interviewing and advising, and negotiation and advocacy. Trainees are encouraged to accept responsibility and expected to act with initiative. The practice has an active social committee and a larger than usual selection of competitive sporting teams.

Vacation Placements
Places for 2000: yes; Duration: 2 weeks; Remuneration: no; Closing Date: 30 April 2000.

Sponsorship & Awards
Discretionary LPC funding.

Contact
R.J. Martindale

Method of Application
Handwritten letter plus CV and passport-sized photograph

Selection Procedure
Normally 1 interview but may include assessment day

Closing date for 2001
1 October 1999

Training
Salary: 1st year(1998) £14,500 minimum
Salary: 2nd Year(1998) £15,000 minimum
Holiday entitlement 4 weeks

Post-Qualification
% of trainees offered job on qualification (1998) 100%

HOLMAN, FENWICK & WILLAN

Marlow House Lloyds Avenue London EC3N 3AL
Tel: (0171) 488 2300 Fax: (0171) 481 0316
Email: gradrecruitment@hfw.co.uk

Partners	67
Assistant Solicitors	97
Total Trainees	16

Firm Profile

Holman, Fenwick & Willan is an international law firm and one of the world's leading specialists in maritime transportation, insurance, reinsurance and trade. The firm is a leader in the field of commercial litigation and arbitration and also offers comprehensive commercial and financial advice. Founded in 1883, the firm is one of the largest operating in its chosen fields with a team of 200 lawyers worldwide, and a reputation for excellence and innovation.

Main Areas of Work

Our range of services include marine, admiralty and crisis management, insurance and reinsurance, commercial litigation and arbitration, international trade and commodities, energy, corporate and financial.

Trainee Profile

Applications are invited from commercially minded under-graduates and graduates of all disciplines with good A-levels and who have, or expect to receive, a IIi degree. Good foreign languages or a scientific or maritime background are an advantage.

Training Environment

During your training period we will ensure that you gain valuable experience in a wide range of areas. We also organise formal training supplemented by a programme of in-house seminars and ship visits in addition to the PSC2. Your training development as an effective lawyer will be managed by our Recruitment & Training Partner, Ottilie Sefton, who will ensure that your training is both successful and enjoyable.

Benefits

Private medical insurance, permanent health and accident insurance, subsidised gym membership, season ticket loan.

Vacation Placements

Places for 1999: 12; Duration: 2 weeks.
Dates: 28 June – 9 July/ 19 July – 30 July; Remuneration: £200 p.w.;
Closing Date: Applications accepted 1 Jan – 12 Feb.

Sponsorship & Awards

CPE Funding: Fees paid + £4,000 maintenance.
LPC Funding: Fees paid + £4,000 maintenance.

Contact
Graduate Recruitment Officer

Method of Application
Handwritten letter and typed CV

Selection Procedure
Two interviews with partners

Closing date for 2001
31 July 1999

Application

Training contracts p.a.	6
Applications p.a.	2,500
% interviewed p.a.	2%
Required degree grade	2:1

Training
Salary: 1st year(1998)

1st six months	£20,000
2nd six months	£20,500
3rd six months	£21,500
4th six months	£22,000
Holiday entitlement	20 days
% of trainees with a non-law degree p.a.	38%

Post-Qualification

Salary (1998)	£32,000
% of trainees offered job on qualification (1998)	67%

Overseas Offices
Paris, Rouen, Nantes, Piraeus, Hong Kong and Singapore

HOLMES HARDINGHAM

22–23 Great Tower Street London EC3R 5AQ
Tel: (0171) 283 0222 Fax: (0171) 283 0768
Email: HoHa@Compuserve.com

Partners	11
Assistant Solicitors	11
Total Trainees	4

Firm Profile
Holmes Hardingham specialises in shipping law and provides a full range of maritime and commercial services, including international road transport matters.

Main Areas of Work
Sale/Purchase Commodities; Salvage; Collision; Cargo Claims: road, rail, air, charter party, bills of lading, yacht matters.

Trainee Profile
A law degree is preferred, though the firm will make exceptions in cases with a strong technical or maritime background. Academic excellence is a pre-requisite in all cases.

Training Environment
Four seats of six-months are spent in shipping, cargo claim (dealing with road, marine and air transport), marine and commodities. The first seat is pre-selected but you are able to choose the order of the following three seats. In every department you will work for a partner and have either your own office or share with a fee earner. Formal training is covered by an externally provided PSC course and by in-house seminars covering the firm's specialist areas of practice. The firm maintains a sociable atmosphere. This is aided by a communal lunch every Monday and Friday.

Benefits
Private health and insurance, interest free season ticket loan.

Vacation Placements
Duration: 1–2 weeks; Remuneration: £250 p.w.; Closing Date: May 1999.

Sponsorship & Awards
Discretionary funding for LPC.

Contact
Glenn Winter

Method of Application
Letter and CV

Selection Procedure
2 interviews

Closing date for 2001
None

Application

Training contracts p.a.	2
Applications p.a.	500
% interviewed p.a.	10
Required degree grade	2:1

Training
Salary: 1st year(1999)   t.b.a.
            (currently £21,000)
Salary: 2nd Year(1999)   t.b.a.
            (currently £22,000)

Holiday entitlement	21 days
% of trainees with a non-law degree p.a.	50%
No. of seats available abroad p.a.	1

Post-Qualification
Salary (1999)   t.b.a
            (currently) £30,000
% of trainees offered job
on qualification (1998)   100%
% of assistants (as at 1/9/98)
who joined as trainees   35%
% of partners (as at 1/9/98)
who joined as trainees   64%

HOWES PERCIVAL

252 Upper Third Street Grafton Gate East Central
Milton Keynes MK9 1DZ.
Tel: (01908) 672 682 Fax: (01604) 620956
Email: law@howes-percival.co.uk
Website: www.howes-percival.co.uk

Partners	30
Assistant Solicitors	15
Total Trainees	9

Firm Profile
Commercial law firm with a committed view to exceeding clients' expectations well into the 21st century. Four offices throughout East Midlands and East Anglia. Areas of outstanding strength within the firm include: Company Commercial (with particular emphasis on Corporate Finance) Commercial Property, Commercial Litigation and Employment. Client profile to be envied by any city firm. Youth is no barrier, most of our partners are under 40 years of age.

Main Areas of Work
Private Client 5%; Employment 10%; Insolvency 10%; Commercial Litigation 20%; Commercial Property 25%; Company Commercial 30%.

Trainee Profile
Beyond excellent academic, technical and professional skills, we are looking for those with a proven track record in team working; are commercially aware; innovative; adaptable to change and that are high on conceptual thinking, analysis and decision making. In addition, successful candidates will be able to demonstrate excellent interpersonal skills.

Training Environment
As the practice is departmentalised, trainees will spend a maximum of six months in four departments (see 'Main Areas of Work'). At our Norwich office trainees may also gain experience in Agriculture and Licensing. Trainees are assigned a departmental training supervisor who, in addition to providing day to day guidance will formally assess the trainee at three and six month intervals, at which time the trainee can also assess the quality of training received. In addition to PSC training, trainees will receive a tailored in-house training programme, including CPD accredited courses, the firm's own Client Care programme and Information Technology training.

Benefits
Payment of PSC course fees.

Contact
Mrs K Collyer

Method of Application
Letter and firm's form

Selection Procedure
Assessment centres and second interview with training principal and partner

Closing date for 2001
1 September 1999

Application

Training contracts p.a.	6
Applications p.a.	300
% interviewed p.a.	13%
Required degree grade	2:1

Training
Salary: 1st year(1999)

(E. Midlands)	£14,750
Salary: 2nd Year(1999)	
(E. Midlands)	£15,750
Holiday entitlement	23 days

Post-Qualification
% of trainees offered job

on qualification (1998)	66%

% of assistants (as at 1/9/98)

who joined as trainees	6%

% of partners (as at 1/9/98)

who joined as trainees	7.5%

INCE & CO

Knollys House 11 Byward Street London EC3R 5EN
Tel: (0171) 623 2011 Fax: (0171) 623 3225
Email: firstname.surname@ince.co.uk

Partners	51*
Assistant Solicitors	61*
Total Trainees	25

* denotes world-wide figures

Firm Profile
Since its foundation in 1870, Ince & Co has specialised in international commercial law and is best known for its shipping and insurance work.

Main Areas of Work
Shipping & International Trade 40%; Insurance/Reinsurance 40%; Professional Indemnity 10%; Company, Commercial Property 10%.

Trainee Profile
Hard-working competitive individuals with initiative who relish challenge and responsibility within a team environment. Academic achievements, positions of responsibility, sport and travel are all taken into account.

Training Environment
Trainees sit with four different partners for six months at a time throughout their training. Under close supervision, they are encouraged from an early stage to meet and visit clients, interview witnesses, liaise with counsel, deal with technical experts and handle opposing lawyers. They will quickly build up a portfolio of cases from a number of partners involved in a cross-section of the firm's practice and will see their cases through from start to finish. They will also attend in-house and outside lectures, conferences and seminars on practical and legal topics.

Benefits
STL, corporate health cover, PHI, LVs.

Vacation Placements
Places for 1999: 16; Duration: 2 weeks; Remuneration: £200 p.w.; Closing Date: February 1999.

Sponsorship & Awards
£6,500 grant (Sponsorship currently under review).

Contact
Sarah Bosley

Method of Application
Typed/handwritten letter and CV

Selection Procedure
Interview with 2 partners from Recruitment Committee and a written test

Closing date for 2001
1 September 1999

Application
Training contracts p.a.	10
Applications p.a.	1,200
% interviewed p.a.	5%
Required degree grade	2:1

Training
Salary: 1st year(1999)	£21,000
Salary: 2nd Year(1999)	£23,000
Holiday entitlement	22 days
% of trainees with a non-law degree p.a.	44%

Post-Qualification
Salary (2000)	£30,000
% of trainees offered job on qualification (1998)	50%
% of assistants (as at 1/9/98) who joined as trainees	64%
% of partners (as at 1/9/98) who joined as trainees	76%

Overseas Offices
Hong Kong, Singapore, Piraeus (consultancy)

IRWIN MITCHELL

St. Peter's House Hartshead Sheffield S1 2EL
Recruitment line: (0114) 274 4580 Fax: (0114) 275 3306
Email: enquiries@irwinmitchell.co.uk
Website: www.irwinmitchell.co.uk

Partners	73
Assistant Solicitors	113
Total Trainees	30

Firm Profile

Irwin Mitchell is a rapidly expanding 73 partner general
practice with over 1000 employees and offices in Sheffield,
Leeds, Birmingham and London. The firm is particularly well
known for commercial law, commercial litigation, insurance
law, business crime and plaintiff personal injury litigation.
Their strong reputation for dealing with novel and complex
areas of law and handling developmental cases (such as the
vibration white finger and CJD cases and the Matrix-Churchill
'arms to Iraq' affair) means that they can offer a broad range of
experience within each of their specialist departments, giving
trainees a high standard of training.

Main Areas of Work

Corporate Services 37%; Plaintiff Personal Injury 28%;
Insurance Litigation 17%; Private Client 12%; Police
Prosecutions 6%.

Trainee Profile

Irwin Mitchell is looking for well motivated individuals with a
real commitment to the law and who can demonstrate above
average academic and social ability. Law and non-law
graduates are recruited. Foreign languages and IT skills are an
asset. The firm believes that trainees are an investment for the
future and as such they prefer to keep their trainees once they
qualify.

Training Environment

The two-year Training Contract consists of 4 seats. Our trainees
also benefit from an Induction programme, monthly training
meetings and the Professional Skills Course which is organised
and financed by the firm. Each trainee has a review every 3
months with their supervising partner. There are numerous
other activities in which trainees are encouraged to participate,
eg. team skills challenges, conferences, mock trials.

Vacation Placements

Places for 1999: 30; Duration: 2 weeks; Remuneration: £50 p.w.;
Closing Date: 1 March 1999.

Sponsorship & Awards

CPE and LPC fees paid and £2,000 maintenance grant.

Contact
Sue Lenkowski/Tracey Easton

Method of Application
Brochures and application forms
are available from the Human
Resources Dept. Call the
recruitment line between
1 March and 30 July

Selection Procedure
Assessment centres are held
in late August and early
September and successful
candidates are invited to a
second interview with 2 partners
in mid-September

Closing date for 2001
30 July 1999

Application

Training contracts p.a.	15
Applications p.a.	1,000
% interviewed p.a.	6%

Training

Salary: 1st year(1999)	£15,000
Salary: 2nd Year(1999)	£17,000
Holiday entitlement	23 days
% of trainees with a non-law degree p.a.	44.5%
No. of seats available abroad p.a.	0

Post-Qualification

% of trainees offered job on qualification (1998)	92%
% of assistants (as at 1/9/98) who joined as trainees	33%
% of partners (as at 1/9/98) who joined as trainees	16.5%

LAWRENCE GRAHAM

190 Strand London WC2R 1JN
Tel: (0171) 379 0000 Fax: (0171) 395 4534
Email: diane.austin@lawgram.com
Website: http://www.lawgram.com

Partners	75
Assistant Solicitors	73
Total Trainees	29

Firm Profile
Lawrence Graham is a full-service City practice dating back before 1730. The firm has particular strengths in commercial insurance, environmental and property litigation, shipping, commercial property, corporate finance and other company and commercial work such as banking, insolvency, mergers and acquisitions, IT and IP and tax and private client.

Main Areas of Work
Litigation/Shipping 31.8%; Commercial Property 27.6%; Company/Commercial 26.6%; Tax/Financial Management 12.6%.

Trainee Profile
Trainees should demonstrate strong technical and interpersonal skills, the ability to understand a client's commercial priorities and objectives, the judgement to deal with complex problems and a life beyond work. Candidates should have or be capable of attaining upper second class degrees and preferably some linguistic ability.

Training Environment
In the first two weeks an introductory course is run to help explain the firm's structure. Various social events are organised and you are assigned a mentor. Training consists of four six month seats including a position in each of the company and commercial, litigation, property and planning departments. The fourth seat is spent either back in a favoured department or in tax and financial management or shipping. All work is supervised but independence and responsibility will increase with experience.

Benefits
PRP, season ticket loan, gym.

Vacation Placements
Places for 2000: 20; Duration: 2 weeks; Remuneration: £160 p.w. (under review); Closing Date: 28 February 1999.

Sponsorship & Awards
CPE Funding: £8,000; LPC Funding: £10,000.

Contact
Diane Austin

Method of Application
Application form

Selection Procedure
Interview and written exercise

Closing date for 2001
31 August 1999

Application

Training contracts p.a.	14
Applications p.a.	1,500
Required degree grade	2:1

Training

Salary: 1st year(1999) £20,000
Salary: 2nd Year(1999) £23,000
Holiday entitlement 21 days
% of trainees with
a non-law degree p.a. Varies

Post-Qualification

Salary (1999) £33,000
% of trainees offered job
on qualification (1998) 80%
% of assistants (as at 1/9/98)
who joined as trainees 42%
% of partners (as at 1/9/98)
who joined as trainees 32%

LAWRENCE TUCKETTS

Bush House 72 Prince Street Bristol BS99 7JZ
Tel: (0117) 929 5252 Fax: (0117) 929 8313
Email: connect@lawrence-tucketts.co.uk

Partners	17
Assistant Solicitors	33
Total Trainees	8

Firm Profile
A progressive, expanding commercial practice advising business and private clients. Particular strengths are in litigation and company/commercial and niche areas include planning/environment.

Main Areas of Work
Litigation 43%; Commercial Property/Planning 23%; Commercial /Corporate 18%; Private Client 16%.

Trainee Profile
A strong academic background is preferred, but the firm appreciates that this is not the only indicator of intelligence, and a resourceful personality is also a consideration. Any other interesting responsibilities/experiences are also considered.

Training Environment
Trainees indicate their preference for three or four seats of six-twelve months each, which the firm tries to match. Although it is not essential for trainees to specialise in their first year, they are encouraged to develop their chosen field in the second. Trainees will be allocated a dedicated supervisor in each department. All trainees sit with another lawyer, but in every case their work is drawn from all parts of the team or department so that they gain as much experience as possible. Review meetings are held regularly. Lawrence Tucketts strives to give you a high level of responsibility and involvement, while ongoing lectures are designed to extend your knowledge. Sports and social activities are available.

Benefits
Subsidised health insurance, subsidised sports and health club facility.

Vacation Placements
Places for 1999: 8; Duration: 1 week; Remuneration: expenses; Closing Date: Good Friday.

Sponsorship & Awards
Interest free loan for LPC.

Contact
Personnel Department

Method of Application
Firm's application form

Selection Procedure
Assessment Day

Closing date for 2001
15 August 1999

Application

Training contracts p.a.	8
Applications p.a.	900
% interviewed p.a.	1.5%
Required degree grade	n/a

Training

Holiday entitlement	4 weeks
% of trainees with a non-law degree p.a.	50%

Post-Qualification

Salary (1999)	n/a
% of trainees offered job on qualification (1998)	100%
% of assistants (as at 1/9/98) who joined as trainees	25%
% of partners (as at 1/9/98) who joined as trainees	25%

LAYTONS

Carmelite 50 Victoria Embankment Blackfriars
London EC4Y 0LS
Tel: (0171) 842 8000 Fax: (0171) 842 8080
Email: laytonsl@laytons.com

Partners	28
Assistant Solicitors	42
Total Trainees	12

Firm Profile

Laytons works closely with clients in long term relationships. The firm combines a range of complementary fields of focused legal expertise with knowledge of the client and its business and a creative, energetic approach to achieving objectives and adding value. High service quality and client care, together with the provision of advice which is technically and commercially effective, are of paramount importance.

Main Areas of Work

Company/Commercial 33%; Commercial Property/Land Development 20%; General Litigation 19%; Building Litigation 11%; Employment 8%; Private Client 5%; Insolvency 4%.

Trainee Profile

Trainees form part of the professional team immediately they start and gain early client contact alongside qualified lawyers. Working closely with a partner, trainees are encouraged to take progressive responsibility whilst undergoing their training programme. Requirements are a first or 2:1 hons degree from a good university, together with a commitment to achieve excellent results and a sense of humour.

Training Environment

Trainees are placed in four six-month seats in each of the firm's principal departments: Company Commercial, Property, Litigation and Private Client.

Benefits

Season ticket loan, Summer bonus, Christmas bonus.

Vacation Placements

Places for 1999: 6; Duration: 1 week; Closing Date: March 1999.

Sponsorship & Awards

CPE and LPC Funding.

Contact
Ian Burman

Method of Application
Application form

Selection Procedure
2 interviews

Closing date for 2001
31 August 1999

Application

Training contracts p.a.	2
Applications p.a.	2,000
% interviewed p.a.	5%
Required degree grade	1 or 2:1

Training

Salary: 1st year(1999)	Market rate
Salary: 2nd Year(1999)	Market rate
Holiday entitlement	22 days

Post-Qualification

Salary (1999)	Market rate
% of trainees offered job on qualification (1998)	83%
% of assistants (as at 1/9/98) who joined as trainees	73%
% of partners (as at 1/9/98) who joined as trainees	22%

LE BRASSEUR J TICKLE

Drury House 34–43 Russell Street London WC2B 5HA
Tel: (0171) 836 0099 Fax: (0171) 831 2215
6–7 Park Place Leeds LS1 2RU
Email: enquiries@lbjt.co.uk
Tel: (0113) 234 1220 Fax: (0113) 234 1573

Partners	25
Assistant Solicitors	25
Total Trainees	8

Contact
Training Partner

Method of Application
Letter and CV

Selection Procedure
2 interviews

Closing date for 2001
Autumn 1999

Application
Training contracts p.a.   4
Applications p.a.   1,000
% interviewed p.a.   4%

Training
Salary: 1st year(1999) £17,500
(London)
Salary: 2nd Year(1999) £18,500
(London)
Holiday entitlement   4 weeks
% of trainees with
a non-law degree p.a.   50%

Post-Qualification
Salary (1999) £28,500 (London)
% of trainees offered job
on qualification (1998)   75%
% of assistants (as at 1/9/98)
who joined as trainees   50%
% of partners (as at 1/9/98)
who joined as trainees   50%

Firm Profile
Le Brasseur J Tickle, founded in 1881, is a medium-sized firm with an enviable reputation for tradition and excellence. The firm has 25 partners and approximately 100 members of staff. The firm is located in two major commercial and legal centres, London and Leeds, from which legal expertise is provided to all types of clients from multi-nationals to individuals.

Main Areas of Work
Health Care: 40%; Personal Injury: 10%; Employment: 10%; Company Commercial: 15%; Commercial Property: 10%; Commercial Litigation: 15%.

Trainee Profile
Le Brasseur J Tickle looks to recruit trainees from a broad academic background with good intellectual ability and an assured outgoing personality who will prove to be responsive to the needs of the firm's clients. When recruiting trainees, the partners look to the future and to appointing trainees as assistant solicitors following qualification. Indeed a significant number of partners trained with the firm.

Training Environment
The firm provides an extensive legal and skills training programme for trainee solicitors and other qualified staff in addition to on-the-job training. Trainees are introduced to the firm with an indication programme covering the work of the firm's departments, the major clients, procedural matters and professional conduct. Training consists of four six-month seats in the following areas: Company Commercial including Property; Health Care Law; and General Litigation. Every endeavour is made to allocate the final seat following discussion as to the area of law in which the trainee wishes to specialise. You will share an office with a partner, who will assist you and formally review your progress at the end of your seat. The PSC is taught externally. The firm is friendly with an open-door policy and there are various sporting and social events organised throughout the year.

LEE BOLTON & LEE

1 The Sanctuary Westminster London SW1P 3JT
Tel: (0171) 222 5381 Fax: (0171) 222 7502
Email: 106102.1723@compuserve.com

Partners	15
Assistant Solicitors	9
Total Trainees	4

Firm Profile
Founded in 1855 Lee Bolton & Lee is a successful medium sized firm based in Westminster. It is closely associated with parliamentary agents and solicitors, Rees and Freres, who provide a specialist service in parliamentary, public and administrative law.

Main Areas of Work
Commercial; Property; Private Client; Litigation; Charity; Education Work.

Trainee Profile
They seek to recruit trainees with a good degree (2:1 or above), first class communication skills, motivation, professionalism, initiative, enthusiasm, and a sense of humour.

Training Environment
Trainees spend six months in each of four seats: Private Client, Property, Litigation and Commercial Property, sitting with either a senior solicitor or a Partner. Training is comprehensive and covers a full induction programme, participation in internal seminars and training sessions and attendance at external courses, including the Professional Skills Course. Trainees are given responsibility for their own files from the beginning, and whilst this might at first seem daunting, the firm operates an open door policy and help is never far away. Progress is reviewed monthly by your elected Supervisor and every three months by the Training Principal. There are various sporting and social events.

Benefits
Season ticket loan, non-guaranteed bonus.

Sponsorship & Awards
A contribution towards LPC funding but dependent upon being offered a training contract.

Contact
Penny Noble

Method of Application
Handwritten letter and CV

Selection Procedure
Panel interview

Closing date for 2001
Mid-August 1999

Application

Training contracts p.a.	2
Applications p.a.	500
% interviewed p.a.	3%
Required degree grade	2:1

Training

Salary: 1st year(1999)	£18,000
Salary: 2nd Year(1999)	£19,000
Holiday entitlement	22 days
% of trainees with a non-law degree p.a.	50%

Post-Qualification

Salary (1999)	£27,000
% of trainees offered job on qualification (1998)	0%
% of assistants (as at 1/9/98) who joined as trainees	33%
% of partners (as at 1/9/98) who joined as trainees	20%

LINKLATERS & PAINES

One Silk Street London EC2Y 8HQ
Tel: (44-171) 456 2000 Fax: (44-171) 456 2222

Firm Profile

Linklaters & Paines has developed into one of the largest law
firms in the world with 1115 fee earners which includes 221
partners and 252 trainee solicitors. In total, staff numbers are
over 2100. The firm is a member of Linklaters & Alliance
which comprises five of Europe's leading law firms (De Bandt,
van Hecke & Lagae (Belgium), De Brauw Blackstone
Westbroek N.V. (Netherlands), Lagerlof & Leman (Sweden),
Linklaters & Paines (UK) and Oppenhoff & Radler
(Germany)). Linklaters & Alliance has 1900 lawyers and other
professionals operating from 28 offices in 16 countries
covering the world's major financial and business centres.

Main Areas of Work

Core businesses include corporate, international finance,
project and asset finance, commercial property and litigation.
They also have specialist groups advising on UK and offshore
investment funds, regulatory compliance, insurance,
competition and EC, corporate recovery and insolvency, and
employment and employee benefits.

Trainee Profile

The firm looks for high academic achievers with a variety of
outside interests. Confidence and commitment to thrive in the
strong client centred, commercial environment is vital as is the
desire for involvement and responsibility early on in their
training. The firm welcomes applications from both law and
non-law students. Any language and IT skills are considered
advantageous.

Training Environment

The training begins with a 2 week induction course,
incorporating the PSC. This is supplemented with many more
courses throughout the training contract to support the practical
experience. Trainees are involved in transactions for blue chip
companies from the outset, contributing as a group resource in
their chosen departments. Your on-the-job training is planned
around your preferred practice area, allowing you to get fully
involved in client work and to take on responsibility from your
first day.

By the end of your training you will have had in-depth experience in your chosen practice area, and a variety of experience in other departments (including offices outside the UK and client secondments) that complements that practice, so the transition to qualification is seamless. The firm's open door policy and mentoring scheme enables any issues to be discussed openly with colleagues in any department. Trainees are also encouraged to volunteer for pro bono activities supported by the firm and to get involved in the various sporting and social opportunities.

Benefits

PPP medical insurance, life assurance, pension, season ticket loan, in-house gym as well as corporate membership to 5 gyms, in-house dentist, doctor and physiotherapist, 24 hour subsidised staff restaurant.

Vacation Placements

Places for 1998/99: 85;
Duration: Christmas – 2 weeks (specifically non-law students).
Easter – 2 weeks.
Summer (2 intakes) – 4 weeks.
Remuneration: £200 p.w.

Sponsorship & Awards

CPE and LPC fees paid in full. A maintenance grant is also provided (which has increased to account for purchase of books) of £4,500 for London and £4,000 for outside of London. Language bursaries are also offered, on application.

Partners	221*
Assistant Solicitors	600*
Total Trainees	252

* denotes world-wide figures

Contact
Jane Leader

Method of Application
Application form

Selection Procedure
2 Interviews (same day)

Application

Training contracts p.a.	120
Applications p.a.	2,500
% interviewed p.a.	20%
Required degree grade	2:1

Training

Salary: 1st year(1999) £21,000
Salary: 2nd Year(1999) £24,000
Holiday entitlement 25 days
% of trainees with
a non-law degree p.a. approx. 40%
No. of seats available
abroad p.a. 80

Post-Qualification

Salary (1999) £32,000
% of trainees offered job
on qualification (1998) 98%

Overseas Offices
Bangkok, Brussels, Frankfurt, Hong Kong, Madrid, Moscow, New York, Paris, Sao Paulo, Shanghai, Singapore, St Petersburg, Tokyo, Washington D.C.

LINKLATERS
& ALLIANCE

LOVELL WHITE DURRANT

65 Holborn Viaduct London EC1A 2DY
Tel: (0171) 236 0066 Fax: (0171) 248 4212
Email: information@lovellwhitedurrant.com
Website: http://www.lovellwhitedurrant.com

Partners	165*
Assistant Solicitors	588*
Total Trainees	125

* denotes world-wide figures

Firm Profile
One of the largest firms of solicitors based in the City of
London with a recognised international practice. They have 12
offices located across North America, Europe and Asia. The
breadth of the practice, and a pre-eminence in so many practice
areas sets them apart from most of their competitors.

Main Areas of Work
Corporate Finance; Banking; EC and Competition Law;
Insurance; Litigation; Intellectual Property; Insolvency;
Commercial Property.

Trainee Profile
Individualists, not clones, whose keen intelligence extends
beyond an excellent degree. A practical and commercial mind
is vital, and so is a talent for analytical thinking.

Training Environment
Six-month seats in the four key sectors: finance, litigation,
property and one other specialised commercial sector. In each
department you will be assigned a partner or senior solicitor.
During each seat, you will have formal and informal reviews to
discuss your progress and preferences for subsequent seats. The
third seat can be spent in an overseas office or on secondment
to the in-house legal department of a major client. Trainees can
help with Lovells' pro bono work such as part-time work at law
centres or in a Citizens Advice Bureau. Numerous social and
sporting activities help staff unwind together.

Benefits
PPP, PHI, season ticket, gym membership, staff restaurant, life
assurance

Vacation Placements
Places for 1999: 70; Duration: 2–3 weeks; Remuneration: £200
p.w.; Closing Date: 19/2/99 for summer, early November 1999
for Christmas.

Sponsorship & Awards
CPE and LPC funding and maintenance allowance. This is
usually in the range of £8,000 – £11,000 a year.

Contact
Clare Walton

Method of Application
Application form

Selection Procedure
Assessment day: interview,
group exercise, critical
reasoning test

Closing date for 2001
End of October 1999

Application
Training contracts p.a.	80
Applications p.a.	2,500
% interviewed p.a.	15%
Required degree grade	2:1 or better

Training
Salary: 1st year(1999)	£21,000
Salary: 2nd Year(1999)	£23,000
Holiday entitlement	25 days
% of trainees with a non-law degree p.a.	30%
No. of seats available abroad p.a.	20

Post-Qualification
Salary (1999)	£32,500

Additional Information

Lovells has a number of support systems which ensure you are getting the help you need. You are assigned a 'contact partner' during training, who will meet with you regularly, to monitor your progress and help you plan your future. Formal training is also vital during your Training Contract because you will be working in specialised areas. You will gain an overview of the numerous areas of Lovells' practice. The courses are given by a combination of external and in-house training and have been adapted for, or developed by the firm. You will also participate in the Professional Skills Course.

Trainee Comments

"I chose to accept a Training Contract from Lovell White Durrant on the basis of my interest in litigation, the friendliness of the people, and the knowledge of the firm that I had gained during the summer placement." (Julian Craughan, first year trainee, read law at University College London).

"The variety of the work and the amount of client contact really appealed to me – as did Lovells' culture" (Paul Brown, newly qualified lawyer, read law at Nottingham).

"I was attracted to Lovell White Durrant by its strong litigation practice and the interest it was developing in advocacy … I was also drawn by the strong EC practice both in London and in Brussels as this an increasingly important and prevalent area of law." (Clare Gibbs, first year trainee, read law at Pembroke College, Cambridge).

"LWD views their employees as individuals, and has the foresight to invest in their trainees for the future benefit of the firm." (Rachel Cunningham, first year trainee, read Biological Sciences at Magdalen College, Oxford).

Overseas Offices

Beijing, Brussels, Chicago, Ho Chi Minh City, Hong Kong, Moscow, New York, Paris, Prague, Singapore, Tokyo

LOVELL WHITE DURRANT

MACFARLANES

10 Norwich Street London EC4A 1BD
Tel: (0171) 831 9222 Fax: (0171) 831 9607
Email: CYR@MACFARLANES.COM
Website: http://www.macfarlanes.com

Partners	50
Assistant Solicitors	102
Total Trainees	33

Firm Profile
A medium-sized City firm serving national and international commercial, industrial, financial and private clients.

Main Areas of Work
Company, Commercial and Banking 48%; Property 20%; Litigation 20%; Tax and Financial Planning 12%.

Trainee Profile
Any degree discipline. Actual or predicted 2:1 or better.

Training Environment
Macfarlanes divides the training contract into four six-month periods. You will usually spend time in each of the firm's four main departments (Company, Commercial and Banking; Litigation; Property; Tax and Financial Planning). There is an extensive in-house training programme. Trainees have responsibility for real work and make a contribution that is acknowledged and appreciated.

Benefits
Twenty-one working days holiday in each calendar year (rising to 26 days upon qualification); profit related pay; interest free season ticket loans; free permanent health insurance*; free private medical insurance*; subsidised conveyancing; subsidised firm restaurant; subscription paid to the City of London Law Society or the London Trainee Solicitors' Group.

*After 12 months service.

Vacation Placements
Places for 1999: 40; Duration: 2 weeks; Remuneration: £180 p.w.; Closing Date: February 1999 but applications considered and places offered from 2 January 1999.

Sponsorship & Awards
CPE and LPC full fees and £3,750 maintenance for each. Prizes for those gaining distinction and commendation.

Contact
Claire Royce

Method of Application
Application form and letter

Selection Procedure
Interview and practical assessment

Closing date for 2001
31 July 1999

Application

Training contracts p.a.	20
Applications p.a.	1,500
% interviewed p.a.	10%
Required degree grade	2:1

Training

Salary: 1st year(1999)	£21,000
Salary: 2nd Year(1999)	£24,000
Holiday entitlement	21 days
% of trainees with a non-law degree p.a.	30%

Post-Qualification

Salary (1998)	£32,000
% of trainees offered job on qualification (1998)	100%
% of assistants (as at 1/9/98) who joined as trainees	62%
% of partners (as at 1/9/98) who joined as trainees	65%

Overseas Offices
Brussels

MANCHES & CO

Aldwych House 81 Aldwych London WC2B 4RP
Tel: (0171) 404 4433 Fax: (0171) 430 1133
Email: personnel@manches.co.uk

Partners	46
Assistant Solicitors	60
Total Trainees	18

Firm Profile
Manches & Co is a full service London commercial law firm at the forefront in a number of specialist legal practice areas and industrial sectors. It has a prestigious Family law practice and an Oxford office. It emphasises a plain speaking, straightforward approach and is run along corporate lines with all non-legal functions handled by the Chief Executive.

Main Areas of Work
Corporate 22%; Commercial Property 20%; Commercial Litigation 20%; Family Law 12%; Intellectual Property 8%; Banking and Insolvency 7%; Social Housing; 4%; Employment 4%; Personal Estate Planning 3%.

Trainee Profile
The firm looks for candidates with a sound academic background, commercial nous and enthusiasm. It wants engaging and outgoing personalities who will contribute to its development and help achieve its business goals. Clear and persuasive communication skills and tenacity are a must.

Training Environment
The firm provides high quality, individual training. Training is generally divided into four periods of 6 months (usually one in a niche practice area). Its comprehensive in-house training programme enables trainees to take responsibility from an early stage ensuring that they become confident and competent solicitors. Trainees are also encouraged to participate in departmental meetings and briefings and receive regular appraisals.

Benefits
Season ticket loan, PRP, permanent health insurance, life insurance.

Vacation Placements
Places for 1999: 30; Duration: 2 weeks; Remuneration: £150 p.w.; Closing Date: 28 February 1998.

Sponsorship & Awards
CPE and LPC Funding: tuition fees and maintenance.

Contact
Philippa Firth

Method of Application
Application form

Selection Procedure
Interview & possible presentation

Closing date for 2001
31 July 1999

Application

Training contracts p.a.	10-12
Applications p.a.	2,200
% interviewed p.a.	3%
Required degree grade	2:1

Training

Salary: 1st year(1998)	£20,550
Salary: 2nd Year(1998)	£23,000
Holiday entitlement	21 days

Post-Qualification

Salary (1998)	£30,600
% of trainees offered job on qualification (1998)	100%

MARRIOTT HARRISON

12 Great James Street London WC1N 3DR
Tel: (0171) 209 2000 Fax: (0171) 209 2001
Email: email@marriottharrison.co.uk

Partners	14
Assistant Solicitors	6
Total Trainees	1

Firm Profile
A leading firm for media law. Marriott Harrison also specialises in corporate finance and tax. The firm deals with every branch of the media industry, covering all aspects of production from intellectual property rights through to satellite operations. A wide variety of company and commercial work is also undertaken, in particular venture capital and corporate acquisitions; much of this work is focused in the Media and Entertainment industries. Commercial litigation is practised with emphasis on media-related cases.

Main Areas of Work
Company/Commercial/Tax 45%; Media 40%; Litigation 10%; Property 5%.

Trainee Profile
Rounded personality allied to ability to grasp legal principles.

Training Environment
Training consists of three eight-month seats in media, company/corporate and litigation departments though some overlapping may be expected. You will share an office with either a partner or assistant solicitor. Supervision will be continuous. The firm is friendly with an open-door policy.

Benefits
Season ticket loan, medical insurance.

Contact
Cathy Parker, Graduate
Recruitment Manager

Method of Application
Handwritten letter and CV

Selection Procedure
2 interviews

Closing date for 2001
December 1999

Application
Training contracts p.a.   1
Required degree grade   2:1

Training
Salary: 1st year(1999)   On
                                          appointment
Holiday entitlement 20 days p.a.

MARTINEAU JOHNSON

St. Philips House St. Philips Place Birmingham B3 2PP
Tel: (0121) 200 3300 Fax: (0121) 200 3330
Email: MartJohn@MartJohn.co.uk

Partners	35
Assistant Solicitors	80
Total Trainees	16

Firm Profile

One of Birmingham's main commercial practices and a member of Multilaw, an association of law firms covering 30 countries in Europe, America and the Pacific Rim. Ten traditional legal departments are supplemented by specialist teams.

Main Areas of Work

Corporate 15%; Property 22%; Litigation 15%; Private Client 10%; Education: 5%; Intellectual Property 6%; Employment 5%; Banking and Insolvency 7%; Finance and Tax 7%; Trade and Energy 8%.

Trainee Profile

The firm seeks trainees who are highly motivated, outgoing with commercial flair and capable of originality.

Training Environment

The firm is committed to ensuring that trainees receive in-depth coaching and supervision throughout their training contract and have their own personal mentor. Trainees follow a unique system of seat rotation. Seats are of four months duration and can be combined so that you spend time in six different seats or longer if desired. During the last eight months, trainees receive priority to experience whichever area(s) of specialisation they choose. In addition to coaching and supervison, all trainees follow a structured training programme. This includes induction, in-house Professional Skills course, and other seminars and workshops on a wide variety of legal and skills-based topics. There is a varied and active sporting and social life both within the firm and with the Birmingham Trainee Solicitor's group.

Benefits

Private medical insurance (second year trainees), life assurance

Vacation Placements

Places for 1999: 60; Duration: Open days only; Remuneration: 0; Closing Date: 26 February 1999.

Sponsorship & Awards

CPE and LPC funding; £3,500 maintenance for LPC.

Contact
Diane Price

Method of Application
Application form

Selection Procedure
Assessment centre – half day

Closing date for 2001
31 July 1999

Application
Training contracts p.a.	10/12
Applications p.a.	600
% interviewed p.a.	7%
Required degree grade	2:1

Training
Salary: 1st year(1999)	£15,500
Salary: 2nd Year(1999)	£16,500
Holiday entitlement	23 days
% of trainees with a non-law degree p.a.	40%
No. of seats available abroad p.a.	0

Post-Qualification
Salary (1999)	£25,000
% of trainees offered job on qualification (1998)	100%
% of assistants (as at 1/9/98) who joined as trainees	53%
% of partners (as at 1/9/98) who joined as trainees	61%

MASONS

30 Aylesbury Street London EC1R 0ER
Tel: (0171) 490 4000 Fax: (0171) 490 2545
Email: info@masons.com
Website: www.masons.com

Partners	77*
Assistant Solicitors	130*
Total Trainees	30

denotes world-wide figures

Firm Profile
Masons is an international city law firm with over 500 staff worldwide. The firm has offices in London, Bristol, Manchester, Leeds and Glasgow and works regularly in Europe, the Middle East, the Pacific Rim, Africa and the sub-continent.

Main Areas of Work
Masons' expertise is recognised around the world – as a commercial law firm known for its involvement in some of the largest major projects across the globe. Masons is recognised as the leading force in contruction and engineering law and one of the leaders in information and technology law and project and asset financing. Other key specialist areas range from commercial litigation and company law to environmental law.

Trainee Profile
Applicants should have or be on line for a 2:1 degree (not necessarily in Law), be commercially aware and ambitious.

Training Environment
Trainees work closely with partners and senior fee earners. This is supplemented by a programme of formal training including the compulsory Professional Skills Course which is conducted in-house. Early contact with clients is encouraged in both work and social environments, as is the acceptance of responsibility.

Benefits
PRP, pension, life assurance, private health care, subsidised restaurant and season ticket loan (London).

Vacation Placements
Places for 1999: 35 (London), 5 (Manchester); Duration: 2 weeks in 2 different departments, June–end of August; Remuneration: £175 p.w. in London, £125 p.w. in Manchester; Closing Date: 12 February 1999.

Sponsorship & Awards
CPE and LPC funding and a living allowance for each.

Contact
Graduate Recruitment

Method of Application
Firm's own application form

Selection Procedure
Assessment day followed by an interview

Closing date for 2001
31 July 1999

Application

Training contracts p.a.	15–17
Applications p.a.	2,000
% interviewed p.a.	6%
Required degree grade	2:1

Training
Salary: 1st year(1998) £21,000 (London)
Salary: 2nd Year(1998) £23,000 (London)
Holiday entitlement 21 days
No. of seats available abroad p.a. 3

Post-Qualification
Salary (1998) £33,000 (London)
% of trainees offered job on qualification (1998) 100%
% of partners (as at 1/9/98) who joined as trainees 25%

Overseas Offices
Brussels, Dublin, Guangzhou (PRC), Hong Kong, Singapore

McCORMICKS

Britannia Chambers 4 Oxford Place Leeds LS1 3AX
Tel: (0113) 246 0622 Fax: (0113) 246 7488
Email: mccormicks@btinternet.com
Wharfedale House 37 East Parade Harrogate HG1 5LQ
Tel: (01423) 530630 Fax: (01423) 530709

Partners	7
Assistant Solicitors	10
Total Trainees	8

Firm Profile
McCormicks is a high profile, progressive and highly regarded firm offering a full range of legal services to both corporate and private clients. It is regarded as one of the leading firms in the North of England and has been described by the Yorkshire Post as 'a law firm in the top rank' and by Yorkshire Television as 'one of the Region's top law firms.' The average age of the partners is 35 and the firm has a reputation for a vibrant and dynamic atmosphere.

Main Areas of Work
(alphabetically) Charities; Commercial Litigation; Company and Commercial; Corporate Crime including VAT and Inland Revenue Investigation work and tribunals; Debt Collection and Mortgage Repossessions; Defamation; Employment; Family; General Crime (especially Road Traffic); Insolvency; Intellectual Property; Media/ Entertainment; Sports Law; Personal Injury; Private Client – the firm is regarded as one of the leading commercial, litigation, fraud, media and sports law practices in the North.

Trainee Profile
A McCormicks trainee will combine intellectual achievement, sense of humour, commitment to hard work and a pro-active disposition to achieving the best possible outcome for the firm and its clients.

Training Environment
Trainees are recruited with the sincere expectation that they will be future partners. You will be assigned to the appropriate department and will be supervised by a mentor. Your work and development will be constantly reviewed by your mentor together with regular file and progress reviews both by your team supervisor and by the Training Partner. This framework provides for your maximum development within a friendly, progressive and supportive environment. There is an open-door policy and a great team spirit.

Vacation Placements
Places for 1999: Available throughout all student vacations – as many students as possible are accommodated.

Contact
Mark Burns, Training Partner

Method of Application
Letter and CV

Selection Procedure
Minimum of one interview with Training Partner

Closing date for 2001
31 July 1999

Application

Training contracts p.a.	4
Applications p.a.	1000
% interviewed p.a.	10%
Required degree grade	2:1

Training
Salary: 1st year(1999)   Highly competitive

Post-Qualification
Salary (1999) Highly competitive
% of trainees offered job on qualification (1998)   75%
% of partners (as at 1/9/98) who joined as trainees   70%

MILLS & REEVE

Francis House 112 Hills Road Cambridge CB2 1PH
Tel: +44(0)1223 364 422 Fax: +44 (0)1223 355848
Email: cp@mills-reeve.com

Partners	47
Assistant Solicitors	82
Total Trainees	22

Firm Profile
Mills & Reeve is one of the largest UK law firms outside London, operating throughout England and Wales from established offices in Cambridge and Norwich.

Main Areas of Work
The firm offers a full range of corporate, commercial, property, litigation and private client services, advising regional businesses, insurers and other financial institutions. In particular they are national specialists in NHS Trust, insurance, agriculture and higher education work and regional leaders in company/commercial work.

Trainee Profile
Lively personalities who listen and communicate effectively. Accuracy, attention to detail and a solid academic background.

Training Environment
Trainees are offered four five-month placements in each of the main departments (corporate services, private client, insurance and property services) followed by a final seat of four months. During these seats you will sit with a partner or experienced solicitor who will advise and monitor you. Early responsibility is encouraged and there are regular two-way appraisals. Staff at all levels are open, friendly and approachable. The firm operates a full induction programme to integrate trainees immediately. Practical training is complemented by a series of in-house lectures and the PSC. The firm encourages its own social and sporting functions outside the office.

Benefits
Life assurance at 2 times pensionable salary and a contributory pension scheme.

Vacation Placements
Places for 1999: 20; Duration: 2 weeks; Remuneration: £80 p.w.; Closing Date: 1 March 1999.

Sponsorship & Awards
CPE funding is discretionary, LPC fees are paid and maintenance grant is offered.

Contact
Charlotte Points
Head of Personnel

Method of Application
Application form

Selection Procedure
A 2:1 degree preferred in either law or non-law subjects

Closing date for 2001
15 August 1999

Application

Training contracts p.a.	10–14
Applications p.a.	400
% interviewed p.a.	14%
Required degree grade	2:1

Training

Salary: 1st year(1999)	£14,250
Salary: 2nd Year(1999)	£15,250
Holiday entitlement	20 days
% of trainees with a non-law degree p.a.	Approx 30%

Post-Qualification

Salary (1999)	£23,500
% of trainees offered job on qualification (1998)	Normally 80%
% of assistants (as at 1/9/98) who joined as trainees	52%
% of partners (as at 1/9/98) who joined as trainees	30%

MISHCON DE REYA

21 Southampton Row London WC1B 5HS
Tel: (0171) 440 7000 Fax: (0171) 404 5982
Email: postmaster@mishcon.co.uk
Website: www.mishcon.co.uk

Partners	30
Assistant Solicitors	45
Total Trainees	20

Firm Profile
An expanding commercial practice based in Central London.
As well as being known for its commercial litigation, defamation
and media work, there has been a conscious expansion of its
non-contentious departments including company commercial
and commercial property. It has recently formed an Art Law
group. The majority of partners are under 40.

Main Areas of Work
Litigation 42%; Company Commercial 23%; Property 22%;
Family 9%; Private Client 4%.

Trainee Profile
Those who read nothing but law books are probably not the
right trainees for this firm. They want people who can meet the
highest intellectual and business standards, while maintaining
outside interests. Candidates should be cheerful, enterprising
and ambitious - they should see themselves as future partners.

Training Environment
Trainees have four six-month seats. Three of these are usually
in the litigation, property and company commercial
departments, with an opportunity to specialise in the fourth
seat. Trainees share a room with an assistant solicitor or a
partner and the firm style is friendly and informal. Computer
literacy is encouraged and access to on-line legal and business
databases is available. Trainees are encouraged to participate in
voluntary work at Law Centres.

Benefits
Health cover, subsidised gym membership, season ticket loan,
permanent health insurance, life assurance.

Vacation Placements
Places for 1999: 8; Duration: 4 weeks; Expenses: £80 p.w.;
Closing Date: 30 April 1999.

Sponsorship & Awards
LPC funding and bursary.

Contact
Joan Simpson

Method of Application
Application form

Selection Procedure
Assessment Day and Interview

Closing date for 2001
31 July 1999

Application

Training contracts p.a.	8
Applications p.a.	1,000+
% interviewed p.a.	10%
Required degree grade	2:1

Training

Salary: 1st year(1999)	£17,500
Salary: 2nd Year(1999)	£19,500
Holiday entitlement	22 days
No. of seats available abroad p.a.	Occasional secondments available

Post-Qualification

% of trainees offered job on qualification (1998)	75%
% of assistants (as at 1/9/98) who joined as trainees	35%
% of partners (as at 1/9/98) who joined as trainees	19%

NABARRO NATHANSON

50 Stratton Street London W1X 6NX
Tel: (0171) 493 9933 Fax: (0171) 629 7900
Email: Graduate Recruitment Freephone: 0800 056 4021
Website: http://www.nabarro.com

Partners	113
Assistant Solicitors	199
Total Trainees	56

Firm Profile
One of the UK's largest commercial practices with offices in London, Reading and Sheffield. The atmosphere in all its offices is friendly and informal, yet highly professional.

Contact
Jane Squire

Method of Application
Application form

Main Areas of Work
Commercial Property; Planning; Pensions & Employment; Corporate Finance; Health & Safety; Commercial Litigation; Intellectual Property; IT; Insolvency; Construction; PFI; Venture Capital; Energy; Health; Charities; Local Government; Environmental Law.

Selection Procedure
Interview and assessment day

Closing date for 2001
31 July 1999

Trainee Profile
Nabarro Nathanson welcomes applications from law and non law undergraduates. Candidates will usually be expecting a minimum 2:1 degree. As well as strong intellectual ability our graduates need exceptional qualities. These include: enthusiasm, drive and initiative, common sense and strong interpersonal and teamworking skills.

Application

Training contracts p.a.	30
Applications p.a.	1,500
Required degree grade	2:1

Training
Salary: 1st year(1999)

London & Reading	£21,000
Sheffield	£15,500

Training Environment
They are a friendly, unstuffy firm with a first-name and open door culture. You will spend six months in each of four seats with supervision provided by a Partner and Solicitor. The seats are: Company Commercial, Commercial Property, Litigation, and a specialist area. The firm is keen to encourage responsibility and high quality work as soon as you are ready for it. By the fourth seat your work will approach the level of a newly qualified solicitor. Nabarro Nathanson is well known for its coherent and integrated training strategy.

Salary: 2nd Year(1999)

London & Reading	£24,000
Sheffield	£17,000
Holiday entitlement	25 days

Post-Qualification
Salary (1998) London £33,000
(reviewed annually)

Benefits
Trainees are given private medical health insurance, 25 days' holiday entitlement per annum, a season ticket loan and access to a subsidised restaurant. Trainee salaries are reviewed annually.

Overseas Offices
Brussels. Associated offices –
Dubai, Hong Kong, Paris

Vacation Placements
Places for 1999: Places available; Duration: 3 weeks – between mid-June and end of August; Closing Date: 28 February 1999.

Sponsorship & Awards
CPE and LPC sponsorship and a maintenance grant.

NICHOLSON GRAHAM & JONES

110 Cannon Street London EC4N 6AR
Tel: (0171) 648 9000 Fax: (0171) 648 9001
Email: info@NGJ.sprint.com
Website: www.ngj.co.uk

Partners	54
Assistant Solicitors	62
Total Trainees	19

Firm Profile
A thriving, broad-based commercial practice in the heart of the City of London. The firm has doubled in size during the 1990s, and has recently expanded its construction and engineering practice. The firm has niche specialisms in sport and leisure.

Main Areas of Work
Company and Commercial 30%; Litigation 30%; Property 25%; Private Client 5%; Construction & Engineering 10%.

Trainee Profile
Recruiters look for both law and non-law graduates with excellent degrees and a practical approach.

Training Environment
Training comprises four to six seats in each of the main departments with supervision by partners or senior assistants. Successful applicants can look forward to good quality City work with plenty of opportunity for early responsibility and contact with clients. Attractions of Nicholson Graham & Jones include a friendly, informal atmosphere and good career prospects upon qualifying.

Vacation Placements
Places for 1999: 8; Duration: 2 weeks; Remuneration: £160.

Sponsorship & Awards
LPC Fees and expenses paid. CPE fees.

Contact
Gail Harcus/Jenny Chapman

Method of Application
Application form

Selection Procedure
Interview and assessment

Closing date for 2001
31 July 1999

Application
Training contracts p.a.	10–11
Applications p.a.	750
% interviewed p.a.	10%
Required degree grade	2:1

Training
Salary: 1st year(1998)	£20,000
Salary: 2nd Year(1998)	£21,500
Holiday entitlement	21 days
% of trainees with a non-law degree p.a.	Varies

Post-Qualification
Salary (1998)	£30,000
% of trainees offered job on qualification (1998)	80%

Overseas Offices
Brussels

NORTON ROSE

Kempson House Camomile Street London EC3A 7AN
Tel: (0171) 283 6000 Fax: (0171) 283 6500
Email: gradrecruitment@nortonrose.com
Website: www.nortonrose.com

Partners	127*
Assistant Solicitors	342*
Total Trainees	103

denotes world-wide figures

Firm Profile
A leading City and international law firm specialising in large-scale corporate and financial transactions. Strong in asset, project and ship finance. More than two thirds of the firm's work has an international element.

Main Areas of Work
Corporate Finance 28%; Banking 29%; Litigation 24%; Property, Planning & Environmental 10%; Taxation 5%; Competition 3%; Human Resources 1%.

Trainee Profile
Successful candidates will be commercially aware, focused, ambitious and team-orientated. High intellect and international awareness are a priority, and language skills are appreciated.

Training Environment
Norton Rose's seat system is innovative. In the first 16 months of the 24-month training contract, trainees will have a seat in each of the core departments of banking, commercial litigation and corporate finance, plus one in a more specialist area. The remaining time can be spent in one of three ways: all eight months in one chosen seat; or four months in one department and four months in the department in which they want to qualify; or six months abroad and two in their chosen department. In-the-field experience is considered as important as formal training at Norton Rose, and trainees are expected to learn by observing experienced lawyers at work, interacting with clients and solicitors, handling sensitive issues and organising their time as well as attending external courses. Internal competition among trainees is discouraged, as great store is placed on team working.

Benefits
Life assurance (25+), private health insurance (optional), season ticket loan, subsidised gym membership.

Vacation Placements
Places for 1999: 45 Summer, 15 Christmas; Duration: Summer: 3 weeks, Christmas: 2 weeks; Remuneration: £185 p.w.; Closing Date: 26 February 1999 for Summer, 5 November 1999 for Christmas.

Sponsorship & Awards
£1,000 travel scholarship, £500 loan on arrival, 4–6 weeks unpaid leave on qualification.

Contact
Brendan Monaghan

Method of Application
Employer's application form

Selection Procedure
Interview and group exercise

Closing date for 2001
6 August 1999

Application
Training contracts p.a.	60–70
Applications p.a.	2,500+
% interviewed p.a.	10%
Required degree grade	2:1

Training
Salary: 1st year(1999)	£21,000
Salary: 2nd Year(1999)	£23,500
Holiday entitlement	22 days
% of trainees with a non-law degree p.a.	35%
No. of seats available abroad p.a.	12

Post-Qualification
Salary (1999)	£32,500
% of trainees offered job on qualification (1998)	97%

Overseas Offices
Bahrain, Brussels, Jakarta, Moscow, Paris, Piraeus, Singapore

OLSWANG

90 Long Acre London WC2E 9TT
Tel: (0171) 208 8888 Fax: (0171) 208 8800
Email: olsmail@olswang.co.uk
Website: http://www.olswang.co.uk

Partners	36
Assistant Solicitors	84
Total Trainees	14

Firm Profile
Olswang does things differently. Established in 1981, the firm has a modern approach and is characterised by its youthful culture and commercial pragmatism. Originally known for its media and entertainment work, the practice has broadened considerably to embrace the full range of commercial issues, with an emphasis on corporate finance and technology.

Main Areas of Work
Company/Commercial 33%; Entertainment/Media 27%; Litigation 20%; Property 20%.

Trainee Profile
The firm looks for confident trainees with a mature attitude, who will develop an early commercial awareness and the ability to think laterally. A willingness to take on responsibility and the ability to handle the pressure that goes with it are essential. Applicants should be individuals who want to make a positive contribution.

Training Environment
There are up to four seats in the major areas: commercial property, corporate/commercial and tax, commercial litigation, and entertainment/media/communications. The firm holds regular lectures on legal topics, and each department has its own training programme. There are various programmes aimed at developing business and interpersonal skills and emphasis is placed on developing IT skills.

Benefits
Excellent salary plus full range of benefits.

Vacation Placements
Places for 1999: 12; Duration: 3 weeks;
Closing Date: 31 January 1999.

Contact
Robert Ivey

Method of Application
Firm's application form

Closing date for 2001
31 July 1999

Application
Training contracts p.a.	12
Applications p.a.	2,000–3,000
% interviewed p.a.	5%
Required degree grade	2:1

Training
Salary: 1st year(1999)	£21,000
Holiday entitlement	20 days

Post-Qualification
Salary (1999)	£32,500
% of trainees offered job on qualification (1998)	100%

289

ORCHARD

99 Bishopsgate London EC2M 3YU
Tel: (0171) 392 0200 Fax: (0171) 392 0201

Firm Profile

Established in 1995, Orchard has quickly made its name as one of the newest, most vibrant firms in London. Built on the expertise of a highly experienced team, it is just one of the reasons why Orchard has already won the business of many major banks and international corporations. The firm is committed to working in partnership with its clients.

Main Areas of Work

Commercial Litigation, Corporate Finance, Mergers & Acquisitions, Banking, Financial Services and Markets, Commercial Contracts, Commercial Property, Employment and Employee Benefits, IT/IP, Corporate Insolvency.

Trainee Profile

Successful candidates are self motivated individuals with excellent interpersonal skills. High standards of academic achievement are important, but so too are commercial awareness and enthusiasm. Essential qualities are flexibility of approach and a sense of humour. All potential trainees should be computer literate.

Training Environment

Trainees will spend six months in four of the firm's main practice areas. They will sit with a Partner or Senior Solicitor and are actively involved in quality work at a very early stage. Trainees will benefit from a system which will allow them to work both independently and as part of a team. Each trainee is assigned a personal mentor to assist them throughout their contract period and regular appraisals are conducted on both an informal and formal basis with either their work supervisor and/or the partner responsible for trainees. Continuing education is supplemented with both in house seminars and video training. The phrase 'work hard, play hard', could have been written for this firm!

Benefits

Under review.

Vacation Placements

No fixed number – please apply in writing.

Partners	9
Assistant Solicitors	10
Total Trainees	4

Contact
Patricia Hart

Method of Application
Application form

Selection Procedure
Two interviews

Closing date for 2002
March 31st 2001

Application
Training contracts p.a.	4–6
Applications p.a.	600
% interviewed p.a.	5%
Required degree grade	2:1

Training
Salary: 1st year(1999)	market rate
Salary: 2nd Year(1999)	market rate
Holiday entitlement	20 days
% of trainees with a non-law degree p.a.	50%

OSBORNE CLARKE

50 Queen Charlotte St Bristol BS1 4HE
Tel: (0117) 984 5350 Fax: (0117) 927 9209
Email: louise.mccalmont@osborne-clarke.co.uk
Website: www.osborne-clarke.co.uk

Partners	51
Assistant Solicitors	126
Total Trainees	27

Firm Profile

Osborne Clarke is widely held to be one of the dominant commercial law firms in the South of England – and one of the fastest growing. It is a major force in its chosen national practice areas – corporate finance, employment, venture capital, IT, telecoms and media – where it competes head on with the largest City and national firms. With 50 partners and over 200 lawyers, the firm is particularly well-endowed with prominent sector specialists in litigation, commercial property, corporate banking, insolvency, tax, environmental and pensions. It also has a growing international client base in the US and Europe particularly in Denmark and in Germany, and is a founding member of the European alliance – Osborne Westphalen International.

Main Areas of Work

Corporate finance, employment, venture capital, IT, telecoms and media.

Trainee Profile

The firm values personality, enthusiasm, the ability to provide practical commercial solutions and the communication skills to deal with clients at all levels. A non-law degree and/or time spent travelling are viewed positively.

Training Environment

Trainees will spend six months in three core departments, either in the UK or in Europe, before choosing to specialise in a particular area. They are expected to take on responsibility at an early stage. There is a structured timetable of external and internal training, with three and six monthly reviews. The firm encourages a wide variety of social and sports activities.

Benefits

None until qualified.

Vacation Placements

Places for 1999: 12; Duration: 1 week; Remuneration: £80 p.w.; Closing Date: 26 February 1999.

Sponsorship & Awards

LPC fees paid.

Contact
Louise McCalmont

Method of Application
Application form and brochure available on request.

Selection Procedure
Individual interviews and group exercises.

Closing date for 2001
31 July 1999

Application
Training contracts p.a.   10–12
Applications p.a.   700–800
% interviewed p.a.   5%
Required degree grade   2:1

Training
Salary: 1st year(1999)   £15,000–
£15,500
Salary: 2nd Year(1999) £16,000–
£16,500
Holiday entitlement   21 days
% of trainees with
a non-law degree p.a.   30%
No. of seats available
abroad p.a.   3

Post-Qualification
Salary (1998)   £23,500
% of trainees offered job
on qualification (1998)   90%

Overseas Offices
Barcelona, Brussels, Copenhagen, Cologne, Frankfurt, Hamburg, Lyon, Milan, Paris, Rotterdam

PAISNER & CO

Bouverie House 154 Fleet St London EC4A 2DQ
Tel: (0171) 353 0299 Fax: (0171) 583 8621
Email: personnel@paisner.co.uk

Partners	45
Assistant Solicitors	72
Total Trainees	13

Firm Profile
Based in the City, Paisner & Co is a broadly-based commercial firm acting for national and international clients.

Main Areas of Work
Company/Commercial 36%; Commercial Property 24%; Litigation 18%; Trusts & Estate Planning 9%; Insurance/Reinsurance 8%; Employment 5%

Trainee Profile
Intelligent, energetic, positive and hard working team players. Individuals who gain a sense of achievement from finding solutions and providing services.

Training Environment
Trainees spend six months in four of the following departments- company and commercial, commercial litigation, commercial property, employment and trusts. You will often work in cross-departmental teams, but will have one-to-one supervision from a partner or senior solicitor. Development is monitored with an assessment every six months. Internal and external lectures, carrying Law Society Continuing Education Points, are given twice a day. Trainees are given library research and Lexis induction courses. Staff are encouraged to get to know each other- partners and senior solicitors are accessible and willing to teach. The office environment is relaxed and informal. Social and sporting events are organised and there is an internal newspaper.

Vacation Placements
Places for 1999: 10; Duration: 4 weeks; Remuneration: £150 p.w.; Closing Date: 30 April 1999.

Sponsorship & Awards
CPE Funding: No; LPC Funding: Yes.

Contact
Personnel Manager

Method of Application
Handwritten letter and CV

Selection Procedure
CV and interview

Closing date for 2001
31 July 1999

Application

Training contracts p.a.	10
Applications p.a.	2,000
% interviewed p.a.	3%
Required degree grade	2:1

Training

Salary: 1st year(1999)	£20,500
Salary: 2nd Year(1999)	£23,000
Holiday entitlement	21 days
% of trainees with a non-law degree p.a.	3%
No. of seats available abroad p.a.	0

Post-Qualification

Salary (1999)	£33,000
% of trainees offered job on qualification (1998)	60%
% of assistants (as at 1/9/98) who joined as trainees	7%
% of partners (as at 1/9/98) who joined as trainees	8%

PANNONE & PARTNERS

123 Deansgate Manchester M3 2BU
Tel: (0161) 909 3000 Fax: (0161) 909 4444
Website: www.pannone.com

Partners	45
Assistant Solicitors	28
Total Trainees	18

Firm Profile

A high profile Manchester firm presently undergoing rapid growth. The firm prides itself on offering a full range of legal services for both personal and commercial clients. The firm was the first to be awarded the quality standard ISO9001 and is a founder member of Pannone Law Group - Europe's first integrated international law group.

Main Areas of Work

Commercial Litigation 25%; Personal Injury 22%; Corporate 15%; Commercial Property 11%; Family 10%; Medical Negligence 10%; Private Client 7%.

Trainee Profile

Selection criteria include a high level of academic achievement, a wide range of interests and a connection with the North West.

Training Environment

An induction course helps trainees adjust to working life, covers the firm's quality procedures and good practice. Seminars throughout the training contract cover the work of other departments within the firm, new legal developments and practice. Four seats of six months, selected by the trainees themselves, are spent in various departments where your development is monitored regularly and any concerns should be dealt with informally as they arise. There are departmental training sessions, sometimes with training videos, to improve your understanding of technical and procedural issues. You are also encouraged to develop IT skills. The PSC is taken externally, and class attendance takes precedence over departmental requirements. Work is tackled with gusto here, but so are the many social gatherings that take place.

Benefits

Study Leave for LPC.

Vacation Placements

Places for 1999: 20; Duration: 1 week; Remuneration: 0; Closing Date: 15 March 1999.

Contact
Julia Hearn

Method of Application
Application form and CV

Selection Procedure
Individual interview, followed with a tour of the firm and informal lunch

Closing date for 2001
13 August 1999

Application

Training contracts p.a.	8
Applications p.a.	650
% interviewed p.a.	10%
Required degree grade	2:1

Training

Salary: 1st year(1999)	£15,000
Salary: 2nd Year(1999)	£17,000
Holiday entitlement	20 days
% of trainees with a non-law degree p.a.	50%
No. of seats available abroad p.a.	0

Post-Qualification

Salary (1999)	£24,000
% of trainees offered job on qualification (1998)	50%
% of assistants (as at 1/9/98) who joined as trainees	30%
% of partners (as at 1/9/98) who joined as trainees	40%

PAYNE HICKS BEACH

10 New Square Lincoln's Inn London WC2A 3QG
Tel: (0171) 465 4300 Fax: (0171) 465 4400
Email: a-palmer@payne-hicks-beach.co.uk

Partners	18
Assistant Solicitors	10
Total Trainees	5

Firm Profile
Payne Hicks Beach is a medium-sized firm based in Lincoln's Inn. It primarily provides specialist tax, trusts and probate advice to individuals and families. It also undertakes corporate and commercial work.

Main Areas of Work
Private Client 33%; Commercial Litigation 13%; Commercial Property 12%; Matrimonial and Family Law/ Litigation 10%; Residential/Agricultural Property 10%; Tax (business and corporate) 10%; Corporate/Commercial 10%; General, Miscellaneous 2%.

Trainee Profile
The firm looks for law and non-law graduates with a good academic record, a practical ability to solve problems, enthusiasm and an ability to work hard and deal appropriately with their colleagues and the firm's clients. French or German may be an advantage.

Training Environment
Following an initial induction course, trainees usually spend six months in four of the firm's departments. Working with a partner, they are involved in the day to day activities of the department, including attending conferences with clients, counsel and other professional advisers. Assessment is continuous and you will be given responsibility as you demonstrate ability and aptitude. To complement the PSC, the firm runs a formal training system for trainees and requires them to attend lectures and seminars on various topics. Sports/social activities including an active arts society are popular.

Benefits
Season travel ticket loan, life assurance 4 x salary, permanent health insurance.

Sponsorship & Awards
Fees for the CPE and LPC are paid.

Contact
Mrs Alice Palmer

Method of Application
Handwritten letter and CV

Selection Procedure
Interview

Closing date for 2001
13 August 1999

Application

Training contracts p.a.	2–3
Applications p.a.	1,000
% interviewed p.a.	3%
Required degree grade	2:1

Training

Salary: 1st year(1998)	£18,500
Salary: 2nd Year(1998)	£20,000
Holiday entitlement	4 weeks
% of trainees with a non-law degree p.a.	50%
No. of seats available abroad p.a.	0

Post-Qualification

Salary (1999)	£29,000
% of trainees offered job on qualification (1998)	100%
% of assistants (as at 1/9/98) who joined as trainees	30%
% of partners (as at 1/9/98) who joined as trainees	39%

PENNINGTONS

Bucklersbury House 83 Cannon Street London EC4N 8PE
Tel: (0171) 457 3000 Fax: (0171) 457 3240

Partners	38*
Assistant Solicitors	52*
Total Trainees	20

denotes world-wide figures

Firm Profile
An international law firm, with offices in the City, Basingstoke, Godalming, Newbury and Paris. There are four main departments. Specialist units cover industry sectors and key overseas jurisdictions.

Main Areas of Work
Litigation (including Shipping) 33%; Property 29%; Corporate/Commercial 24%; Private Client (including Family) 14%.

Trainee Profile
Penningtons is looking for bright, enthusiastic, highly motivated and well rounded individuals with a keen interest in the practice of law.

Training Environment
Six-month seats are provided in three or four of the following departments: corporate/commercial, property, litigation, and private client (including family). Individual preference is usually accommodated in the second year. Trainees are given a thorough grounding in the law. International opportunities do arise. There are in-house lectures and reviews and appraisals occur regularly. The firm aims to utilise trainees' talents to their full, but is careful not to overburden them. All staff are supportive and the atmosphere is both professional and informal.

Benefits
Subsidised sports and social club.

Vacation Placements
Places for 1999: 60 on London Open Days at Easter; Remuneration: expenses; Closing Date: 28 February 1999. Some summer vacation placements out of London.

Sponsorship & Awards
LPC Funding is available. Awards are given for commendation or distinction in LPC.

Contact
Lesley Lintott

Method of Application
Handwritten letter, CV and application form

Selection Procedure
1 interview with a partner and director of studies

Closing date for 2001
31 August 1999

Application
Training contracts p.a.	10
Applications p.a.	2,000
% interviewed p.a.	5%
Required degree grade	2:1

Training
Salary: 1st year(1998) £19,500 (London)
Salary: 2nd Year(1998) £20,500 (London)
Holiday entitlement 22 days
% of trainees with
a non-law degree p.a. 40%

Post-Qualification
Salary (1998) £27,500
% of trainees offered job
on qualification (1998) 60%
% of assistants (as at 1/9/98)
who joined as trainees 45%
% of partners (as at 1/9/98)
who joined as trainees 49%

Overseas Offices
Paris

PICTONS

Keystone 60 London Rd St. Albans AL1 1NG

Tel: (01727) 798000 Fax: (01727) 798002

Partners	31
Assistant Solicitors	37
Total Trainees	14

Firm Profile

Operating from offices in Hertfordshire, Bedfordshire and Buckinghamshire, Pictons is a broad-based commercial practice offering services to private and commercial clients. The latter range from multi-national corporations to owner managed businesses.

Main Areas of Work

Commercial, Property and Company 25%; Crime 20%; Domestic Conveyancing 15%; Commercial Litigation/ Personal Injury 15%; Family 15%; Probate Trusts, Tax Planning 10%.

Trainee Profile

Dynamic, ambitious and personable with a good academic record. Preference for candidates with work experience in a law firm.

Training Environment

The training contract consists of four six-month seats. The branch manager oversees your structural training alongside a partner or senior solicitor from each department. You are a working member of the team assuming responsibility and direct contact with clients. An in-house training programme is organised for trainees and staff with regular outside speakers.

Vacation Placements

Duration: 2 weeks;
Closing Date: 31 April 1999.

Contact
Nicola Wright/Jessica Beers

Method of Application
CV with covering letter

Closing date for 2001
31 July 1999

Application
Required degree grade 2:1 or above

PINSENT CURTIS

Dashwood House 69 Old Broad Street London EC2M 1NR
Tel: (0171) 418 7000 Fax: (0171) 418 7050
3 Colmore Circus Birmingham B4 6BH
Tel: (0121) 200 1050 Fax: (0121) 626 1040
41 Park Square Leeds LS1 2NS
Tel: (0113) 244 500 Fax: (0113) 244 8000
Email: nimisha.gosrani@pinsent-curtis.co.uk
Website: www.pinsent-curtis.co.uk

Partners	125
Assistant Solicitors	130
Total Trainees	58

Contact
Nimisha Gosrani

Method of Application
Application form

Selection Procedure
Interview

Closing date for 2001
31 July 1999

Application
Training contracts p.a.   35
Applications p.a.   4000
Required degree grade   2:1

Training
Holiday entitlement   20 days
No. of seats available
abroad p.a.   1

Overseas Offices
Brussels

Firm Profile
Pinsent Curtis is a major national commercial firm. It has a first class reputation based on its work for a substantial list of quality corporate clients. The firm also has strong contacts with merchant banks, underwriters and insurers, and has the largest tax department outside London.

Main Areas of Work
Litigation & Professional Indemnity 38%;
Corporate/Commercial 34%; Property 19%; Tax 9%.

Trainee Profile
The firm seeks applications from both law and non-law graduates with a good honours degree. However, not only is a good academic background required, but also personality, commitment and common sense. Given that the bulk of work is business oriented, trainees need to communicate with the business community, be interested in its problems and have the ability to give positive commercial advice.

Training Environment
Trainees sit in four seats of six months ranging from corporate, property, litigation, commercial, tax and employment. Hands-on experience is seen as an essential part of the learning process, so early responsibility and contact with clients are encouraged. Partners or associates oversee your work and are on hand to help and advise. The PSC is taught in-house, and there is an internal structured development programme to broaden your knowledge. The firm has an open-door policy and informal atmosphere, and there are many social and sporting activities for its staff.

Vacation Placements
Places for 1999: 100; Duration: 1 week;
Remuneration: £85 p.w.;
Closing Date: 28 February 1999.

Sponsorship & Awards
CPE/ LPC funding. In addition maintenance grants are offered.

PRITCHARD ENGLEFIELD

14 New St London EC2M 4TR
Tel: (0171) 972 9720 Fax: (0171) 972 9722
Email: po@pritchardenglefield.co.uk

Partners	21
Assistant Solicitors	22
Total Trainees	8

Firm Profile

A medium-sized City firm practising a mix of general commercial and non-commercial law with many German and French clients. Despite its strong commercial departments, the firm still undertakes family and private client work and is known for its medical negligence and PI practice and its strong international flavour.

Main Areas of Work

All main areas of commercial practice including litigation, company/commercial (UK, German, French and some Italian), employment also private client/probate, personal injury, medical negligence and some family.

Trainee Profile

Normally only high academic achievers with a second European language (especially German and French) are considered. However, a lower second degree coupled with exceptional subsequent education or experience could suffice.

Training Environment

An induction course acquaints trainees with the computer network, library and administrative procedures and there is a formal in-house training programme. Four six-month seats make up most of your training. You can usually choose some departments, and you could spend two six-month periods in the same seat. Over two years, you learn advocacy, negotiating, drafting and interviewing, attend court, use your language skills and meet clients. Occasional talks and seminars explain the work of the firm, and you can air concerns over bi-monthly lunches with the partners comprising the Trainee panel. PSC is taken externally over two years. Quarterly drinks parties, musical evenings and ten-pin bowling number amongst popular social events.

Benefits

Some subsidised training, luncheon vouchers.

Sponsorship & Awards

None at present.

Contact
Marian Joseph

Method of Application
Standard application
form available from
Graduate Recruitment

Selection Procedure
1 interview only in September

Closing date for 2001
31 July 1999

Application
Training contracts p.a.   4
Applications p.a.   300–400
% interviewed p.a.   10%
Required degree grade
                    generally 2:1

Training
Salary: 1st year(1998) £17,500
Salary: 2nd Year(1999) £18,000
Holiday entitlement   4 weeks
% of trainees with
a non-law degree p.a. Approx
                    50%
No. of seats available
abroad p.a.   0

Post-Qualification
Salary (1999)   Approx £27,000
% of trainees offered job
on qualification (1998)   75%
% of assistants (as at 1/9/98)
who joined as trainees   75%
% of partners (as at 1/9/98)
who joined as trainees   50%

Overseas Offices
Frankfurt, Hong Kong

RADCLIFFES

5 Great College Street Westminster London SW1P 3SJ
Tel: (0171) 222 7040 Fax: (0171) 222 6208
Email: marie.o'shea@radcliffes.co.uk
Website: www.radcliffes.co.uk

Partners	36
Assistant Solicitors	22
Total Trainees	7

Firm Profile
Founded in 1844, Radcliffes is a medium-sized commercial firm providing a broad range of advice in the fields of Company Commercial law, Litigation and Dispute Resolution, Property and Development, Tax and Private Client and Family Law.

Contact
Marie O'Shea
Administration Secretary

Method of Application
CV and covering letter or EAF

Main Areas of Work
The firm has specific high profile experience in the fields of healthcare, charities, IT and Telecommunications and deals with a substantial amount of international work to include Italy and South Africa.

Selection Procedure
2 Interviews with partners

Closing date for 2001
31 July 1999

Trainee Profile
Its aim is to recruit trainee solicitors who have a real prospect of becoming partners in due course. The firm seeks not just academic but also extra curricular activities, self-confidence, determination and a sense of humour.

Application
Training contracts p.a.   4
Applications p.a.   1030
% interviewed p.a.   7%
Required degree grade   2:1

Training Environment
Trainees are introduced to the firm with a full induction week.

Training
Salary: 1st year(1999) £18,500
Salary: 2nd Year(1999) £19,500
Holiday entitlement 22 days p.a.

Benefits
Health insurance, season ticket loan, life assurance, PHI.

Vacation Placements
Places for 1999: 10; Duration: 2 weeks;
Remuneration: £130 p.w.;
Closing Date: 31 March 1999.

Post-Qualification
Salary (1999)   £28,000
% of trainees offered job
on qualification (1998)   67%
% of assistants (as at 1/9/99)
who joined as trainees   50%
% of partners (as at 1/9/99)
who joined as trainees   50%

REYNOLDS PORTER CHAMBERLAIN

Chichester House 278–282 High Holborn
London WC1V 7HA
Tel: (0171) 242 2877 Fax: (0171) 242 1431
Email: rpc@rpc.co.uk
Website: www.rpc.co.uk

Partners	42
Assistant Solicitors	68
Total Trainees	16

Firm Profile

Reynolds Porter Chamberlain is a leading Central London practice with over 160 lawyers. In addition to its main offices in Holborn, the firm has an expanding office in Leadenhall Street in the City. Best known as a major litigation practice, particularly professional negligence, they also have thriving corporate, commercial property, private client and construction departments.

Main Areas of Work

Litigation 60%; Corporate 12.5%; Commercial Property 12.5%; Construction 10%; Family/ Private Client 5%.

Trainee Profile

The firm appoints seven Trainees each year from law and non-law backgrounds. Although proven academic ability is important to them (they require a 2.1 or above) Reynolds Porter Chamberlain also values flair, energy, business sense, commitment and the ability to communicate and relate well to others.

Training Environment

As a Trainee you will receive first rate training in a supportive working environment. You will work closely with a Partner and be given real responsibility as soon as you are ready to handle it. At least six months will be spent in each of the three main areas of the practice and Trainees are encouraged to express a preference for their seats. This provides a thorough grounding and the chance to develop confidence as you see matters through to their conclusion. In addition to the externally provided Professional Skills Course a complimentary programme of in-house training is provided.

Benefits

Four weeks' holiday, two bonus schemes, season ticket loan, subsidised gym membership, four office parties per year.

Vacation Placements

Places for 1999: 12; Duration: 2 weeks; Remuneration: £175 p.w.; Closing Date: 28 February 1999.

Sponsorship & Awards

CPE Funding: Fees paid + £3,500 maintenance.
LPC Funding: Fees paid + £3,500 maintenance.

Contact
Sally Andrews
Head of Personnel

Method of Application
Hand-written covering letter and application form

Selection Procedure
Assessment Days held in September

Closing date for 2001
14 August 1999

Application
Training contracts p.a.	7
Applications p.a.	1000
% interviewed p.a.	4%
Required degree grade	2.1

Training
Salary: 1st year(1999) £19,000
Salary: 2nd Year(1999) £21,000
Holiday entitlement 20 days
% of trainees with
a non-law degree p.a. 50%
No. of seats available
abroad p.a. N/A

Post-Qualification
Salary (1999) £31,000
% of trainees offered job
on qualification (1998) 75%
% of assistants (as at 1/9/98)
who joined as trainees 55%
% of partners (as at 1/9/98)
who joined as trainees 35%

RICHARDS BUTLER

Beaufort House 15 St. Botolph Street London EC3A 7EE
Tel: (0171) 247 6555 Fax: (0171) 247 5091
Email: law@richardsbutler.com

Firm Profile

Established in 1920, Richards Butler is noted for the
exceptional variety of its work. It has acknowledged strengths
in shipping, commodities, company/commercial, litigation,
property, insurance, media/ entertainment, competition and
energy law, in each of which it has international prominence.

Main Areas of Work

Corporate/ Commercial/ Banking/ Finance 43% Shipping/
International Trade & Commodities/ Insurance 23%
Commercial Litigation 20% Commercial Property 14%.

Trainee Profile

Candidates should be players rather than onlookers, work well
under pressure and be happy to operate as a team member or
team leader as circumstances dictate. Candidates from diverse
backgrounds are welcome, including mature students with
commercial experience and management skills.

Training Environment

Richards Butler provides practical experience across as wide a
spectrum of the law as possible. Training is divided into four
periods of five months and one period of four months. Trainees
start in general corporate, litigation and commercial property
seats, however there are opportunities to work in other
additional specialised areas such as shipping, media law, or
international trade in later seats.

Benefits

Life insurance, Private Patients' Plan, Interest free season
ticket loan, subsidised staff restaurant.

Vacation Placements

Places for 1999: 30; Duration: 2 weeks; Remuneration: £200
p.w.; Closing Date: 13 March 1999. In addition, the firm offers
overseas scholarships to 4 students.

Sponsorship & Awards

CPE and LPC fees and maintenance paid.

Partners	95*
Assistant Solicitors	162*
Total Trainees	40

denotes world-wide figures

Contact
Jill Steele

Method of Application
Firm's application form

Selection Procedure
1 interview

Closing date for 2001
31 July 1999

Application

Training contracts p.a.	20
Applications p.a.	1,500
% interviewed p.a.	7.5%
Required degree grade	n/a

Training

Salary: 1st year(1998) £21,000
Salary: 2nd Year(1998) £23,500
Holiday entitlement 22 days
% of trainees with
a non-law degree p.a. 33%
No. of seats available
abroad p.a. 10

Post-Qualification

Salary (1998) £31,500
% of trainees offered job
on qualification (1998) 60%
% of assistants (as at 1/9/98)
who joined as trainees 65%
% of partners (as at 1/9/98)
who joined as trainees 51%

Overseas Offices
Abu Dhabi, Beijing, Brussels,
Doha, Hong Kong, Islamabad,
Muscat, Paris, Piraeus, Sao
Paulo, Warsaw

ROSS & CRAIG

12A Upper Berkeley Street London W1H 7PE
Tel: (0171) 262 3077 Fax: (0171) 724 6427
Email: reception@rosscraig.com

Partners	9
Assistant Solicitors	11
Total Trainees	3

Firm Profile
Established in the 1950's with an emphasis on commercial work, Ross & Craig acts for public and private companies, businesses and individual entrepreneurs. Half the firm's workload is in commercial property.

Main Areas of Work
Property (inc. Environmental) 50%; Company/Commercial 20%; Litigation 18%; Family 9%; Private Client 3%.

Trainee Profile
Candidates need relevant work experience, a variety of interests and a confident personality.

Training Environment
Trainees will spend 6 months in the Litigation and Property departments and 1 year in the Company Commercial department. Appraisals are given at the end of each seat. There is no formal social committee as the firm is relatively small.

Vacation Placements
Duration: 1 week-3 months;
Remuneration: dependent upon duration;
Closing Date: January 1999.

Contact
Suzanna Sloan

Method of Application
Handwritten letter and CV

Selection Procedure
Individual interviews

Closing date for 2001
Early 2000

Application
Training contracts p.a.	2
Applications p.a.	500
% interviewed p.a.	10%
Required degree grade	2:1

Training
Salary: 1st year(1999)	£15,000
Salary: 2nd Year(1999)	£17,000
Holiday entitlement	20 days
No. of seats available abroad p.a.	0

Post-Qualification
Salary (1999)	£27,000
% of trainees offered job on qualification (1998)	50%
% of assistants (as at 1/9/98) who joined as trainees	50%
% of partners (as at 1/9/98) who joined as trainees	22%

ROWE & MAW

20 Black Friars Lane London EC4V 6HD
Tel: (0171) 248 4282 Fax: (0171) 248 2009
Email: roweandmaw@roweandmaw.co.uk
Website: www.roweandmaw.co.uk

Partners	68*
Assistant Solicitors	122*
Total Trainees	45

denotes world-wide figures

Firm Profile
Founded 100 years ago, Rowe & Maw is a leading commercial firm, with offices in London, including one at Lloyds, and in Brussels. Its strength lies in advising companies and businesses on day-to-day work and special projects.

Main Areas of Work
Corporate 37%; Litigation 22%; Property 12%; Construction 8%; Pensions 9%; Intellectual property 7%; Employment 4%; Private client 1%.

Trainee Profile
The firm is interested in students with a good academic record and a strong commitment to law. Commercial awareness gained through legal or business work experience is an advantage. Extra-curricular activities are taken into consideration. The firm wants trainees to become future partners. The current senior partner trained with the firm.

Training Environment
There are September and March intakes. Training divides into four six-month seats. All trainees spend time in the corporate, litigation and property departments, frequently working for blue chip clients. Secondments to Brussels or to clients in the UK or abroad are an option for some. The firm has a professional development and training programme which covers subjects like EU law and the workings of the City. Advocacy and drafting skills are also taught. Trainees are encouraged to join in the sports and social life.

Benefits
Interest free season ticket loan, subsidised membership of sport clubs, private health scheme.

Vacation Placements
Places for 1999: 25; Duration: 2 weeks; Remuneration: £200 p.w.; Closing Date: 26 February 1999.

Sponsorship & Awards
CPE and LPC fees paid and £4,000 maintenance p.a.

Contact
Vicky Barnbrook

Method of Application
Application form

Selection Procedure
Selection workshops including an interview and a business exercise

Closing date for 2001
31 August 1999

Application
Training contracts p.a.	25
Applications p.a.	1,250
% interviewed p.a.	10%
Required degree grade	2:1

Training
% of trainees with a non-law degree p.a.	50%
No. of seats available abroad p.a.	2

Post-Qualification
Salary (1999)	£33,000
% of trainees offered job on qualification (1998)	80%
% of assistants (as at 1/9/98) who joined as trainees	50%
% of partners (as at 1/9/98) who joined as trainees	38%

Overseas Offices
Brussels

RUSSELL-COOKE

2 Putney Hill London SW15 6AB

Tel: (0181) 789 9111 Fax: (0181) 785 4286

Firm Profile

A medium-sized practice with three offices in the London area. The City office deals primarily with commercial property. The Putney office has a range of specialist departments including company/commercial, crime, judicial review, commercial litigation, matrimonial, domestic and commercial conveyancing, personal injury litigation and private client work. The Kingston-upon-Thames office is a general practice with a specialist child-care department.

Main Areas of Work

Commercial Property/General Commercial 30%; Litigation (Commercial, PI and Property) 20%; Private Client 10%; Domestic Conveyancing 10%; Matrimonial 10%; Crime 20%.

Trainee Profile

Trainees will need at least two A grades and a B grade at A Level and a 2:1 degree, though not necessarily in law. You will also need to be good at the practical business of advising and representing clients. Intellectual rigour, adaptability and the ability, under pressure, to handle a diverse range of people and issues efficiently and cost-effectively are vital attributes.

Training Environment

Trainees are offered four seats lasting six months each. Photocopying and researching points of law will not take up all your time in the firm. You will have the chance to manage your own case work and deal directly with clients, with supervision suited to your needs and the needs of the department and clients. Internal training and an annual executive staff conference supplements the externally provided PSC. Social events include quiz nights, wine tasting, summer and Christmas parties.

Partners	20
Assistant Solicitors	25
Total Trainees	6

Contact
J.M. Thornton

Method of Application
Application form

Selection Procedure
First and second interviews.

Closing date for 2001
13 August 1999

Application

Training contracts p.a.	3–4
Applications p.a.	500
% interviewed p.a.	7%
Required degree grade	2:1

Training

Salary: 1st year(1999)	£16,000
Salary: 2nd Year(1999)	£16,750
Holiday entitlement	20 days
% of trainees with a non-law degree p.a.	50%
No. of seats available abroad p.a.	0

Post-Qualification

Salary (1999)	Market
% of trainees offered job on qualification (1998)	75%
% of assistants (as at 1/9/98) who joined as trainees	30%
% of partners (as at 1/9/98) who joined as trainees	50%

RUSSELL JONES & WALKER

Swinton House 324 Gray's Inn Road London WC1X 8DH
Tel: (0171) 837 2808 Fax: (0171) 837 2941
Email: 101317.2022@compuserve.com
Website: www.rjw.co.uk

Partners	38
Assistant Solicitors	58
Total Trainees	9

Firm Profile
Russell Jones & Walker was founded in London in the 1920's but has expanded in recent years to become one of the largest litigation practices in the country with more than 350 lawyers and support staff and offices in Leeds, Birmingham, Bristol, Manchester, Sheffield, Newcastle-upon-Tyne and Cardiff.

Main Areas of Work
Personal Injury 66%; Criminal 13%; Commercial Litigation 12%; Employment 5%; Family/Probate 2%; Commercial and Domestic Conveyancing 2%.

Trainee Profile
They are looking for candidates who are motivated and hard-working with a sense of humour and the ability and confidence to accept responsibility in fee earning work and client care.

Training Environment
Each trainee will spend six months in four of the following departments under the supervision of a partner or senior solicitor - personal injury; commercial litigation, family and probate; medical negligence; criminal and investigation; employment/trade union regulation and commercial conveyancing. Your supervisor will conduct a three-month assessment and six-month review. The PSC is taught externally at present. The firm is extremely sociable and trainees are encouraged to participate in social and sporting events. There is a comprehensive in-house education timetable. Jeremy Clarke-Williams, the training partner supervises all aspects of the training contract. IT training and an induction progamme are provided.

Benefits
Season ticket loan.

Vacation Placements
Places for 1999: Available – various dates and locations as needs dictate.

Sponsorship & Awards
CPE/LPC Funding: interest free loan to assist with fees available.

Contact
Lorraine Hunt
Training Co-ordinator

Method of Application
Application form

Closing date for 2001
31 July 1999

Application
Training contracts p.a.   5–6
Applications p.a. 1,000–1,500
% interviewed p.a.   5-7%
Required degree grade
All applications considered

Training
Salary: 1st year(1999) £18,000
Salary: 2nd Year(1999) £19,750
Holiday entitlement   4 weeks
% of trainees with
a non-law degree p.a.   50%
No. of seats available
abroad p.a.   0

Post-Qualification
Salary (1999)   £27,000
% of trainees offered job
on qualification (1998)   100%
% of assistants (as at 1/9/98)
who joined as trainees   c.25%
% of partners (as at 1/9/98)
who joined as trainees   10%

SALANS HERTZFELD & HEILBRONN HRK

Clements House 14–18 Gresham Street London EC2V 7NN
Tel: (0171) 509 6000 Fax: (0171) 726 6191
Email: shh@salans-hrk.com

Partners	86
Assistant Solicitors	210
Total Trainees	3

Firm Profile

Salans Hertzfeld & Heilbronn ('SHH') is a multinational law firm with full-service offices in the City of London, Paris and New York, together with further offices in Moscow, St Petersburg, Warsaw, Kyiv and Almaty. The firm has currently over 350 fee-earners, including 86 partners.

Main Areas of Work

Banking & Finance/Corporate 50%; Litigation 25%; Employment 15%; Commercial Property 10%.

Trainee Profile

Candidates need to have high academic qualifications and the ability to approach complex problems in a practical and commercial way. The firm looks to recruit those who demonstrate an ability and a willingness to assume responsibility at an early stage, possess common sense and good judgement. Language and IT skills are also valued.

Training Environment

The firm operates an in-house training scheme for both trainees and assistant solicitors. In addition, trainees will be offered the opportunity to attend external courses wherever possible. Trainees are at all times supervised by a partner and encouraged to take an active part in the work of their department. The caseload of the trainee will, in each case, depend on the trainee's level of expertise and experience. Where possible the firm seeks to recruit its trainees at the end of the training periods.

Contact
Alison Gaines
Partner

Method of Application
Handwritten Letter and CV

Selection Procedure
2 interviews with partners

Closing date for 2001
31 July 1999

Application

Training contracts p.a.	3
Applications p.a.	500
% interviewed p.a.	5%
Required degree grade	2:1

Training
Salary: 1st year(1999) Not less than £19,500
Holiday entitlement 20 days
% of trainees with
a non-law degree p.a. Variable
No. of seats available
abroad p.a. None at present

Post-Qualification
Salary (1999) Variable
% of trainees offered job
on qualification (1998) 2 out of 3
% of assistants (as at 1/9/98)
who joined as trainees 6 out of 22
% of partners (as at 1/9/98)
who joined as trainees none

Overseas Offices
Paris, New York, Moscow, St Petersburg, Warsaw, Kyiv, Almaty

SHADBOLT & CO

Chatham Court Lesbourne Road Reigate RH2 7LD
Tel: (01737) 226277 Fax: (01737) 226165
Email: shadboltlaw.co.uk
Website: www.shadboltlaw.co.uk

Partners	13*
Assistant Solicitors	10*
Total Trainees	5*

* denotes world-wide figures

Firm Profile
Established in 1991, Shadbolt & Co is a specialist firm servicing business clients in the UK and internationally. Well known for its strengths in major projects, construction and engineering and more recently for its company commercial practice. All partners have City backgrounds.

Main Areas of Work
Corporate and Commercial Disputes 40%; Projects/non-contentious Construction and engineering 30%; Company and Commercial 30%.

Trainee Profile
Mature self-starters with a strong academic background and outside interests. They should be able to take responsibility, have good interpersonal skills and be able to play an active role in the future of the firm. Linguists (especially French) are particularly welcome. Travel is favourably viewed.

Training Environment
Four six-month seats from: corporate, commercial, commercial property, projects/non contentious construction, and litigation. Where possible, individual preference is noted. Work has an international bias. French speaking trainees work temporarily in an associated Paris office. Trainees are seconded to major plc construction/engineering clients. As a small firm, trainees are rapidly integrated and immediately take active roles and early responsibility. All trainees sit with partners/senior solicitors who monitor progress. There are two appraisals per seat. In certain seats trainees may be given their own files. Lunch time lectures occur twice a month, and trainees participate in publishing a construction law and other updates. The PSC is taught externally. The firm's atmosphere is young and informal, and there are various social and sporting activities.

Benefits
Permanent health insurance, bonus scheme.

Vacation Placements
Places for 1999: 5; Duration: 2 weeks; Remuneration: £100 p.w.; Closing Date: April 1999.

Sponsorship & Awards
CPE and LPC fees partly payable when trainee commences work.

Contact
Helen Boddy

Method of Application
Handwritten letter and CV

Selection Procedure
Interview(s)

Closing date for 2001
September 1999

Application
Training contracts p.a.	4–5
Applications p.a.	175
% interviewed p.a.	7%
Required degree grade	2:1

Training
Salary: 1st year(1999)	£17,500
Salary: 2nd year(1999)	£21,000
Holiday entitlement	20 days
% of trainees with a non-law degree p.a.	60%
No. of seats available abroad p.a.	1/2

Post-Qualification
Salary (1999)	£27,000
% of trainees offered job on qualification (1998)	100%
% of assistants (as at 1/9/98) who joined as trainees	20%
% of partners (as at 1/9/98) who joined as trainees	0%

Overseas Offices
Hong Kong, Paris

SHERIDANS

14 Red Lion Square London WC1R 4QL
Tel: (0171) 404 0444 Fax: (0171) 831 1982
Email: general@sheridans.co.uk

Partners	16
Assistant Solicitors	9
Total Trainees	7

Firm Profile
A Holborn firm specialising in litigation and the entertainment and media industry, and offering private client and commercial services including property and company work.

Main Areas of Work
Commercial and other litigation including media, family and crime 40%; Entertainment and Media 35%; Property and Planning 15%; Company/Commercial 10%.

Trainee Profile
Candidates should be intelligent, ambitious and self-confident with excellent communication and interpersonal skills.

Training Environment
Trainees spend six to eight months in each department (litigation, company/commercial, property and planning). Working alongside senior partners or solicitors, you will be involved with a whole variety of work. There are regular trainee and department meetings. In the second year, trainees may be given a limited number of their own files. Early responsibility is encouraged. Trainees are not usually placed in media and entertainment (at least not until their last six months, due to its particularly specialised nature). The training programme is being expanded to include in-house seminars and video assisted learning schemes. Full computer and technology training is provided. Trainees are expected to work hard and think on their feet. The firm is friendly and informal and organises a range of social/sporting activities.

Benefits
Life assurance.

Sponsorship & Awards
LPC funding is variable for those who have accepted training contracts.

Contact
Cyril Glasser

Method of Application
Letter and CV

Selection Procedure
2 interviews

Application date for 2001
1–31 August 1999

Application
Training contracts p.a.	2.5
Applications p.a.	850
% interviewed p.a.	7%
Required degree grade	2:1

Training
Salary: 1st year(1998)	£18,500
Salary: 2nd Year(1998)	£19,250
Holiday entitlement	20 days
% of trainees with a non-law degree p.a.	28%
No. of seats available abroad p.a.	0

Post-Qualification
Salary (1998)	£26,500
% of trainees offered job on qualification (1998)	67%
% of assistants (as at 1/9/98) who joined as trainees	100%
% of partners (as at 1/9/98) who joined as trainees	38%

SHOOSMITHS & HARRISON

The Lakes Bedford Road Northampton NN4 7SH
Tel: (01604) 543000 Fax: (01604) 543543
Email: Northampton@shoosmiths.co.uk
Website: www.shoosmiths.co.uk

Partners	69
Assistant Solicitors	95
Total Trainees	31

Firm Profile
A leading regional practice, providing services for commercial and private clients throughout the country. The firm has particular strengths in insurance litigation, commercial property and town and country planning.

Main Areas of Work
Insurers 39.9%; Business Services, Property & Banking 41.4%; Financial Institutions 10%; Private Client 8.7%.

Trainee Profile
Candidates must show academic and personal achievement and commitment to work and the firm.

Training Environment
The training contract is divided into four seats of six months. Occasionally a trainee may choose to specialise and spend two seats in one department. It is compulsory for trainees to sit in either the commercial/corporate or in the litigation department. Trainees may move around the regional offices. Trainees sit with a partner who is responsible for giving hands-on training. Lectures are held internally for trainees and staff and the PSC is also taught in-house. All the staff in the firm are accessible and happy to give assistance. The firm has invested over four million pounds in IT over the past year and trainees will develop IT skills. Social and sporting activities are organised by every office and the practice as a whole.

Benefits
Life assurance, contributory pension after 3 months.

Vacation Placements
Places for 1999: 20; Duration: 2 weeks;
Remuneration: £100 p.w.;
Closing Date: 31 March 1999.

Sponsorship & Awards
CPE and LPC funding.

Contact
Liz Cheaney

Method of Application
Application form

Selection Procedure
Assessment centre – one day

Closing date for 2001
31 July 1999

Application
Training contracts p.a.	16
Applications p.a.	1,200
% interviewed p.a.	7%
Required degree grade	2:1

Training
Salary: 1st year(1997)	£14,750
Salary: 2nd Year(1997)	£15,750
Holiday entitlement	23 days

Post-Qualification
Salary (1999)	£24,000

SIDLEY & AUSTIN

1 Threadneedle Street London EC2R 8AW
Tel: (0171) 360 3600 Fax: (0171) 626 7937
Email: LWhite01@sidley.com
Website: www.sidley.com

Partners	11
Assistant Solicitors	36
Total Trainees	8

Firm Profile
Founded in Chicago in 1866, Sidley & Austin is now one of the largest law firms in the world, with more than 850 lawyers practising on three continents. They have nearly 50 lawyers in London and are expanding fast.

Main Areas of Work
Banking Regulation, Structured Finance and Securitisation, Corporate and Commercial Law, Corporate Tax, the Information Industries (Telecoms, Information Technology, Internet, Media, Networks etc.) and Intellectual Property.

Trainee Profile
Sidley & Austin is looking for focused, intelligent and enthusiastic individuals with personality and humour who have a real interest in practising law in the commercial world. Trainees normally have at least a 2.1 degree (not necessarily in law) and three A-levels at A and B grades. Trainees would normally be expected to have passed the CPE (if required) and the LPC at the first attempt.

Training Environment
Sidley & Austin aims to recruit 4–6 trainee solicitors to start in September 2001/March 2002 so there is no risk of you being just a number. The team at Sidley & Austin in London is young, dynamic and collegiate. Everyone is encouraged to be proactive and to create their own niche when they are ready to do so. Trainees normally spend 3-6 months in the following departments: International Finance, Information Industries, Corporate, Tax and Property. Sidley & Austin in London does not have a separate litigation department, although they do undertake some litigation work. Litigation training includes an internal course, run in conjunction with their Chicago office, culminating in attendance at a mock trial in Chicago. In addition, there is a structured timetable of training on a cross-section of subjects and an annual residential weekend.

Benefits
Healthcare, disability cover, life assurance, contribution to gym membership, annual health check, interest free season ticket loan.

Sponsorship & Awards
CPE and LPC fees paid and maintenance p.a.

Contact
Louise White

Method of Application
Covering letter and application form – Please call 0800 731 5015

Selection Procedure
Interview(s)

Closing date for 2001
End July 1999

Application
Training contracts p.a.   4–6
Applications p.a.   300 (98)
% interviewed p.a.   20% (98)
Required degree grade   2:1

Training
Salary: 1st year(1998) £21,500
Salary: 2nd Year(1998) £24,750
Holiday entitlement   22 days
% of trainees with
a non-law degree p.a.   50%

Overseas Offices
Chicago, Dallas, Los Angeles, New York, Singapore, Tokyo, Washington D.C.

SIMMONS & SIMMONS

21 Wilson Street London EC2M 2TX
Tel: (0171) 628 2020 Fax: (0171) 628 2070
Email: simmons-simmons.com
Website: www.simmons-simmons.com

Partners	156
Assistant Solicitors	316
Total Trainees	126

Firm Profile
Simmons & Simmons is one of the top ten London law firms providing advice worldwide to corporations, governments and other institutions. There is a culture of business management and development in which every new member of the firm is involved. The firm has particular expertise in corporate finance, mergers and acquisitions, privatisations, banking and capital markets, employment, environmental law and IP. Over 20 languages are spoken within the practice. The firm also has significant strength and depth in property, taxation, pensions, and dispute resolution.

Main Areas of Work
Corporate Finance and Company 41%; Commercial/Intellectual Property/EC 15%; Property 14%; Litigation 12%; Banking and Capital Markets 10%; Tax 7%; Environmental 1%.

Trainee Profile
While a good academic record and sound commercial judgement are important, strength of character and outside interests are also taken into consideration.

Training Environment
Trainees are involved in the firm's work from the start of their contract. Simmons & Simmons allocate each trainee a training principal to oversee their training and career development. Each move to a new department is accompanied by a structured series of seminars on relevant areas of law. Simmons & Simmons supports the Battersea Legal Advice Centre and provides advice on a *pro bono* basis to prisoners on 'death row' in Jamaica.

Benefits
Season ticket loan, fitness loan, PRP, group travel insurance, group accident insurance, group health insurance.

Vacation Placements
Places for 1999: 40; Duration: 4 weeks; Remuneration: £200 p.w.; Closing Date: 26 February 1999.

Sponsorship & Awards
In the absence of Local Authority funding the firm will pay LPC and, where necessary, CPE fees and offer a maintenance allowance of £4,000 for those at Law School in London or Guildford and £3,600 elsewhere.

Contact
Katharyn White

Method of Application
Application form, CV and covering letter

Selection Procedure
Assessment day: document exercise, interview and group session

Closing date for 2001
20 August 1999

Application

Training contracts p.a.	60
Applications p.a.	2,700
% interviewed p.a.	10%
Required degree grade	2:1

Training

Salary: 1st year(1999)	£21,000
Salary: 2nd Year(1999)	£24,000
Holiday entitlement	22 days
% of trainees with a non-law degree p.a.	40%
No. of seats available abroad p.a.	18

Post-Qualification

Salary (1999)	£32,000
% of trainees offered job on qualification (1998)	91%

Overseas Offices
Abu Dhabi, Brussels, Hong Kong, Lisbon, Milan, New York, Paris, Rome, Shanghai

311

SINCLAIR ROCHE & TEMPERLEY

Royex House 5 Aldermanbury Square London EC2V 7LE
Tel: (0171) 452 4000 Fax: (0171) 452 4001

Partners	36
Assistant Solicitors	64
Total Trainees	19

Firm Profile
They are a major international law firm, founded in 1934.
Over two thirds of the work handled in their London office is for
non-UK clients. Their particular expertise is in shipping,
aviation, international trade and energy, also emerging markets.
Areas of work include shipping litigation and arbitration,
collision, salvage and marine insurance, ship finance, aviation,
oil and gas, company commercial and tax, commercial property,
project, asset and trade finance and EC law.

Main Areas of Work
Shipping and Commercial; Litigation; Ship and Project
Finance; Company/Commercial; Marine Casualty and
Insurance; Commercial Property; Aviation; EU; Tax.

Trainee Profile
An equal opportunities employer looking for motivated trainees
with a strong personality and good academic record.
Commitment and interest in the firm's and their clients'
business are essential.

Training Environment
Four six month seats. Trainees sit with a partner or senior
assistant. As well as gaining the requisite legal skills, business
development and management skills will be covered. Client
contact is encouraged. A thorough programme of continuing
professional training through lectures, seminars and external
courses is provided.

Benefits
Private health cover, discretionary bonus, luncheon vouchers,
PHI, accident insurance, subsidised sports club membership.

Vacation Placements
Places for 1999: 12; Duration: 2 weeks; Remuneration: £150
p.w.; Closing Date: 28 February 1999, subject to availability.

Sponsorship & Awards
CPE and LPC fees paid and £4,000 maintenance p.a.

Contact
Dawn Morgan

Method of Application
CV and covering letter

Selection Procedure
Interview

Closing date for 2001
31 October 1999 subject to
availability

Application

Training contracts p.a.	8
Applications p.a.	1,750
% interviewed p.a.	6%
Required degree grade	2:1

Training

Salary: 1st year(1999)	£20,000
Salary: 2nd Year(1999)	£21,000
Holiday entitlement	20 days
% of trainees with	
a non-law degree p.a.	Varies
No. of seats available	
abroad p.a.	Varies

Post-Qualification

Salary (1999)	£31,500
% of trainees offered job	
on qualification (1998)	82%
% of assistants (as at 1/9/98)	
who joined as trainees	50%

Overseas Offices
Bucharest, Hong Kong,
Shanghai, Singapore

SLAUGHTER AND MAY

35 Basinghall Street London EC2V 5DB
Tel: (0171) 600 1200 Fax: (0171) 600 0289
Website: www.slaughterandmay.com

Partners	108*
Assistant Solicitors	350*
Total Trainees	140

* denotes world-wide figures

Firm Profile

One of the leading law firms in the world, Slaughter and May enjoys a reputation for quality and expertise. The corporate and financial practice is particularly strong and lawyers are known for their business acumen and technical excellence. International work is central to the practice and lawyers travel widely. No London partner has ever left the firm to join a competing practice.

Main Areas of Work

Corporate and Financial 66%; Commercial Litigation 11%; Tax 7%; Property (Commercial) 6%; Pensions and Employment 5%; EC and Competition Law 3%; Intellectual Property 2%.

Trainee Profile

The work is demanding and the firm looks for intellectual agility and the ability to work with people from different countries and walks of life. Common sense, a mature outlook and the willingness to accept responsibility are all essential. The firm expects to provide training in everything except the fundamental principles of law, so does not expect applicants to know much of commercial life. Trainees are expected to remain with the firm on qualification.

Training Environment

Four or five seats of three or six months' duration. Two seats will be in the corporate and financial department and one seat in either Litigation, Intellectual Property or Pensions and Employment. In each seat, a partner is responsible for monitoring your progress and reviewing your work. There is an extensive training programme which includes the PSC. There are also discussion groups covering general and specialised legal topics.

Benefits

BUPA, STL, pension scheme, membership of various sports clubs, 24 hour accident cover.

Vacation Placements

Places for 1999: 60; Duration: 2 weeks; Remuneration: £200 p.w.; Closing Date: ASAP from December but before 26 February 1999.

Sponsorship & Awards

CPE and LPC fees and maintenance grants are paid; some grants are available for postgraduate work.

Contact
Neil Morgan

Method of Application
Covering letter and CV

Selection Procedure
Interview

Application

Training contracts p.a.	75
Applications p.a.	3,000
% interviewed p.a.	20%
Required degree grade	Good 2:1

Training

Salary: 1st year(1999) £21,000
Salary: 2nd Year(1999) £24,000
Holiday entitlement 25 days on qualification

% of trainees with a non-law degree p.a.	50%
No. of seats available abroad p.a.	30

Post-Qualification

Salary (1999)	£32,000
% of trainees offered job on qualification (1998)	100%

Overseas Offices
Brussels, Hong Kong, New York, Paris, Singapore

313

STEPHENSON HARWOOD

One, St Paul's Churchyard London EC4M 8SH
Tel: (0171) 329 4422 Fax: (0171) 606 0822

Firm Profile
Established in the City of London in 1828, Stephenson Harwood has developed into a large international practice, with a commercial focus and a wide client base.

Main Areas of Work
Corporate; Banking; Litigation; Property; Shipping; Tax

Trainee Profile
The firm looks for high calibre graduates with excellent academic records and an outgoing personality.

Training Environment
As the graduate intake is relatively small, the firm feels able to give trainees individual attention. Their well-structured and challenging programme involves four six-month seats in either corporate or banking, litigation, property and another seat of your choice. These seats include 'on the job' training, sharing an office and working with a partner or senior solicitor. In-house lectures complement your training and there is continuous review of your career development. You will have the opportunity to spend six months abroad and have language tuition where appropriate. You will be given your own caseload and as much responsibility as you can shoulder. The firm plays a range of team sports, has its own gym, subsidised membership of a city health club and has privileged seats for concerts at the Royal Albert Hall and the London Coliseum and access to private views at the Tate Gallery.

Benefits
LVs, subsidised membership of health club, season ticket loan, 22 days paid holiday per year.

Vacation Placements
Places for 1999: 21; Duration: 2 weeks; Remuneration: £175 p.w.; Closing Date: 26 February 1999.

Sponsorship & Awards
£6,400 fees paid for CPE and LPC and £4,000 maintenance p.a.

Partners	72*
Assistant Solicitors	109*
Total Trainees	38

* denotes world-wide figures

Contact
Ms Alison Warner
Legal and Graduate
Recruitment Manager

Method of Application
Application form

Selection Procedure
Interview with 2 partners

Closing date for 2001
13 August 1999

Application

Training contracts p.a.	25
Applications p.a.	2,000
% interviewed p.a.	n/a
Required degree grade	2:1

Training

Salary: 1st year(1999)	£20,000
Salary: 2nd Year(1999)	£22,000
Holiday entitlement	22 days
% of trainees with a non-law degree p.a.	46%
No. of seats available abroad p.a.	8

Post-Qualification

Salary (1999)	£30,000
% of trainees offered job on qualification (1998)	95%
% of assistants (as at 1/9/98) who joined as trainees	37%
% of partners (as at 1/9/98) who joined as trainees	46%

Overseas Offices
Brussels, Guangzhou,
Hong Kong, Madrid, Piraeus,
Singapore

TARLO LYONS

Watchmaker Court 33 St. John's Lane London EC1M 4DB
Tel: (0171) 405 2000 Fax: (0171) 814 9421
Email: info@tarlo-lyons.com
Website: www.tarlo-lyons.com

Partners	22
Assistant Solicitors	14
Total Trainees	4

Firm Profile

Tarlo Lyons was founded in 1927 as a general practice and undertakes a wide variety of commercial work. The Firm has particular expertise in Computer and Information Technology and Telecommunications Law, Entertainment Law (specifically live stage, TV and film), Commercial Litigation and Gaming and Licensing Law. It recently acquired Investor in People accreditation.

Main Areas of Work

Litigation 23%; Commercial 20%; Property 20%; Information Technology 23%; Entertainment 14%.

Trainee Profile

Candidates need to demonstrate intellectual capacity combined with common sense, resourcefulness and a sense of humour. Basic IT skills essential; languages valued. A well spent gap year or commercial experience can be an advantage.

Training Environment

Trainees are introduced to the Firm during a two day induction course. Training consists of four six month seats in the following departments: property, litigation, IT and company/commercial (the latter offering some entertainment work). You will be allocated to a Supervisor in each Department, who will monitor your workflow and training. In addition you will meet with the Training Partner every 2-3 months for a formal review. Some in-house training, especially on skills eg., IT, personal management, client care etc. Trainees are encouraged to attend relevant external courses on technical matters. The PSC is taught externally. The Firm has a friendly, open door policy and trainees take part in a wide range of marketing, sporting and social events.

Benefits

Contribution to private health insurance and season ticket loan.

Contact
R.L. Hails

Method of Application
Letter and CV

Selection Procedure
2 Interviews with partners.

Closing date for 2001
31 August 1999

Application

Training contracts p.a.	2
Applications p.a.	400+
% interviewed p.a.	5%
Required degree grade	2:1

Training

Salary: 1st year(1999)	£20,000 on average
Salary: 2nd Year(1999)	£22,000 on average
Holiday entitlement	20 days
% of trainees with a non-law degree p.a.	50%

Post-Qualification

Salary (1999)	£30,000
% of trainees offered job on qualification (1998)	100%
% of assistants (as at 1/9/98) who joined as trainees	30%
% of partners (as at 1/9/98) who joined as trainees	40%

TAYLOR JOYNSON GARRETT

Carmelite 50 Victoria Embankment Blackfriars
London EC4Y 0DX
Tel: (0171) 353 1234 Fax: (0171) 936 2666
Website: www.tjguk.com

Partners	77
Assistant Solicitors	99
Total Trainees	44

Firm Profile
Taylor Joynson Garrett is a major City and International law firm, with an impressive UK and international client base. As well as offices in London, Brussels and Bucharest, it is affiliated with the US law firm Graham & James and Deacons Graham & James in the Pacific Rim. The firm has recognised expertise in its corporate and intellectual property practices, as well as strength in depth across the full range of commercial disciplines.

Main Areas of Work
Corporate/Commercial 25%; Litigation 23%; Intellectual Property 17%; Private Client 10%; Commercial Property 11%; Banking 9%; Employment 5%.

Trainee Profile
Academic achievement is high on the firm's list of priorities, and a 2:1 or better is expected. It wants individuals who have good communication skills and will flourish in a competitive environment. Strength of character, determination and the ability to think laterally are also important.

Training Environment
Trainees will have six-month seats in four different departments, with the possibility of some time in Brussels. You will be supervised by a partner or assistant and appraised both two months into, and at the end of, each seat. There will be plenty of opportunity to take early responsibility. The firm works closely with external training providers to meet the needs of the PSC. The course is tailored to suit the firm's needs, and most of the training is conducted in-house. A full sports and social calendar is available.

Benefits
Private medical care, permanent health insurance, STL, non-contributory pension scheme on qualification

Vacation Placements
Places for 1999: 30; Duration: 2 weeks; Remuneration: £180 p.w.; Closing Date: 26 February 1999.

Sponsorship & Awards
CPE and LPC fees paid and £4,000 maintenance p.a.

Contact
Trainee Solicitors' Manager

Method of Application
Firm's application form, CV and covering letter

Selection Procedure
2 interviews, 1 with a partner.

Closing date for 2001
13 August 1999

Application
Training contracts p.a.	22
Applications p.a.	3,000
% interviewed p.a.	4%
Required degree grade	2:1

Training
Salary: 1st year(1999)	£21,000
Salary: 2nd Year(1999)	£23,000
Holiday entitlement	25 days
% of trainees with a non-law degree p.a.	40%
No. of seats available abroad p.a.	4

Post-Qualification
Salary (1999)	£33,000
% of trainees offered job on qualification (1998)	80%
% of assistants (as at 1/9/98) who joined as trainees	60%
% of partners (as at 1/9/98) who joined as trainees	31%

Overseas Offices
Brussels, Bucharest

TEACHER STERN SELBY

37–41 Bedford Row London WC1R 4JH
Tel: (0171) 242 3191 Fax: (0171) 242 1156
Email: tss@tsslaw.co.uk
Website: www.tsslaw.co.uk

Partners	14
Assistant Solicitors	14
Total Trainees	6

Firm Profile
A London-based firm, specialising in commercial litigation and commercial property. It also gives specialist tax planning advice and has a wide range of contacts overseas.

Main Areas of Work
Commercial Litigation 40%; Commercial Property 25%; Company and Commercial 20%; Secured Lending 9%; Residential Conveyancing/Probate 3%; Personal Injury/Education/Judicial review 3%.

Trainee Profile
Emphasis falls equally on academic excellence and personality. The firm looks for flexible and motivated individuals, who have outside interests and who have demonstrated responsibility in the past. Languages an advantage.

Training Environment
Trainees spend six months in three departments (Company Commercial, Litigation and Property) with, where possible, an option to return to a preferred department in the final six months. Most trainees are assigned to actively assist a partner who monitors and supports them. Trainees are expected to fully immerse themselves and take early responsibility. After a short period you will conduct your own files. Trainees are welcome to attend the in-house seminars and lectures for continuing education. With strong links in Israel and Eastern Europe, there are opportunities for travel. The atmosphere is relaxed and informal with an open door policy.

Vacation Placements
Places for 1999: None anticipated.

Sponsorship & Awards
CPE Funding: none; LPC Funding: unlikely.

Contact
Russell Raphael, Partner

Method of Application
Letter and application form

Selection Procedure
2 interviews

Closing date for 2001
31 October 1999

Application

Training contracts p.a.	3
Applications p.a.	500
% interviewed p.a.	5%
Required degree grade	2:1

Training

Salary: 1st year(1999) £17,000
Salary: 2nd Year(1999) £18,000
Holiday entitlement 4 weeks
% of trainees with
a non-law degree p.a. 50%

Post-Qualification

Salary (1999) £26,000
% of trainees offered job
on qualification (1998) 33%
% of assistants (as at 1/9/98)
who joined as trainees 40%
% of partners (as at 1/9/98)
who joined as trainees 33%

THEODORE GODDARD

150 Aldersgate St London EC1A 4EJ
Tel: (0171) 606 8855 Fax: (0171) 606 4390
Email: tg@theodoregoddard.co.uk
Website: http//www.theogoddard.com

Partners	52
Assistant Solicitors	100
Total Trainees	40

Firm Profile

A long established medium-sized City firm with a particular
reputation in media/communications and banking/finance. The
firm provides a full range of services to household name and
blue chip clients in all sectors of commerce and industry.
International work has long been central to its business, and it
has an office in Brussels, an associated firm in Paris and
associates worldwide.

Main Areas of Work

Company/corporate finance 29%; Commercial litigation 13%;
Property 17%; Banking and finance 12%; Media/IP 17%; Tax
6%.

Trainee Profile

Graduates of all disciplines are recruited. While proven
academic ability, strong communication skills and confidence
are sought, the overriding need is for individuals with drive and
business acumen. Trainees are expected to make a real
contribution and to deal with clients from the outset.

Training Environment

Training consists of four six-month placements with the option
of three-month secondments to our associate firm in Paris or to a
commercial client. Trainees are consulted about seat allocation.
Most of the PSC is run in-house and the firm has won four
coveted training awards for the quality of its in-house training.

Benefits

Permanent employment offered from the outset. Contributory
pension, permanent health insurance, private medical
insurance, death in service benefit, subsidised sports club
membership and staff restaurant.

Vacation Placements

Places for 1999: c20 in the Summer vacation (with 70 open day
places in the Easter vacation); Duration: 2 weeks;
Remuneration: £200 p.w.; Closing Date: End February 1999
for both vacation placements and open days.

Sponsorship & Awards

CPE and LPC fees paid in full. £3,900 maintenance p.a. in
London and Guildford, £3,300 elsewhere.

Contact
Deborah Dalgleish

Method of Application
Application form

Selection Procedure
Initial interview, followed by
short assessment or second
interview

Closing date for 2001
31 August 1999

Application

Training contracts p.a.	20
Applications p.a.	3,500+
% interviewed p.a.	10%
Required degree grade	2:1+

Training

Salary: 1st year(1998)	£21,000
Salary: 2nd Year(1998)	£24,000
Holiday entitlement	22 days
% of trainees with a non-law degree p.a.	50%
No. of seats available abroad p.a.	4

Post-Qualification

Salary (1998)	£33,000
% of trainees offered job on qualification (1998)	100%

Overseas Offices
Brussels, Paris. Associated
firms – Associates worldwide

THOMSON SNELL & PASSMORE

3 Lonsdale Gardens Tunbridge Wells TN1 1NX
Tel: (01892) 51 00 00 Fax: (01892) 549884
Email: solicitors@ts-p.co.uk

Partners	36
Assistant Solicitors	13
Total Trainees	7

Firm Profile
One of the oldest firms in the country, dating back to 1570, Thomson Snell & Passmore is a wide-ranging general practice which is continuing to expand. It is a founder member of The Law South Group and services private clients and businesses both national and regional from its two offices in the south.

Main Areas of Work
Probate & Trusts 21%; Residential Property 16%; Professional Negligence 13%; Commercial Property 12%; Commercial Litigation 11%; PI/Medical Negligence 11%; Company/Commercial 9%; Family Law 7%.

Trainee Profile
Candidates should be personable with a good academic record and relevant work experience. Ability to fit into the office and work under pressure are essential, together with good communication and interpersonal skills. An outgoing personality and non-academic achievements are fundamental.

Training Environment
The firm involves trainees from the outset and are given responsibility as soon as possible. They must complete four seats of six months, but can express a preference for a particular department, subject to the firm's requirements. They are assigned to a partner and a trainee advisor in each department and there is also a training principal with whom they will have an opportunity to discuss their progress and obtain feedback on a regular basis. Lectures and courses aid their progression. A programme of social events is organised and trainees are encouraged to mix socially. Trainees will move between the Tunbridge Wells and Tonbridge offices during their contract. The environment within the firm is both friendly and supportive.

Benefits
Eligible for discretionary bonus in second year.

Vacation Placements
Places for 1999: are full, but exceptional candidates are always considered.

Sponsorship & Awards
LPC funding.

Contact
Mrs Val Butcher

Method of Application
Firm's own application form

Selection Procedure
By interview on selection following screening

Closing date for 2001
20 August 1999

Application
Training contracts p.a.	3–4
Applications p.a.	500–700
% interviewed p.a.	4–5%
Required degree grade	2:1

Training
Salary: 1st year(1999)	£12,750
	to £13,500
Salary: 2nd Year(1999)	£14,250
	to £15,000
Holiday entitlement	20 days
% of trainees with	
a non-law degree p.a.	50–60%
No. of seats available	
abroad p.a.	0

Post-Qualification
Salary (1999)	£21,500
% of trainees offered job	
on qualification (1998)	33%
% of assistants (as at 1/9/98)	
who joined as trainees	50%
% of partners (as at 1/9/98)	
who joined as trainees	30%

TITMUSS SAINER DECHERT

2 Serjeants' Inn London EC4Y 1LT
Tel: (0171) 583 5353 Fax: (0171) 353 3683
Email: info@titmuss-dechert.com

Partners	45
Assistant Solicitors	69
Total Trainees	23

Firm Profile

Titmuss Sainer Dechert is the combination of Titmuss, Sainer & Webb and US firm, Dechert, Price and Rhoads. Together they are a world-wide commercial practice with over five hundred lawyers. The London office majors in business law, commercial property, litigation and investigations. Additionally, it has a number of specialist areas (all of them recommended in Chambers' clients' guide to Law Firms), where trainees may gain experience. These included Customs & Excise; insurance; intellectual property; tax; private client and financial services.

Main Areas of Work

Property 40%; Business Law 22%; Litigation 18%; Financial and Insurance services 15%; Tax and Private Client 5%.

Trainee Profile

All candidates interviewed have already shown themselves to be high achievers academically. The firm looks for qualities over and above that. They want you to be able to empathise with a wide range of people, as their clients come from all walks of life. They are looking for enthusiasm, intelligence, an ability to find a practical solution to a problem and for powers of expression and persuasion. Also wanted are those with a desire and ability to promote the firm's business at every opportunity. Titmuss Sainer Dechert want people who will remain with them on qualifying and make their careers with the firm. They take fewer trainees than comparable firms of this size because they regard as paramount the quality of training and opportunities for individual progression which is provided for their trainees; and those believed to be the best are guaranteed by keeping their intake relatively small in number.

Training Environment

Unusually for a city firm, the training period is divided into six periods of four months, giving trainees the chance to sample a wide range of core and speciality work. In each seat you will be supervised by a senior lawyer who will provide regular feedback on your work. In addition he or she will participate with you and a Trainee Panel Partner (to whom you will be assigned and who will be responsible for your wellbeing throughout your training contract) in a formal oral and written assessment of your work towards the end of each seat. Trainees have the opportunity to spend four months at Dechert Price & Rhoads' Brussels office.

Contact
Lynn Muncey

Method of Application
Letter and application form

Selection Procedure
1 interview with at least
2 partners

Closing date for 2001
13 August 1999

Application
Training contracts p.a. Up to 12
Applications p.a.   1,000
% interviewed p.a.   12%
Required degree grade   2:1
(or capability of attaining a 2:1)

Training
Salary: 1st year(1999) £21,000
Salary: 2nd Year(1999) £23,000
Holiday entitlement   20 days
% of trainees with
a non-law degree p.a.   Varies
No. of seats available
abroad p.a.   3

Post-Qualification
Salary (1999)   £33,000
                (to be reviewed)
% of trainees offered job
on qualification (1998)   90%
% of partners (as at 1/9/98)
who joined as trainees   30%

The greater number of seats makes it easier for us to fit in with any special requests to work in specific areas of the firm. Titmus Sainer Dechert was the first English firm to appoint a training director in the early 1980s and their most recent appointee is a senior educator and the former director of the College of Law in London. The PSC is provided in a tailored format by the firm in conjunction with the College of Law, with some modules taking place in-house. That apart there is an extensive training programme in which trainees are encouraged to participate (numerous aspects being particularly aimed at trainees).

Benefits

Free permanent health and life assurance, subsidised membership of a local gym and interest-free season ticket loans.

Vacation Placements

Places for 1999: 8; Duration: Monday 5 July to Friday 16 July; Remuneration: competitive allowance; Closing Date: Applications considered between Monday 4 January and Friday 26 February 1999.

Sponsorship & Awards

LPC fees paid and £4,000 maintenance p.a. for those living in London and £3,750 for those outside (where local authority grants unavailable).

Trainee Comments

"My four month stint in Brussels was a tremendous experience. The firm provided me with a very comfortable flat, only five minutes from the office. I had the opportunity to work with English, Belgian and American lawyers. It was quite a challenge to work in an environment where English, French and Flemish were spoken at once." (Caroline Boxall, second year trainee, graduated in law from New Hall, Cambridge.)

"As a trainee, I had plenty of opportunity to do real hands-on client work and I was involved in basic drafting. I also advised clients on various regulatory rules and assisted their applications to the appropriate regulatory body. Taking initiative and early responsibility is encouraged – I helped to set up a new Russian fund for investment into smaller Russian companies." (Paul Dehadray describes his time as a trainee in Financial Services. He read law at King's College, London).

The firm is renowned for its friendly and supportive atmosphere and the wealth of sports and social activities within the firm are a reflection of this.

Overseas Offices

Through its union with Dechert Price and Rhoads the firm has other offices in Brussels, New York, Paris, Washington, Philadelphia, Boston, Hartford, Harrisburg and Princeton.

Titmuss Sainer Dechert

2 Serjeants' Inn, London EC4Y 1LT. Telephone 0171-583 5353.

TRAVERS SMITH BRAITHWAITE

10 Snow Hill London EC1A 2AL

Tel: (0171) 248 9133 Fax: (0171) 236 3728 or 696 3500

Email: Graduate.Recruitment@TraversSmith.co.uk

Partners	46
Assistant Solicitors	71
Total Trainees	30

Firm Profile

A leading medium-sized corporate, financial and commercial law firm with the capability to advise on a wide range of business activities. The practice offers small, closely-knit teams providing consistent service to clients.

Main Areas of Work

Corporate 30%; Litigation 15%; Property 15%; Finance 15%; Commercial 13%; Tax 5%; Pensions 5%; Employment 2%.

Trainee Profile

Candidates should have a strong academic background and show ambition and determination. A sense of humour is vital.

Training Environment

Training consists of four six-month seats taken from the corporate, commercial, banking/insolvency, employment, litigation, property, pensions and tax departments. There is no crowd to get lost in; trainees quickly get to know each other and everyone else in the firm. They are treated as individuals and given immediate responsibility for handling deals and clients. Formal training includes a comprehensive programme of in-house training and seminars, a weekly technical bulletin to keep staff abreast of changes in the law, a good library, and a computerised information centre. The office is designed to ensure there is close contact between staff members at all times. Social and sporting activities are enjoyed by the whole firm.

Benefits

Private health insurance, season ticket loans, luncheon vouchers, subsidised sports club membership.

Vacation Placements

Places for 1999: 45; Duration: 3 weeks;
Remuneration: £200 p.w.;
Closing Date: End March 1999.

Sponsorship & Awards

LPC and CPE fees paid and £4,000 maintenance p.a.

Contact
Christopher Jon Carroll

Method of Application
Handwritten letter and CV

Selection Procedure
Interviews

Closing date for 2001
September 1999

Application

Training contracts p.a.	20
Applications p.a.	1,600
% interviewed p.a.	15%
Required degree grade	2:1

Training

Salary: 1st year(1999)	£21,000
Salary: 2nd Year(1999)	£24,000
Holiday entitlement	20 days
% of trainees with a non-law degree p.a.	Approx 50%
No. of seats available abroad p.a.	0

Post-Qualification

Salary (1999)	£33,000
% of trainees offered job on qualification (1998)	100%
% of assistants (as at 1/9/98) who joined as trainees	75%
% of partners (as at 1/9/98) who joined as trainees	33%

TROWERS & HAMLINS

Sceptre Court 40 Tower Hill London EC3N 4DX
Tel: (0171) 423 8000 Fax: (0171) 423 8001
Email: gradrecruitment@trowers.com
Website: http://www.trowers.com

Partners	56
Assistant Solicitors	78
Total Trainees	25

Firm Profile
Trowers & Hamlins is a substantial international firm. A leader in housing and public sector law, the firm also has a strong commercial side. The firm has regional offices in the UK, offices in the Gulf and links with Jordan, Yemen, Singapore, USA and Europe.

Main Areas of Work
Property (Housing, Public Sector, Comm.) 33.9%; Corporate/Company and Commercial 31.3%; Litigation 28.2%; Private Client 6.6%.

Trainee Profile
Personable, enthusiastic candidates with a good academic record and wide-ranging outside interests. The ability to work under pressure and with others, combined with versatility are essential characteristics.

Training Environment
Trainees will gain experience in four seats from: company/commercial, property, public sector, litigation and private client. Trainees are encouraged to learn from direct contact with clients and assume responsibility. The training programme is flexible and with reviews held every six months, individual preferences will be considered. A training officer assists partners with the training programme and in-house lectures and seminars are held regularly. There are opportunities to work in Manchester, Exeter or the Arabian Gulf. The firm encourages a relaxed atmosphere and blends traditional qualities with contemporary attitudes. Activities are organised outside working hours.

Benefits
Season ticket loan, private health care after one year's service, Employee Assistance Programme & discretionary bonus.

Vacation Placements
Places for 1999: 25-30; Duration: 3 weeks; Remuneration: £160 p.w.; Closing Date: 31 January (Easter); 1 March (Summer).

Sponsorship & Awards
CPE and LPC fees paid and £3,000 maintenance p.a.

Contact
Graduate Recruitment Office

Method of Application
Letter, application form and CV

Selection Procedure
Interview(s), essay and practical test

Closing date for 2001
1 August 1999

Application
Training contracts p.a.	12–15
Applications p.a.	2,000
% interviewed p.a.	4%
Required degree grade	2:1+

Training
Salary: 1st year(1999) £20,500
Salary: 2nd Year(1999) £22,500
Holiday entitlement 20 days
% of trainees with
a non-law degree p.a. 40%
No. of seats available
abroad p.a. Between 4 and 6

Post-Qualification
Salary (1999) £33,000
% of trainees offered job
on qualification (1998) 100%
% of assistants (as at 1/9/98)
who joined as trainees 40%
% of partners (as at 1/9/98)
who joined as trainees 45%

Overseas Offices
Abu Dhabi, Dubai, Oman, Bahrain

UK Branch Offices
Manchester, Exeter

WALKER MORRIS

Kings Court 12 King Street Leeds LS1 2HL
Tel: (0113) 283 2500 Fax: (0113) 245 9412
Email: info@walkermorris.co.uk
Website: http://www.walkermorris.co.uk

Partners	30
Assistant Solicitors	72
Total Trainees	18

Firm Profile
Based in Leeds, Walker Morris is one of the largest commercial
law firms in the North, providing a full range of legal services
to commercial and private clients. It is increasingly gaining an
international reputation.

Main Areas of Work
Commercial Litigation 32%; Commercial Property 30%;
Company and Commercial 22%; Building Societies 12%;
Private Clients 4%.

Trainee Profile
Bright, articulate, highly motivated individuals who will thrive
on early responsibility in a demanding yet friendly
environment.

Training Environment
Trainees commence with an induction programme, before
spending four months in each main department (commercial
property, corporate, commercial litigation and private client).
Trainees can choose in which departments they wish to spend
their second year. Formal training workshops and seminars
complement what is largely a hands-on learning style. The PSC
is covered internally. Individual IT training and, where
necessary, foreign language tuition, are provided. An option
exists for a four-month trainee exchange programme with a
leading Parisian law firm. Emphasis is placed on teamwork,
inside and outside the office. The firm's social and sporting
activities are an important part of its culture and are organised
by a committee drawn from all levels of the firm. A trainee
solicitors committee also organises events and liaises with the
Leeds Trainee Solicitors Group.

Vacation Placements
Places for 1999: 32 – over 4 weeks; Duration: 1 week;
Remuneration: £100 p.w.; Closing Date: 28 February 1999.

Sponsorship & Awards
CPE Funding: Fees + £1,000; LPC Funding: Fees + £1,000.

Contact
Paul Emmett

Method of Application
Application form and covering
letter

Selection Procedure
Telephone and face to face
interviews

Closing date for 2001
31 July 1999

Application

Training contracts p.a.	8–10
Applications p.a.	800
	approximately
% interviewed p.a.	
	Telephone: 10%
	Face to face: 5%
Required degree grade	2:1

Training

Salary: 1st year(1999)	£15,750
Salary: 2nd Year(1999)	£17,500
Holiday entitlement	24 days
% of trainees with a non-law	
degree p.a.	30% on average
No. of seats available	
abroad p.a.	1

Post-Qualification

Salary (1999)	£24,000
% of trainees offered job	
on qualification (1998)	85%
% of assistants (as at 1/9/98)	
who joined as trainees	70%
% of partners (as at 1/9/98)	
who joined as trainees	55%

WARNER CRANSTON

Pickfords Wharf Clink St London SE1 9DG
Tel: (0171) 403 2900 Fax: (0171) 403 4221
Email: warner_cranston@compuserve.com

Partners	17
Assistant Solicitors	42
Total Trainees	7

Firm Profile
A London and Coventry based firm formed in 1979 with an international reputation for handling all types of commercial transactions. Its underlying principle is one of big firm expertise, coupled with a personal service.

Contact
Joy Iley
Human Resources Manager

Main Areas of Work
Company Commercial and Finance 37%; Commercial Litigation 20%; Employment 15%; Construction and Arbitration 7%; Property 14%; Personal Injury 4%; Debt Recovery 3%.

Method of Application
Application form and covering letter

Selection Procedure
Assessment Day: 2 interviews, aptitude test and presentation.

Trainee Profile
Proactive, commercially-minded graduates with a practical hands-on approach, who welcome responsibility.

Closing date for 2001
31 July 1999

Training Environment
The firm invests heavily in training, with in-house seminars (including advocacy course), drafting programmes and vital business skills courses. The firm aims to provide an informal but fast-paced working environment, where trainees are immediately given demanding work. A fine balance between supervision and responsibility is observed. There are four seats available, in company commercial, litigation, employment and property. Progress is reviewed regularly by a senior partner. An entrepreneurial atmosphere is encouraged, allowing trainees to flourish in what the firm calls the 'Warner Cranston Alternative'. The firm is located in attractive offices near London Bridge, overlooking the Thames.

Application

Training contracts p.a.	4
Applications p.a.	1000
% interviewed p.a.	3%
Required degree grade	2:1

Training

Salary: 1st year(1998)	£21,500
Salary: 2nd Year(1998)	£23,000
Holiday entitlement	23 days
% of trainees with a non-law degree p.a.	25%
No. of seats available abroad p.a.	0

Benefits
BUPA, IFSTL, life assurance, PHI, pension contributions (after qualifying period).

Post-Qualification

Salary (1998)	£31,500
% of trainees offered job on qualification (1998)	100%
% of assistants (as at 1/9/98) who joined as trainees	14%
% of partners (as at 1/9/98) who joined as trainees	6%

Vacation Placements
Places for 1999: 12; Duration: 2 weeks; Remuneration: £400; Closing Date: 31 March 1999.

Sponsorship & Awards
CPE/LPC fees and maintenance grant.

WATSON, FARLEY & WILLIAMS

15 Appold Street London EC2A 2HB
Tel: (0171) 814 8000 Fax: (0171) 814 8141
Website: http://www.wfw.com

Partners	60*
Assistant Solicitors	108*
Total Trainees	23

* denotes world-wide figures

Firm Profile
Established in 1982, Watson, Farley & Williams has its strengths in corporate, banking and asset finance, particularly ship and aircraft finance. The firm aims to provide superior service in specialist areas and to build long-lasting relationships with its clients.

Main Areas of Work
Shipping; Aviation; Banking; Asset Finance;Corporate; Litigation; Intellectual Property; EC and Competition; Taxation; Property; Insolvency.

Trainee Profile
Outgoing graduates who exhibit energy, ambition, self-assurance, initiative and intellectual flair.

Training Environment
Trainees are introduced to the firm with a comprehensive induction course covering legal topics and practical instruction. Seats are available in at least four of the firm's main areas, aiming to provide trainees with a solid commercial grounding. There is also the opportunity to spend time abroad, working on cross-border transactions. Operating in an informal, friendly and energetic atmosphere, trainees will receive support whenever necessary. You will be encouraged to take on early responsibility and play an active role alongside a partner at each stage of your training. The practice encourages continuous learning for all employees and works closely with a number of law lecturers, producing a widely-read 'digest' of legal developments, to which trainees are encouraged to contribute. All modules of the PSC are held in-house. The firm has its own sports teams and organises a variety of social functions.

Benefits
Life assurance, PHI, BUPA, STL, pension, subsidised gym membership.

Vacation Placements
Places for 1999: 30; Duration: 2 weeks; Remuneration: £200 p.w.; Closing Date: 31 March 1999.

Sponsorship & Awards
CPE and LPC Fees paid and £4,000 maintenance p.a. (£3,600 outside London).

Contact
Graduate Recruitment Officer

Method of Application
Handwritten letter and application form

Selection Procedure
Interview

Closing date for 2001
31 July 1999

Application

Training contracts p.a.	10–12
Applications p.a.	1,500
% interviewed p.a.	5%
Required degree grade	2:1
	ideally

Training
Salary: 1st year(1998) £21,000–£22,000
Salary: 2nd Year(1998) £23,000–£24,000

Holiday entitlement	22 days
% of trainees with a non-law degree p.a.	50%
No. of seats available abroad p.a.	8

Post-Qualification

Salary (1999)	£33,000
% of trainees offered job on qualification (1998)	95%
% of assistants (as at 1/9/98) who joined as trainees	35%
% of partners (as at 1/9/98) who joined as trainees	4%

Overseas Offices
Copenhagen, Moscow, New York, Paris, Piraeus, Singapore

WEDLAKE BELL

16 Bedford Street Covent Garden London WC2E 9HF
Tel: (0171) 395 3000 Fax: (0171) 836 9966
Email: legal@wedlakebell.co.uk

Partners	32*
Assistant Solicitors	34*
Total Trainees	9

denotes world-wide figures

Firm Profile
Based in Covent Garden, this medium-sized friendly firm, offers corporate, litigation, property and private client advice. It has an office in Guernsey, and links with the European Union through TELFA and Russia.

Main Areas of Work
Corporate/Commercial 33%; Property 24%; Litigation 23%; Private Client 20%.

Trainee Profile
In addition to academic excellence, Wedlake Bell looks for flexibility, communication skills, a personable nature, confidence, mental agility and computer literacy in their candidates. Languages are not crucial.

Training Environment
Trainees have four seats of six months. You will be encouraged to meet clients and accept responsibility as soon as possible. There is an in-house training programme, attended by trainees and qualified solicitors.

Benefits
On qualification: life assurance, medical insurance, PHI, subsidised gym membership and travel loan.

Vacation Placements
Places for 1999: 4; Duration: 3 weeks in July; Remuneration: £150 p.w.; Closing Date: End of February.

Contact
Anne Campbell

Method of Application
CV and covering letter

Selection Procedure
Interviews in September

Closing date for 2001
End of August 1999

Application
Training contracts p.a.   4
Applications p.a.   800
% interviewed p.a.   3%
Required degree grade   2:1

Training
Salary: 1st year(1999) Not known
Salary: 2nd year(1999) Not known
Holiday entitlement   20 days
% of trainees with
a non-law degree p.a.   25%

Post-Qualification
% of trainees offered job
on qualification (1998)   66%
% of assistants (as at 1/9/98)
who joined as trainees   50%

Overseas Offices
Guernsey

WEIGHTMANS

Richmond House 1 Rumford Place Liverpool L3 9QW
Tel: (0151) 227 2601 Fax: (0151) 227 3223
DX: 14201 Liverpool X400 Weightmans
79–83 Colmore Row Birmingham B3 2AP
Tel: (0121) 233 2601 Fax: (0121) 233 2600

Partners	41
Assistant Solicitors	44
Total Trainees	17

Firm Profile
Weightmans is one of the country's largest defendant insurance-based practices. It also has a thriving commercial division. Its strengths are its commercial and cost efficient approach, expertise which has been passed down over 160 years. Weightmans has a strong team spirit and is driven by ideas, rather than automatic process. It keeps an open mind to alternatives and solutions which are focused around the business needs of its clients.

Main Areas of Work
Litigation 85%. Also: Employment, Commercial, Property, Licensing, Company, Commercial.

Trainee Profile
Weightmans' people are unique in their approach to the law and candidates need to demonstrate excellent people skills, and an innovative yet realistic approach. Particular emphasis is placed on instinctive 'business savy' and mature trainees who can offer a broad range of expertise outside the confines of the law are encouraged.

Training Environment
Weightmans offers a comprehensive legal, team building and management programme. The induction programme focuses on the work of the firm, the firm's philosophies and its values. Trainees rotate on a six monthly basis working closely with partners from the following departments - Commercial property, licensing, company commercial, litigation (including professional indemnity). Where possible, trainees are able to choose the order of their seats and receive regular appraisals and progress reports.

Benefits
Interest free loan towards LPC fees.

Method of Application
Application form

Selection Procedure
Interview with partners

Closing date for 2001
9th August 1999

Application
Training contracts p.a.   8–10

Training
Salary: 1st year(1999) £15,200
Salary: 2nd Year(1999) £17,000
Holiday entitlement   20 days

WHITE & CASE

7–11 Moorgate London EC2R 6HH
Tel: (0171) 726 6361 Fax: (0171) 726 4314

Partners	9
Assistant Solicitors	25
Total Trainees	7

Firm Profile
A global firm formed in 1901, with over 800 lawyers in 29 offices around the world. Its strengths lie in capital markets, corporate finance, project finance, and domestic and international litigation.

Main Areas of Work
Capital Markets 20%; Project Finance 20%; Corporate Finance/M&A 15%; Construction 15%; Company/Commercial/Joint Ventures 15%; Litigation 15%.

Trainee Profile
Candidates should have a good degree, self-confidence and an interest in the firm and its practice areas. Languages are a useful asset.

Training Environment
Trainees will benefit from practical training obtained by sitting in the same office as and working with a partner or senior associate. They will enjoy a friendly environment, smaller and more personal than some City firms, while simultaneously gaining experience working with large domestic and multi-national corporations and governments on a variety of commercial matters. Training will involve spending four six-month periods in a different practice area (including banking, corporate and commercial, project finance, litigation and construction), and will usually include a placement in a foreign office. The compulsory Professional Skills Course is spread throughout the contract. There is also an induction and skills course for all trainees.

Benefits
BUPA, 6 months in an overseas office.

Vacation Placements
Places for 1999: 10; Duration: 2 weeks; Remuneration: not less than £250 p.w.; Closing Date: End February 1999.

Sponsorship & Awards
CPE and LPC fees paid and £4,000 maintenance p.a.

Contact
Elizabeth Normand

Method of Application
Covering letter and CV

Selection Procedure
Interview

Closing date for 2001
End July 1999

Application
Training contracts p.a.	7
Applications p.a.	1200
% interviewed p.a.	2%
Required degree grade	2:1

Training
Salary: 1st year   not less than £25,000
Holiday entitlement   22 days
No. of seats available abroad p.a.   under review

Post-Qualification
Salary (1998)   £45,000

Overseas Offices
Almaty, Ankara, Bangkok, Bombay, Brussels, Budapest, Hanoi, Helsinki, Ho Chi Minh City, Hong Kong, Istanbul, Jakarta, Jeddah, Johannesburg, London, Los Angeles, Mexico City, Miami, Moscow, New York, Paris, Prague, Riyadh, Sao Paulo, Singapore, Stockholm, Tokyo, Warsaw, Washington D.C.

329

WIGGIN AND CO

The Quadrangle Imperial Square Cheltenham GL50 1YX
Tel: (01242) 224 114 Fax: (01242) 224223
Email: law@wiggin.co.uk

Firm Profile
Based in Cheltenham, with offices in London and Los Angeles, Wiggin and Co is a 'city-type' practice. It has strengths in the tax, company/commercial, media, communications, technology and entertainment fields.

Main Areas of Work
Private Client 40%; Media and Entertainment 40%; Litigation 12%; Property 8%.

Trainee Profile
Candidates will have a strong academic background, be personable and show a willingness to work hard individually or as part of a team.

Training Environment
The training is divided into four six-month seats. Trainees will spend time in four out of five departments, namely the company/commercial, media, property, litigation and private client departments. In each department you will sit with a partner or a senior solicitor. You will be encouraged to take an active role in transactions, assume responsibility and deal directly with clients. In-house lectures and seminars are held regularly and training reviews are held every three months. The firm offers the attraction of Cheltenham combined with technical ability and experience akin to a large City firm. Its relatively small size encourages a personal approach towards staff and client relations.

Benefits
Life assurance, private health cover, pension scheme, permanent health insurance.

Sponsorship & Awards
CPE and LPC Fees and £3,000 maintenance p.a. Brochure available on request.

Partners	12
Assistant Solicitors	14
Total Trainees	4

Contact
Sean James

Method of Application
Letter and CV

Selection Procedure
2 interviews

Closing date for 2001
21 August 1999

Application

Training contracts p.a.	2/3
Applications p.a.	1,700
% interviewed p.a.	2%
Required degree grade	2:1

Training

Salary: 1st year(1999)	£21,200
Salary: 2nd Year(1999)	£24,700
Holiday entitlement	20 days
% of trainees with a non-law degree p.a.	50%
No. of seats available abroad p.a.	0

Post-Qualification

Salary (1999)	£31,000
% of trainees offered job on qualification (1998)	100%
% of assistants (as at 1/9/98) who joined as trainees	15%
% of partners (as at 1/9/98) who joined as trainees	17%

Overseas Offices
Los Angeles

WILDE SAPTE

1 Fleet Place London EC4M 7WS
Tel: (0171) 246 7000 Fax: (0171) 246 7777
Email: njg@wildesapte.com
Website: http://www.wildesapte.com

Partners	77*
Assistant Solicitors	162*
Total Trainees	62

* denotes world-wide figures

Firm Profile
Founded in 1785, Wilde Sapte is a commercial City firm handling a wide range of work for UK and international clients, with a particular emphasis on banking, finance and insurance markets.

Main Areas of Work
Banking & Finance 46%; Litigation 24%; Property 11%; Company & Commercial 11%; Taxation 7%; Misc.1%

Trainee Profile
Law graduates or graduates with a highly developed second language (ideally French, Spanish, German, Russian, Japanese or Mandarin). Non-law graduates should expect to achieve a first class degree.

Training Environment
Training consists of four six month seats. The third or fourth seat is either spent abroad in one of Wilde Sapte's Paris, Brussels or Tokyo offices or in a chosen specialist area, subject to availability. Trainees complete the PSC in the first year. Language training is available throughout the 2 year training contract.

Benefits
Subsidised gym, interest free season ticket loan, death in service benefit, PPP, PRP, contributory pension at age 28 after qualification, staff restaurant.

Vacation Placements
Places for 1999: 75; Duration: 1 week; Remuneration: £160 p.w.; Closing Date: 28 February 1998.

Sponsorship & Awards
CPE and LPC fees paid and £4,000 maintenance p.a.

Contact
Nicola Graham

Method of Application
CV with covering letter (including breakdown of university examination results)

Selection Procedure
Initial interview and test with Personnel Department, followed by interview with partner

Closing date for 2001
Non-law: 31/1/99; Law 31/8/99

Application

Training contracts p.a.	30
Applications p.a.	2,500
% interviewed p.a.	10%
Required degree grade	2:1

Training

Salary: 1st year(1999)	£21,500
Salary: 2nd Year(1999)	£24,000
Holiday entitlement	20 days
% of trainees with a non-law degree p.a.	25%
No. of seats available abroad p.a.	8

Post-Qualification

Salary (1999)	£33,000
% of trainees offered job on qualification (1998)	95%
% of assistants (as at 1/9/98) who joined as trainees	40%
% of partners (as at 1/9/98) who joined as trainees	25%

Overseas Offices
Brussels, Hong Kong, Paris, Tokyo

331

WITHERS

12 Gough Square London EC4A 3DW
Tel: (0171) 936 1000 Fax: (0171) 936 2589
Email: mailto@withers.co.uk
Website: www.withers.co.uk

Partners	48*
Assistant Solicitors	80*
Total Trainees	22

denotes world-wide figures

Firm Profile
A thriving, medium-sized practice, based between the High Court and the City. Half the firm's work is for corporate clients and institutions, the balance is for individuals and families. Withers has specialist practices ranging from an agriculture department to an Alternative Investment Market sector.

Main Areas of Work
Private Client and Charities 40%; Litigation 19%; Corporate, Company and Commercial 17%; Property (Agricultural, Commercial and Residential) 13%; Family 11%; International 5%.

Trainee Profile
As well as a keen intellect, trainees should have the confidence and social skills to interact successfully with clients and colleagues, and the determination and ambition to do well. They should show business acumen, entrepreneurial flair and commercial awareness. A genuine international outlook and foreign languages, particularly Italian, would be an advantage.

Training Environment
After a two week induction period, trainees spend six months in four of the main departments (corporate, family law, private client, property, litigation), sitting with senior assistants or partners. You will work as part of a small team within each department and be given responsibilities at an early stage.

Benefits
Interest free season ticket loan, life assurance, social events, cafe facilities.

Vacation Placements
Places for 1999: 16; Duration: Easter (3 weeks), summer (3 weeks); Remuneration: £130 p.w.; Closing Date: 19 February 1999.

Sponsorship & Awards
LPC and CPE fees paid and £4,000 maintenance p.a. and cash prize for distinction or commendation in CPE and LPC.

Contact
Andrea Stapleton

Method of Application
Application form

Selection Procedure
2 interviews

Closing date for 2001
2 August 1999

Application

Training contracts p.a.	10
Applications p.a.	2,000
% interviewed p.a.	5%
Required degree grade	2:1

Training

Salary: 1st year(1999)	£20,500
Salary: 2nd Year(1999)	£22,600
Holiday entitlement	20 days
% of trainees with a non-law degree p.a.	40%

Post-Qualification

Salary (1999)	£32,000
% of trainees offered job on qualification (1998)	90%
% of assistants (as at 1/9/98) who joined as trainees	8%
% of partners (as at 1/9/98) who joined as trainees	36%

Overseas Offices
Paris and Associate Italian office

WRAGGE & CO

55 Colmore Row Birmingham B3 2AS
Tel: +44 0121 233 1000 Fax: +44 0121 214 1099
Email: lucy_gibson@wragge.com
Website: www.wragge.com

Partners	61
Assistant Solicitors	258
Total Trainees	32

Firm Profile

Wragge & Co is the largest single office law firm outside London. Its rapid growth and success are a result of a distinctive strategy to develop a national law firm from a single office in Birmingham. Wragge & Co's clients continue to appreciate the benefits of its consistent and integrated approach to client service, whilst its people enjoy working in a strong and cohesive culture.

Main Areas of Work

As a full service commercial law firm, Wragge & Co provides a comprehensive range of legal services to large companies, public authorities and financial institutions, in the UK and overseas, including over 165 listed companies. Wragge & Co enjoys a national reputation in areas such as corporate, litigation, property, employment, tax, pensions, IP, transport and logistics, utilities, project finance, PFI and EC/competition law.

Trainee Profile

Graduates should show commercial acumen as well as academic excellence. Adaptability, ambition and enthusiasm are valued and candidates should be problem solvers and clear communicators.

Training Environment

Wragge & Co places considerable emphasis on transforming trainees into high quality, commercially-minded lawyers. You will spend six months in four different practice areas (usually property, corporate and litigation, with a chance to specialise in a final seat of your choice). From day one, you will work on live files with direct client contact. The more aptitude you show, the greater the responsibility you will be given. You will be supported by a monitoring partner and a second year trainee who will be assigned to 'mind' you. Introductory courses are provided at the start of each seat in addition to the Professional Skills Course training requirements. This formal training complements 'on the job' learning. There is a 'hyperactive' sports and social club, and the Birmingham Trainee Solicitors Group is equally dynamic. It is hoped that trainees will work hard and play hard!

Benefits

Life ass., perm. health scheme, pension, int. free travel loans

Contact
Lucy Gibson

Method of Application
Application form

Selection Procedure
Assessment day and interview

Closing date for 2001
16 August 1999

Application
Training contracts p.a.   18–20
Applications p.a.   1,000
% interviewed p.a.   10%
Required degree grade   2:1
                                    (preferred)

Training
Salary: 1st year(1999) £15,000
Salary: 2nd Year(1999) £17,000
Holiday entitlement   23 days
% of trainees with
a non-law degree p.a.   40%

▶

WRAGGE & CO *continued*

Vacation Placements

Places for 1999: 40; Duration: 2 weeks; Remuneration: £125 p.w.; Closing Date: 12 February 1999 – apply by letter and CV; Open Day dates: March and April 1999 (all students) December 1998 (non-law students). Apply by letter and CV.

Sponsorship & Awards

CPE and LPC fees paid and £3,500 maintenance grant.

Trainee Comments

"I was accepted for a training contract at Wragge & Co in September 1994, just before I started to study for the CPE. I chose Wragge & Co because of its excellent reputation both regionally and nationally, and I was made to feel very welcome on the day of my interview. I started at Wragge & Co in September 1996 and commenced my training in the Commercial Litigation Department. This was a good first seat not least of all because I was well supervised, and not exposed to too much too quickly. Nevertheless, towards the end of this seat, I was running files of my own.

I then moved to the Property Department for my second seat where I experienced planning and general development work. From the outset, I was running files of my own, and was again supervised on larger scale work.

My third seat was in the Corporate Department where I was involved in general PLC work. Such work does not lend itself to individual files for trainees, and so I worked as part of a team on larger projects, with considerable client contact.

As a fourth seat trainee, I was given as much client contact and responsibility as I wanted and was given several files to run on my own, particularly in the run up to qualification.

My option seat was spent in the Employment and Pensions teams. Now that I have qualified into the Employment team, my experience of pensions work has proved invaluable. Socially, I have always found Wragge & Co a friendly firm, with each department holding social events to help you to get to know new members of the team. Birmingham itself is regenerating fast, and with the decision to knock down the Bull Ring, it may one day shake off the bad reputation it has earned itself. In the meantime, it is a well kept secret which can only be good for those of us in the know!"

(Selwyn Blyth, studied French and Spanish at Cambridge University, completed the CPE at Birmingham University and did the LPC at the College of Law in York).

Post-Qualification

Salary (1999)	£25,500
% of trainees offered job on qualification (1998)	100%
% of assistants (as at 1/9/98) who joined as trainees	28%
% of partners (as at 1/9/98) who joined as trainees	47%

ABSON HALL

30 Greek Street Stockport SK3 8AD
Tel: (0161) 480 1221 Fax: (0161) 480 4246
Contact: Mr C.P. Bowen

Partners	10
Assistant Solicitors	7
Training contracts p.a.	1–2

ACTONS

2 King St Nottingham NG1 2AX
Tel: (0115) 9100 200 Fax: (0115) 9100 290
Contact: Gary Chadwick

Partners	10
Assistant Solicitors	11
Training contracts p.a.	3

ALLAN HENDERSON BEECHAM AND PEACOCK

7 Collingwood Street Newcastle upon Tyne NE1 1JE
Tel: (0191) 232 3048 Fax: (0191) 261 7255
Contact: Anne Anderson

Partners	5
Assistant Solicitors	3
Training contracts p.a.	2

ALSTERS

30A College Green Bristol BS1 1TB
Tel: (0117) 929 7612 Fax: (0117) 927 2889
Contact: Pat Powell

Partners	6
Assistant Solicitors	3
Training contracts p.a.	2

AMHURST BROWN COLOMBOTTI

2 Duke Street St. James's London SW1Y 6BJ
Tel: (0171) 930 2366 Fax: (0171) 930 2250
Contact: Training Principal

Partners	18
Assistant Solicitors	3
Training contracts p.a.	2

ANDREW GREGG & CO

6 Queen Square Bristol BS1 4JE
Tel: (0117) 925 8123 Fax: (0117) 925 5567
Contact: Andrew Gregg

Partners	1
Assistant Solicitors	2
Training contracts p.a.	1

ANDREW M. JACKSON & CO

Essex House Manor Street Hull HU1 1XH
Tel: (01482) 325 242 Fax: (01482) 212974
Contact: Mrs Sue Brown

Partners	23
Assistant Solicitors	27
Training contracts p.a.	3–4

ANTHONY COLLINS SOLICITORS

St Philip's Gate 5 Waterloo Street Birmingham B2 5PG
Tel: (0121) 200 3242 Fax: (0121) 212 7442
Contact: Mrs B. Macdonald

Partners	11
Assistant Solicitors	18
Training contracts p.a.	2+

ARCHERS

Barton House 24 Yarm Road Stockton-on-Tees TS18 3NB
Tel: (01642) 673431 Fax: (01642) 613602
Contact: John Richardson

Partners	9
Assistant Solicitors	8
Training contracts p.a.	2

ASHTON BOND GIGG

Pearl Assurance House 5 Friar Lane Nottingham NG1 6BX
Tel: (0115) 947 6651 Fax: (0115) 947 5244
Contact: Lorraine Wheatley, Practice Manager

Partners	6
Assistant Solicitors	3
Training contracts p.a.	1

ASHTON GRAHAM

81 Guildhall Street Bury St. Edmunds IP33 1PZ
Tel: (01284) 762331 Fax: (01284) 764214
Contact: Mr. Paul S. Whittingham

Partners	7
Assistant Solicitors	9
Training contracts p.a.	3

ATTEY BOWER & JONES

82 Cleveland Street Doncaster DN1 3DR
Tel: (01302) 340400 Fax: (01302) 323710
Contact: P.J. Farmer

Partners	17
Assistant Solicitors	7
Training contracts p.a.	4

BANNERS

Marsden Chambers 2 Marsden Street Chesterfield S40 1JY
Tel: (01246) 209773 Fax: (01246) 231188
Contact: Julie Dyson

Partners	7
Assistant Solicitors	3
Training contracts p.a.	1

BARKER, BOOTH & EASTWOOD

346 Lytham Rd Blackpool FY4 1DW
Tel: (01253) 362500 Fax: (01253) 341032
Contact: Miss Morley

Partners	7
Assistant Solicitors	3
Training contracts p.a.	1

BARKER GOTELEE

41 Barrack Square Martlesham Heath Ipswich IP5 3RF	Partners	3
Tel: (01473) 611211 Fax: (01473) 610560	Assistant Solicitors	8
Contact: James Skellorn	Training contracts p.a.	1

BARLOWS

55 Quarry Street Guildford GU1 3UE	Partners	11
Tel: (01483) 562901 Fax: (01483) 573325	Assistant Solicitors	20
Contact: Helen Archibald	Training contracts p.a.	3

BARNETT ALEXANDER CHART

60 Grays Inn Road London WC1X 8LT	Partners	11
Tel: (0171) 242 4422 Fax: (0171) 242 1102	Assistant Solicitors	11
Contact: Mr Jeffrey Rubenstein	Training contracts p.a.	3

BATTENS (WITH POOLE & CO)

Church House Yeovil BA20 1HB	Partners	26
Tel: (01935) 423685 Fax: (01935) 706054	Assistant Solicitors	20
Contact: Mrs Jean Venus	Training contracts p.a.	4

T.G. BAYNES & SONS

208 Broadway Bexleyheath DA6 7BG	Partners	13
Tel: (0181) 301 2525 Fax: (0181) 304 1475	Assistant Solicitors	8
Contact: Simon Potts	Training contracts p.a.	4

BEACHCROFT STANLEYS

20 Furnival Street London EC4A 1BN	Partners	38
Tel: (0171) 242 1011 Fax: (0171) 831 6630	Assistant Solicitors	74
Contact: Miss Emma Falder	Training contracts p.a.	12

BEALE AND COMPANY

Garrick Hse 27-32 King St London WC2E 8JD	Partners	8
Tel: (0171) 240 3474 Fax: (0171) 240 9111	Assistant Solicitors	6
Contact: Michael Archer	Training contracts p.a.	4

BEAUMONT AND SON

Lloyds Chambers 1 Portsoken St London E1 8AW
Tel: (0171) 481 3100 Fax: (0171) 481 3353
Contact:Virginia Pritchard

Partners	10
Assistant Solicitors	33
Training contracts p.a.	3

BELL LAMB & JOYNSON

39 Walton Vale Liverpool L9
Tel: (0151) 474 8463 Fax: (0151) 474 8468
Contact: Mr J.D. Rawson

Partners	13
Assistant Solicitors	4
Training contracts p.a.	1

BELL LAX LITIGATION

Mill House 2 High Street Sutton Coldfield B72 1XA
Tel: (0121) 355 0011 Fax: (0121) 355 0099
Contact: Heather Bell

Partners	2
Assistant Solicitors	6
Training contracts p.a.	4

BERG & CO

Scottish Mutual House 35 Peter Street Manchester M2 5BG
Tel: (0161) 833 9211 Fax: (0161) 834 5566
Contact: Stephanie Klass

Partners	8
Assistant Solicitors	9
Training contracts p.a.	2

BERMANS

Pioneer Buildings 65-67 Dale St Liverpool L2 2NS
Tel: (0151) 227 3351 Fax: (0151) 236 2107
Contact: Mr Feargal O'Cleirigh

Partners	10
Assistant Solicitors	5
Training contracts p.a.	1–2

BERRY & BERRY

11 Church Road Tunbridge Wells, Kent TN1 1JA
Tel: (01892) 526344 Fax: (01892) 511223
Contact: Mrs Z.E. Koder

Partners	8
Assistant Solicitors	8
Training contracts p.a.	2

BERRYMAN & CO

Park House Friar Lane Nottingham NG1 6DN
Tel: (0115) 941 7574 Fax: (0115) 941 9623
Contact: Lynn Morgan

Partners	13
Assistant Solicitors	10
Training contracts p.a.	2

BERRY, REDMOND & ROBINSON

19 The Boulevard Weston-super-Mare BS23 1NR	Partners	5
Tel: (01934) 619000 Fax: (01934) 614148	Assistant Solicitors	4
Contact: Mr Pat Maxwell	Training contracts p.a.	1

BERWIN LEIGHTON

Adelaide House London Bridge London EC4R 9HA	Partners	71
Tel: 0171 760 1000 Fax: +44 171 760 1111	Assistant Solicitors	138
Contact: Claire Benson	Training contracts p.a.	20

BETESH FOX & CO

17 Ralli Courts West Riverside Manchester M3 5FT	Partners	9
Tel: (0161) 832 6131 Fax: (0161) 832 8172	Assistant Solicitors	15
Contact: Michael Rainford	Training contracts p.a.	2

BEVAN ASHFORD

35 Colston Avenue Bristol BS1 4TT	Partners	62
Tel: (0117) 923 0111 Fax: (0117) 929 1865	Assistant Solicitors	113
Contact: Mrs Jean Brierley	Training contracts p.a.	19

BEVERIDGE ROSS & PREVEZER

10-11 New Street London EC2M 4TP	Partners	9
Tel: (0171) 626 1533 Fax: (0171) 929 4982	Assistant Solicitors	3
Contact: Richard Marshall	Training contracts p.a.	1

BEVISS & BECKINGSALE

Law Chambers Holyrood Street Chard TA20 2AJ	Partners	8
Tel: (01460) 61494 Fax: (01460) 63821	Assistant Solicitors	5
Contact: Mr Anthony Osborne	Training contracts p.a.	1–2

BINDMAN & PARTNERS

275 Gray's Inn Rd London WC1X 8QF	Partners	13
Tel: (0171) 833 4433 Fax: (0171) 837 9792	Assistant Solicitors	10
Contact: Ms Felicity Crowther	Training contracts p.a.	3

BIRCHALL BLACKBURN

Crystal House Birley Street Preston PR1 2AQ
Tel: (01772) 561663 Fax: (01772) 202438
Contact: Mrs M. K. Boyce

Partners	12
Assistant Solicitors	10
Training contracts p.a.	1–2

BIRCHAM & CO.

1 Dean Farrar St Westminster London SW1H 0DY
Tel: (0171) 222 8044 Fax: (0171) 222 3480
Contact: Miss Sarah Stowell

Partners	23
Assistant Solicitors	18
Training contracts p.a.	4

BIRKETT LONG

Essex House 42 Crouch St Colchester CO3 3HH
Tel: (01206) 217300 Fax: (01206) 572393
Contact: Mr Philip Hoddell

Partners	16
Assistant Solicitors	8
Training contracts p.a.	2–4

BIRKETTS

24-26 Museum St Ipswich IP1 1HZ
Tel: (01473) 232300 Fax: (01473) 230524
Contact: Karen Benneworth

Partners	20
Assistant Solicitors	9
Training contracts p.a.	2

BISHOP LONGBOTHAM & BAGNALL

Rodney Hse 5 Roundstone St Trowbridge BA14 8DH
Tel: (01225) 755656 Fax: (01225) 753266
Contact: Mr Terry Bishop

Partners	11
Assistant Solicitors	9
Training contracts p.a.	1

BISHOP & SEWELL

90 Great Russell Street London WC1B 3RJ
Tel: (0171) 631 4141 Fax: (0171) 636 5369
Contact: Stephen Bishop

Partners	6
Assistant Solicitors	3
Training contracts p.a.	1

BLACKS

Hanover House 22 Clarendon Road Leeds LS2 9NZ
Tel: (0113) 207 0000 Fax: (0113) 242 1703
Contact: Mr Christopher Allen

Partners	12
Assistant Solicitors	10
Training contracts p.a.	2

BLAKEMORES

Station Tower Station Square Coventry CV1 2GR	Partners	12
Tel: (01203) 525858 Fax: (01203) 228440	Assistant Solicitors	11
Contact: Mr Gerard Whitehouse	Training contracts p.a.	2–3

BOLITHO WAY

13/18 Kings Terrace Portsmouth PO5 3AL	Partners	6
Tel: (01705) 820747 Fax: (01705) 862831	Assistant Solicitors	2
Contact: Mr. D.G. Grinstead	Training contracts p.a.	1

BOLT BURDON

16 Theberton Street Islington London N1 0QX	Partners	10
Tel: (0171) 288 4700 Fax: (0171) 288 4701	Assistant Solicitors	23
Contact: Miss Nicki Franklin	Training contracts p.a.	2

BOODLE HATFIELD

61 Brook Street London W1Y 2BL	Partners	25
Tel: (0171) 629 7411 Fax: (0171) 629 2621	Assistant Solicitors	16
Contact: Miss Christine Jones	Training contracts p.a.	4

BOWER & BAILEY

Anchor House 269 Banbury Road Oxford OX2 7JF	Partners	16
Tel: (01865) 311133 Fax: (01865) 311722	Assistant Solicitors	24
Contact: Mr T.C. Bailey	Training contracts p.a.	6

BOWER COTTON

36 Whitefriars Street London EC4Y 8BH	Partners	8
Tel: (0171) 353 3040 Fax: (0171) 583 2869	Assistant Solicitors	4
Contact: Mr R. Perrin	Training contracts p.a.	2

BRABNER HOLDEN BANKS WILSON

1 Dale St Liverpool L2 2ET	Partners	18
Tel: (0151) 236 5821 Fax: (0151) 227 3185	Assistant Solicitors	25
Contact: Mark Glenville	Training contracts p.a.	3

BRACHERS

Somerfield House 59 London Road Maidstone ME16 8JH

Tel: (01622) 690 691 Fax: (01622) 681430

Contact: Mr Jim Day

Partners	19
Assistant Solicitors	15
Training contracts p.a.	4

BREEZE & WYLES

114 Fore Street Hertford SG14 1AG

Tel: (01992) 558411 Fax: (01992) 582834

Contact: Mrs M. Nickson

Partners	7
Assistant Solicitors	4
Training contracts p.a.	2

BREMNER SONS & CORLETT

1 Crosshall Street Liverpool L1 6DH

Tel: (0151) 227 1301 Fax: (0151) 227 1300

Contact: Mr Withinshaw

Partners	10
Assistant Solicitors	2
Training contracts p.a.	1

BRETHERTON PRICE ELGOODS

123 Promenade Cheltenham GL50 1NW

Tel: (01242) 224433 Fax: (01242) 574285

Contact: Mrs Helen King

Partners	12
Assistant Solicitors	27
Training contracts p.a.	2

BRIDGE MCFARLAND SOLICITORS

19 South St. Mary's Gate Grimsby DN31 1JE

Tel: (01472) 311711 Fax: (01472) 311500

Contact: Steven Lambert

Partners	9
Assistant Solicitors	5
Training contracts p.a.	1

BROWN COOPER

7 Southampton Place London WC1A 2DR

Tel: (0171) 404 0422 Fax: (0171) 831 9856

Contact: Mr M.J. Coyne

Partners	4
Assistant Solicitors	3
Training contracts p.a.	1

BUCKLE MELLOWS

45-51 Priestgate Peterborough PE1 1LB

Tel: (01733) 568175 Fax: (01733) 562064

Contact: Mr R.E. Clarke

Partners	10
Assistant Solicitors	10
Training contracts p.a.	1

BULLER JEFFRIES

36 Bennetts Hill Birmingham B2 5SN	Partners	7
Tel: (0121) 212 2620 Fax: (0121) 212 2210	Assistant Solicitors	8
Contact: Mr G.J. Lewis	Training contracts p.a.	1–2

BURNETTS

6 Victoria Place Carlisle CA1 1ES	Partners	16
Tel: (01228) 552222 Fax: (01228) 522399	Assistant Solicitors	4
Contact: Mr T.S. Leach, Managing Partner	Training contracts p.a.	1

BURROUGHS DAY

14-16 Charlotte St Bristol BS1 5PT	Partners	13
Tel: (0117) 929 0333 Fax: (0117) 927 2342	Assistant Solicitors	20
Contact: Miss Fiona Dawrant	Training contracts p.a.	2

BURSTOWS

8 Ifield Road Crawley RH11 7YY	Partners	15
Tel: (01293) 828000 Fax: (01293) 603666	Assistant Solicitors	12
Contact: Miss Carol Fletcher	Training contracts p.a.	3

BURY & WALKERS

Britannic Hse Regent St Barnsley S70 2EQ	Partners	11
Tel: (01226) 733533 Fax: (01226) 207610	Assistant Solicitors	7
Contact: Andrew Crothers	Training contracts p.a.	1

BUSS MURTON

The Priory Tunbridge Wells TN1 1JJ	Partners	16
Tel: (01892) 510222 Fax: (01892) 510333	Assistant Solicitors	12
Contact: Philip Davis	Training contracts p.a.	2

CAMPBELL HOOPER

35 Old Queen St London SW1H 9JD	Partners	15
Tel: (0171) 222 9070 Fax: (0171) 222 5591	Assistant Solicitors	18
Contact: Mrs Jill Wilson-Brown	Training contracts p.a.	2

CANTER LEVIN & BERG

46-48 Stanley St Liverpool L1 6AL	Partners	12
Tel: (0151) 474 5757 Fax: (0151) 474 5763	Assistant Solicitors	10
Contact: Mr Max Marcus	Training contracts p.a.	2

CARRICK CARR & WRIGHT

Norwich House Savile Street Kingston upon Hull HU1 3ES	Partners	7
Tel: (01482) 325385/590000 Fax: (01482) 327584	Assistant Solicitors	3
Contact: Michael East	Training contracts p.a.	1

CARTER HODGE

18 Hoghton St Southport PR9 0PB	Partners	8
Tel: (01704) 531991 Fax: (01704) 537475	Assistant Solicitors	6
Contact: Derek Alman	Training contracts p.a.	0–1

CARTMELL SHEPHERD

Viaduct House Carlisle CA3 8EZ	Partners	12
Tel: (01228) 516666 Fax: (01228) 401490	Assistant Solicitors	13
Contact: Mrs M.M. Hendry	Training contracts p.a.	2

CARTWRIGHT & LEWIS

100 Hagley Road Edgbaston Birmingham B16 8LT	Partners	9
Tel: (0121) 452 1989 Fax: (0121) 456 3977	Assistant Solicitors	10
Contact: Mrs Sue Harris	Training contracts p.a.	3

CHALLINORS LYON CLARK

Guardian Hse Cronehills Linkway West Bromwich B70 8SW	Partners	20
Tel: (0121) 553 3211 Fax: (0121) 553 2079	Assistant Solicitors	26
Contact: Mr David Higson	Training contracts p.a.	3

CHRISTIAN FISHER

42 Museum Street Bloomsbury London WC1A 1LY	Partners	2
Tel: (0171) 831 1750 Fax: (0171) 831 1726	Assistant Solicitors	6
Contact: Louise Christian	Training contracts p.a.	2

CHURCH BRUCE HAWKES BRASINGTON & PHILLIPS

51-54 Windmill St Gravesend DA12 1BD	Partners	6
Tel: (01474) 560361 Fax: (01474) 328315	Assistant Solicitors	4
Contact: Mr J. V. Brasington	Training contracts p.a.	1

CLARKE WILLMOTT & CLARKE

The Waterfront Welsh Back Bristol BS1 4SB	Partners	37
Tel: (0117) 941 6600 Fax: (0117) 941 6622	Assistant Solicitors	43
Contact: Alan Burnmams	Training contracts p.a.	8

CLARKS

Great Western House Station Rd Reading RG1 1SX	Partners	15
Tel: (0118) 958 5321 Fax: (0118) 960 4611	Assistant Solicitors	20
Contact: Antony Morris	Training contracts p.a.	4

CLARKSON WRIGHT & JAKES

Valiant House 12 Knoll Rise Orpington BR6 0PG	Partners	8
Tel: (01689) 871621 Fax: (01689) 878537	Assistant Solicitors	2
Contact: Mrs Gay Marchant	Training contracts p.a.	2

CLAUDE HORNBY & COX

35-36 Great Marlborough Street London W1V 2JA	Partners	2
Tel: (0171) 437 8873 Fax: (0171) 494 3070	Assistant Solicitors	6
Contact: Michael Butler	Training contracts p.a.	2

COBBETTS

Ship Canal House King St Manchester M2 4WB	Partners	30
Tel: (0161) 833 3333 Fax: (0161) 833 3030	Assistant Solicitors	40
Contact: Simon Jones	Training contracts p.a.	6–8

COFFIN MEW & CLOVER

17 Hampshire Terrace Portsmouth PO1 2PU	Partners	20
Tel: (01705) 812511 Fax: (01705) 291847	Assistant Solicitors	18
Contact: Mrs Sara Lloyd	Training contracts p.a.	3–4

COLEMANS

27 Marlow Road Maidenhead SL6 7AE	Partners	4
Tel: (01628) 631051 Fax: (01628) 622106	Assistant Solicitors	4
Contact: Colin Hellmuth	Training contracts p.a.	0–1

COLEMANS SOLICITORS

Elisabeth House 16 St. Peter's Square Manchester M2 3DF	Partners	5
Tel: (0161) 236 5623 Fax: (0161) 228 7509	Assistant Solicitors	6
Contact: Mr Roger Coleman	Training contracts p.a.	1

COLES MILLER

44-46 Parkstone Road Poole BH15 2PG	Partners	13
Tel: (01202) 673011 Fax: (01202) 675868	Assistant Solicitors	14
Contact: David Parfitt	Training contracts p.a.	2

CONSTANT & CONSTANT

Sea Containers Housese 20 Upper Ground		
Blackfriars Bridge London SE1 9QT	Partners	30
Tel: (0171) 261 0006 Fax: (0171) 401 2161	Assistant Solicitors	13
Contact: Mr M. Bundock	Training contracts p.a.	2

COUDERT BROTHERS

60 Cannon Street London EC4N 6JP	Partners	15
Tel: (0171) 248 3000 Fax: (0171) 248 3001	Assistant Solicitors	26
Contact: Mrs C.A. de Ferras Green	Training contracts p.a.	4

COZENS-HARDY & JEWSON

Castle Chambers Opie St Norwich NR1 3DP	Partners	9
Tel: (01603) 625231 Fax: (01603) 627160/ 612690	Assistant Solicitors	8
Contact: Mrs Philippa G. Daniels	Training contracts p.a.	1–2

CROCKERS OSWALD HICKSON

10 Gough Square London EC4A 3NJ	Partners	9
Tel: (0171) 353 0311 Fax: (0171) 583 1417	Assistant Solicitors	12
Contact: Christina Cronin	Training contracts p.a.	2

CROMBIE WILKINSON

Clifford House 19 Clifford Street York YO1 1RJ
Tel: (01904) 624185 Fax: (01904) 623078
Contact: Mrs Jennie Bartram

Partners	8
Assistant Solicitors	5
Training contracts p.a.	1–2

CRUTES

7 Osborne Terrace Newcastle-upon-Tyne NE2 1RQ
Tel: (0191) 281 5811 Fax: (0191) 281 3608
Contact: Miss Jane Lister

Partners	22
Assistant Solicitors	24
Training contracts p.a.	1–2

CUFF ROBERTS

100 Old Hall Street Liverpool L3 9TD
Tel: (0151) 227 4181 Fax: (0151) 227 2584
Contact: Peter Higgins

Partners	20
Assistant Solicitors	7
Training contracts p.a.	2

CUMBERLAND ELLIS PEIRS

Columbia Hse 69 Aldwych London WC2B 4RW
Tel: (0171) 242 0422 Fax: (0171) 831 9081
Contact: Miss N.J. Walman

Partners	12
Assistant Solicitors	7
Training contracts p.a.	1

CUNNINGHAM, JOHN & CO

Fairstead House 7 Bury Road Thetford IP24 3PL
Tel: (01842) 752401 Fax: (01842) 753555
Contact: Mrs Sandra Clarke

Partners	8
Assistant Solicitors	10
Training contracts p.a.	4

CURWENS

Crossfield House Gladbeck Way Enfield EN2 7HT
Tel: (0181) 363 4444 Fax: (0181) 367 1301
Contact: Mrs Norma Morris

Partners	12
Assistant Solicitors	8
Training contracts p.a.	1

DARBYS

Sun Alliance House 52 New Inn Hall St Oxford OX1 2QA
Tel: (01865) 247294 Fax: (01865) 793411
Contact: Mr Stephen Dyde

Partners	9
Assistant Solicitors	20
Training contracts p.a.	2

DAVID GIST & CO

21/23 Clare Street Bristol BS1 1TZ
Tel: (0117) 927 9111 Fax: (0117) 927 9101
Contact: Susan Brewster

Partners	5
Assistant Solicitors	7
Training contracts p.a.	1

DAVID GRAY & COMPANY

Old County Court 56 Westgate Road
Newcastle upon Tyne NE1 5XU
Tel: (0191) 232 9547 Fax: (0191) 230 4149
Contact: Mr Graham Anderson

Partners	7
Assistant Solicitors	7
Training contracts p.a.	2

DAVID & SNAPE

Wyndham House Wyndham Street Bridgend CF31 1EP
Tel: (01656) 661115 Fax: (01656) 660545
Contact: Mr Chubb

Partners	6
Assistant Solicitors	6
Training contracts p.a.	1

DAVIES AND PARTNERS

Rowan House Barnett Way Barnwood Gloucester GL4 3RT
Tel: (01452) 612 345 Fax: (01452) 611922
Contact: Mrs Gill Wells

Partners	18
Assistant Solicitors	45
Training contracts p.a.	4

DAVIES LAVERY

Palace Court 17 London Road Maidstone ME16 8JE
Tel: (01622) 688171 Fax: (01622) 672847
Contact: Mr Jerome Curran

Partners	9
Assistant Solicitors	11
Training contracts p.a.	1

DAVIES WALLIS FOYSTER

5 Castle Street Liverpool L2 4XE
Tel: (0151) 236 6226 Fax: (0151) 236 3088
Contact: Ms Pat Modlinsky

Partners	41
Assistant Solicitors	85
Training contracts p.a.	6

DAVIS BLANK FURNISS

90 Deansgate Manchester M3 2QJ
Tel: (0161) 832 3304 Fax: (0161) 834 3568
Contact: Peter Heginbotham

Partners	10
Assistant Solicitors	10
Training contracts p.a.	1–2

DAWSON & CO

2 New Square Lincoln's Inn London WC2A 3RZ	Partners	18
Tel: (0171) 421 4800 Fax: (0171) 421 4848	Assistant Solicitors	9
Contact: Miss Joanne Keddie	Training contracts p.a.	5

DAWSON CORNWELL & CO

16 Red Lion Square London WC1R 4QT	Partners	7
Tel: (0171) 242 2556 Fax: (0171) 831 0478	Assistant Solicitors	2
Contact: Mr M.P. Beard	Training contracts p.a.	0–1

DEAN WILSON

96 Church Street Brighton BN1 1UJ	Partners	7
Tel: (01273) 327241 Fax: (01273) 770913	Assistant Solicitors	4
Contact: Joanna M. Ward	Training contracts p.a.	1

DICKINSON MANSER

5 Parkstone Rd Poole BH15 2NL	Partners	7
Tel: (01202) 673071 Fax: (01202) 680470	Assistant Solicitors	5
Contact: Mr L.H. Parkyn	Training contracts p.a.	1

DOBERMAN HORSMAN

College Chambers 92-94 Borough Road

Middlesbrough TS1 2HL	Partners	4
Tel: (01642) 230130 Fax: (01642) 230133	Assistant Solicitors	4
Contact: Mr Bell	Training contracts p.a.	1

DOLMANS

17 Windsor Place Cardiff CF1 4PA	Partners	12
Tel: (01222) 345531 Fax: (01222) 398206	Assistant Solicitors	15
Contact: Mrs Susannah Elroon	Training contracts p.a.	4–5

DONNS SOLICITORS

PO Box 41 201 Deansgate Manchester M60 1DZ	Partners	8
Tel: (0161) 834 3311 Fax: (0161) 834 2317	Assistant Solicitors	5
Contact: Joseph Glass	Training contracts p.a.	4

DOUGLAS-JONES MERCER

147 St. Helens Rd Swansea SA1 4DB	Partners	12
Tel: (01792) 650000 Fax: (01792) 458212	Assistant Solicitors	9
Contact: Ms Beverly Webb	Training contracts p.a.	2

DOWNS

156 High Street Dorking, Surrey RH4 1BQ	Partners	11
Tel: (01306) 880110 Fax: (01306) 876266	Assistant Solicitors	6
Contact: Mr O. I. Miller	Training contracts p.a.	0–2

DRUCES & ATTLEE

Salisbury House London Wall London EC2M 5PS	Partners	14
Tel: (0171) 638 9271 Fax: (0171) 628 7525	Assistant Solicitors	16
Contact: Mr R. Monkcom	Training contracts p.a.	4

EATONS

22 Blades Court Deodar Rd Putney London SW15 2NU	Partners	7
Tel: (0181) 877 9727 Fax: (0181) 877 9940	Assistant Solicitors	3
Contact: Martin Dacre	Training contracts p.a.	1

EDWARD FAIL BRADSHAW & WATERSON

402 Commercial Road Stepney London E1 0LG	Partners	5
Tel: (0171) 790 4032 Fax: (0171) 790 2739	Assistant Solicitors	7
Contact: Nigel Dean	Training contracts p.a.	3

EDWARDS GELDARD

Dumfries House Dumfries Place Cardiff CF1 4YF	Partners	30
Tel: (01222) 238 239 Fax: (01222) 237268	Assistant Solicitors	37
Contact: Mr O.M. Golding	Training contracts p.a.	10

EDWIN COE

2 Stone Buildings Lincoln's Inn London WC2A 3TH	Partners	16
Tel: (0171) 691 4000 Fax: (0171) 691 4111	Assistant Solicitors	9
Contact: Russel Shear	Training contracts p.a.	2

ELLIOTT & COMPANY

Centurion House Deansgate Manchester M3 3WT
Tel: (0161) 834 9933 Fax: (0161) 832 3693
Contact: Miss Catherine Mellor

Partners	10
Assistant Solicitors	24
Training contracts p.a.	2

ELLIS JONES

Sandbourne House 302 Charminster Road
Bournemouth BH8 9RU
Tel: (01202) 525333 Fax: (01202) 535935
Contact: Mr Alan Redsern

Partners	6
Assistant Solicitors	5
Training contracts p.a.	1

ENSOR BYFIELD

Equity Court 73-75 Millbrook Road East
Southampton SO15 1RJ
Tel: (01703) 483200 Fax: (01703) 212127
Contact: Mr Christopher Crowcroft

Partners	8
Assistant Solicitors	13
Training contracts p.a.	1–2

EPSTEIN GROWER & MICHAEL FREEMAN

One Great Cumberland Place London W1H 8DQ
Tel: (0171) 724 2526 Fax: (0171) 723 2988
Contact: Mr Epstein

Partners	5
Assistant Solicitors	4
Training contracts p.a.	1

ERIC ROBINSON & CO

18 West End Rd Bitterne Southampton SO18 1DN
Tel: (01703) 425000 Fax: (01703) 446594
Contact: Mr G. Onoufrilou

Partners	11
Assistant Solicitors	12
Training contracts p.a.	2

EVILL & COLEMAN

113 Upper Richmond Road Putney London SW15 2TL
Tel: (0181) 789 9221 Fax: (0181) 789 7978
Contact: Stewart Graham

Partners	10
Assistant Solicitors	4
Training contracts p.a.	2

FARLEYS

22-27 Richmond Terrace Blackburn BB1 7AQ
Tel: (01254) 606000 Fax: (01254) 583526
Contact: Andrew Taylor

Partners	9
Assistant Solicitors	21
Training contracts p.a.	2–3

FAULKNERS

Argyll House Bath Street Frome BA11 1DP	Partners	10
Tel: (01373) 465051 Fax: (01373) 467414	Assistant Solicitors	8
Contact: Mr Nicholas Rheinberg	Training contracts p.a.	2

FENNEMORES

200 Silbury Boulevard Central Milton Keynes MK9 1LL	Partners	14
Tel: (01908) 678241 Fax: (01908) 665985	Assistant Solicitors	12
Contact: Mrs Elizabeth Wood	Training contracts p.a.	2

FIELD CUNNINGHAM & CO

St. John's Court 70 Quay St Manchester M3 3EJ	Partners	4
Tel: (0161) 834 4734 Fax: (0161) 834 1772	Assistant Solicitors	3
Contact: Mr Stephen J. Hawkins	Training contracts p.a.	1

FINERS

179 Great Portland St London W1N 6LS	Partners	29
Tel: (0171) 323 4000 Fax: (0171) 580 7069	Assistant Solicitors	19
Contact: Mark Fenton/Philip Rubens	Training contracts p.a.	4–6

FINN, GLEDHILL

1-4 Harrison Rd Halifax HX1 2AG	Partners	8
Tel: (01422) 330000 Fax: (01422) 342604	Assistant Solicitors	2
Contact: S.J. Mattock	Training contracts p.a.	1

FITZHUGH GATES

3 Pavilion Parade Brighton BN2 1RY	Partners	9
Tel: (01273) 686811 Fax: (01273) 676837	Assistant Solicitors	1
Contact: Maureen Waller	Training contracts p.a.	1

FLADGATE FIELDER

25 North Row London W1R 1DJ	Partners	26
Tel: (0171) 323 4747 Fax: (0171) 629 4414	Assistant Solicitors	24
Contact: Julie Kimber	Training contracts p.a.	4

FLINT, BISHOP & BARNETT

Royal Oak House Market Place Derby DE1 2EA
Tel: (01332) 340211 Fax: (01332) 347107
Contact: Angie Whittingham, Personnel Manager

Partners	19
Assistant Solicitors	13
Training contracts p.a.	2

FORD & WARREN

Westgate Point Westgate Leeds LS1 2AX
Tel: (0113) 243 6601 Fax: (0113) 242 0905
Contact: Ms Frank Sutcliffe

Partners	12
Assistant Solicitors	23
Training contracts p.a.	3

FOSTER BAXTER COOKSEY

6-10 George Street Snow Hill Wolverhampton WV2 4DN
Tel: (01902) 311711 Fax: (01902) 311102
Contact: Mrs Kim Carr

Partners	14
Assistant Solicitors	20
Training contracts p.a.	2

FOSTERS

60 London Street Norwich NR2 1JY
Tel: (01603) 620508 Fax: (01603) 624090
Contact: Andrew Saul

Partners	9
Assistant Solicitors	10
Training contracts p.a.	3

FREETH CARTWRIGHT HUNT DICKINS

Willoughby House 20 Low Pavement Nottingham NG1 7EA
Tel: (0115) 936 9369 Fax: (0115) 936 9370
Contact: Sue Bradley

Partners	40
Assistant Solicitors	69
Training contracts p.a.	8

FURLEY PAGE FIELDING & BARTON

39 St. Margaret's Street Canterbury CT1 2TX
Tel: (01227) 763939 Fax: (01227) 762829
Contact: Mrs S. Hoger

Partners	16
Assistant Solicitors	5
Training contracts p.a.	1–2

GAMLINS

31-37 Russell Road Rhyl LL18 3DB
Tel: (01745) 343500 Fax: (01745) 343616
Contact: Mr Sethi

Partners	7
Assistant Solicitors	14
Training contracts p.a.	3

GEORGE DAVIES & CO

Fountain Court 68 Fountain Street Manchester M2 2FB
Tel: (0161) 236 8992 Fax: (0161) 228 0030
Contact: Mr Mark Hovell

Partners	13
Assistant Solicitors	10
Training contracts p.a.	2

GEORGE GREEN & CO

195 High St Cradley Heath Warley B64 5HW
Tel: (01384) 410410 Fax: (01384) 634237
Contact: Neill Robb

Partners	9
Assistant Solicitors	9
Training contracts p.a.	2

GILL AKASTER

Scott Lodge Milehouse Plymouth PL2 3DD
Tel: (01752) 500111 Fax: (01752) 563403
Contact: Mrs J. Ashley

Partners	11
Assistant Solicitors	7
Training contracts p.a.	1

GIRLINGS

158 High Street Herne Bay CT6 5NP
Tel: (01227) 373874 Fax: (01227) 365897
Contact: Simon Gurr

Partners	20
Assistant Solicitors	4
Training contracts p.a.	1

GLAISYERS

10 Rowchester Court Printing House St
Birmingham B4 6DZ
Tel: (0121) 233 2971 Fax: (0121) 236 1534
Contact: Mr Charles Royle

Partners	10
Assistant Solicitors	8
Training contracts p.a.	1

GLANVILLES

16 Landport Terrace Portsmouth PO1 2QT
Tel: (01705) 827231 Fax: (01705) 753611
Contact: Miss Sue Craven

Partners	16
Assistant Solicitors	11
Training contracts p.a.	1–2

GLAZER DELMAR

223-229 Rye Lane Peckham London SE15 4TZ
Tel: (0171) 639 8801 Fax: (0171) 358 0581
Contact: Ruth Wallwork

Partners	3
Assistant Solicitors	9
Training contracts p.a.	2

GLOVERS

115 Park Street London W1Y 4DY
Tel: (0171) 629 5121 Fax: (0171) 491 0930
Contact: Ms Frances Dewhurst

Partners	10
Assistant Solicitors	10
Training contracts p.a.	2

GODLOVES

Russell House 15 St. Pauls Street Leeds LS1 2LZ
Tel: (0113) 225 8811 Fax: (0113) 2258844
Contact: Mr Malcolm Jones

Partners	12
Assistant Solicitors	4
Training contracts p.a.	1

GORNA & CO

Virginia House Cheapside King St Manchester M2 4NB
Tel: (0161) 832 3651 Fax: (0161) 834 8572
Contact: Mr S.C. Hindmarsh

Partners	9
Assistant Solicitors	15
Training contracts p.a.	1

GOSSCHALKS

Queens Gardens Hull HU1 3DZ
Tel: (01482) 324 252 Fax: (01482) 590290
Contact: Chris Burton

Partners	27
Assistant Solicitors	16
Training contracts p.a.	3

GREEN SHEIKH & CO

45 Crawford Place London W1H 2BY
Tel: (0171) 258 0055 Fax: (0171) 724 0385
Contact: Mr Harvey Posemer

Partners	6
Assistant Solicitors	5
Training contracts p.a.	2

GREENWOODS

30 Priestgate Peterborough PE1 1JE
Tel: (01733) 555244 Fax: (01733) 347988
Contact: Rosemary Gearing

Partners	17
Assistant Solicitors	14
Training contracts p.a.	2–3

GRINDEYS

Glebe Court Stoke on Trent ST4 1ET
Tel: (01782) 825871 Fax: (01782) 416220
Contact: David James

Partners	13
Assistant Solicitors	30
Training contracts p.a.	2–4

HALLETT & CO

11 Bank St Ashford TN23 1DA	Partners	9
Tel: (01233) 625711 Fax: (01233) 643841	Assistant Solicitors	3
Contact: Mark Dewey	Training contracts p.a.	0–1

HAMLIN SLOWE

Roxburghe House 273-287 Regent St London W1A 4SQ	Partners	21
Tel: (0171) 629 1209 Fax: (0171) 491 2259	Assistant Solicitors	7
Contact: Laurence Gilmore	Training contracts p.a.	4

HANSELL STEVENSON

13 Cathedral Close Norwich NR1 4DS	Partners	8
Tel: (01603) 615731 Fax: (01603) 633585	Assistant Solicitors	12
Contact: Philip Peaston	Training contracts p.a.	2

HAROLD MICHELMORE & CO

15-21 Market Street Newton Abbot TQ12 2RN	Partners	6
Tel: (01626) 332266 Fax: (01626) 331700	Assistant Solicitors	4
Contact: Mr Chris N. Thomas	Training contracts p.a.	1

HARRIS & CARTWRIGHT

Windsor Crown House 7 Windsor Rd Slough SL1 2DX	Partners	7
Tel: (01753) 810710 Fax: (01753) 810720	Assistant Solicitors	10
Contact: Mr Kent Pattinson	Training contracts p.a.	2

HARRIS & HARRIS

14 Market Place Wells BA5 2RE	Partners	8
Tel: (01749) 674747 Fax: (01749) 676585	Assistant Solicitors	4
Contact: Alison Macaulay	Training contracts p.a.	1

HARROWELL SHAFTOE

1 St. Saviourgate York YO1 2NQ	Partners	11
Tel: (01904) 620331 Fax: (01904) 655855	Assistant Solicitors	11
Contact: Mrs J.M. Knights	Training contracts p.a.	1

HART BROWN

20 Bedford Road Guildford GU1 4TH
Tel: (01483) 887766 Fax: (01483) 887752
Contact: Susan Tasker

Partners	16
Assistant Solicitors	20
Training contracts p.a.	4

HARTLEY & WORSTENHOLME

20 Bank St Castleford WF10 1JD
Tel: (01977) 732222 Fax: (01977) 603105
Contact: Mr. Tom Day

Partners	8
Assistant Solicitors	11
Training contracts p.a.	0–2

HATCHER ROGERSON

25 Castle Street Shrewsbury SY1 1DA
Tel: (01743) 248545 Fax: (01743) 242979
Contact: Mr David Saunders

Partners	10
Assistant Solicitors	8
Training contracts p.a.	2

HAY & KILNER

Merchant House 30 Cloth Market
Newcastle-upon-Tyne NE1 1EE
Tel: (0191) 232 8345 Fax: (0191) 221 0514
Contact: Bruce N.Howarth

Partners	24
Assistant Solicitors	7
Training contracts p.a.	2

HENMANS

116 St. Aldates Oxford OX1 1HA
Tel: (01865) 722181 Fax: (01865) 792376
Contact: Julia Iball

Partners	15
Assistant Solicitors	24
Training contracts p.a.	2–3

HEPTONSTALLS

7-15 Gladstone Terrace Goole DN14 5AH
Tel: (01405) 765661 Fax: (01405) 764201
Contact: Mr B. Withington

Partners	6
Assistant Solicitors	11
Training contracts p.a.	2

HICKMAN & ROSE

144 Liverpool Road London N1 ORE
Tel: (0171) 700 2211 Fax: (0171) 609 6044
Contact: Ms Jane Hickman

Partners	5
Assistant Solicitors	15
Training contracts p.a.	4

HIGGS & SONS

Blythe House 134 High Street Brierley Hill DY5 3BG	Partners	23
Tel: (01384) 342100 Fax: (01384) 342000	Assistant Solicitors	16
Contact: Mr. Vernon	Training contracts p.a.	3

HILL TAYLOR DICKINSON

Irongate House Duke's Place London EC3A 7LP	Partners	24
Tel: (0171) 283 9033 Fax: (0171) 283 1144	Assistant Solicitors	31
Contact: Malcolm Taylor	Training contracts p.a.	4

HOBSON AUDLEY HOPKINS & WOOD

7 Pilgrim Street London EC4V 6DR	Partners	13
Tel: (0171) 450 4500 Fax: (0171) 450 4545	Assistant Solicitors	22
Contact: Andrew Joyce	Training contracts p.a.	2

HODGE JONES & ALLEN

Twyman House 31-39 Camden Road London NW1 9LR	Partners	15
Tel: (0171) 482 1974 Fax: (0171) 267 3476	Assistant Solicitors	23
Contact: Ms Sarah Firth	Training contracts p.a.	3–4

HOOD VORES & ALLWOOD

The Priory Church St Dereham NR19 1DW	Partners	6
Tel: (01362) 692424 Fax: (01362) 698858	Assistant Solicitors	2
Contact: Mr D.A.W. Rose	Training contracts p.a.	0–1

HOOPER & WOLLEN

Carlton House 30 The Terrace Torquay TQ1 1BS	Partners	10
Tel: (01803) 213251 Fax: (01803) 296871	Assistant Solicitors	4
Contact: Mrs Pat Bear	Training contracts p.a.	1

HORWICH FARRELLY

National House 36 St Ann Street Manchester M60 8HF	Partners	10
Tel: (0161) 834 3585 Fax: (0161) 834 3630	Assistant Solicitors	6
Contact: Mr Nigel Yates	Training contracts p.a.	2

HOWARD KENNEDY

19 Cavendish Square London W1A 2AW
Tel: (0171) 636 1616 Fax: (0171) 499 6871
Contact: Mr Andrew Farmiloe

Partners	29
Assistant Solicitors	19
Training contracts p.a.	2

HOWARTH GOODMAN

8 King Street Manchester M60 8HG
Tel: (0161) 832 5068 Fax: (0161) 833 2917
Contact: Mr S. Baddiel

Partners	4
Assistant Solicitors	3
Training contracts p.a.	2

HOWELL & CO

1341 Stratford Road Hall Green Birmingham B28 9HW
Tel: (0121) 778 5031 Fax: (0121) 777 3967
Contact: Mr Jobling

Partners	2
Assistant Solicitors	4
Training contracts p.a.	3

HOWELLS

427-431 London Road Sheffield S2 4HJ
Tel: (0114) 249 6666 Fax: (0114) 250 0656
Contact: Mr John McSweeney

Partners	11
Assistant Solicitors	15
Training contracts p.a.	2

HUGH JAMES

Arlbee House Greyfriars Rd Cardiff CF1 4QB
Tel: (01222) 224 871 Fax: (01222) 388222
Contact: Wendy Stamp

Partners	42
Assistant Solicitors	34
Training contracts p.a.	5

HUMPHREYS & CO.

14 King St Bristol BS1 4EF
Tel: (0117) 929 2662 Fax: (0117) 929 2722
Contact: R.A.Humphreys

Partners	4
Assistant Solicitors	6
Training contracts p.a.	1

HUMPHRIES KIRK

Glebe House North Street Wareham BH20 4AN
Tel: (01929) 552141 Fax: (01929) 556701
Contact: Mrs J.E. Murray

Partners	8
Assistant Solicitors	10
Training contracts p.a.	1

HUNT & COOMBS

35 Thorpe Rd Peterborough PE3 6AG
Tel: (01733) 565312 Fax: (01733) 552748
Contact: Paul Tate

Partners	10
Assistant Solicitors	4
Training contracts p.a.	1–2

HUNTERS

9 New Square Lincoln's Inn London WC2A 3QN
Tel: (0171) 412 0050 Fax: (0171) 412 0049
Contact: Mr P. Almy

Partners	11
Assistant Solicitors	6
Training contracts p.a.	1

HUTTONS

16-18 St Andrews Crescent Cardiff CF1 3DD
Tel: (01222) 378621 Fax: (01222) 388450
Contact: Clare Strowbridge

Partners	5
Assistant Solicitors	7
Training contracts p.a.	2

JAMES CHAPMAN & CO

76 King Street Manchester M2 4NH
Tel: (0161) 828 8000 Fax: (0161) 828 8018
Contact: Mrs Sarah Grant

Partners	24
Assistant Solicitors	16
Training contracts p.a.	2

JEFFREY GREEN RUSSELL

Apollo House 56 New Bond Street London W1Y OSX
Tel: (0171) 339 7000 Fax: (0171) 499 2449
Contact: Mark Spragg

Partners	26
Assistant Solicitors	25
Training contracts p.a.	2–3

JOELSON WILSON & CO

70 New Cavendish Street London W1M 8AT
Tel: (0171) 580 5721 Fax: (0171) 580 2251
Contact: Paul Wilson

Partners	6
Assistant Solicitors	4
Training contracts p.a.	2

JOHN HODGE & CO

27/31 Boulevard Weston-super-Mare BS23 1NY
Tel: (01934) 623511 Fax: (01934) 418210
Contact: Hugh Langley

Partners	7
Assistant Solicitors	4
Training contracts p.a.	1

JOHN PICKERING & PARTNERS

9 Church Lane Oldham OL1 3AN
Tel: (0161) 633 6667 Fax: (0161) 626 1671
Contact: Anthony Coombs

Partners	5
Assistant Solicitors	4
Training contracts p.a.	0–1

THE JOHNSON PARTNERSHIP

Cannon Courtyard Long Row Nottingham NG1 6JE
Tel: (0115) 941 9141 Fax: (0115) 947 0178
Contact: Mr Digby Johnson

Partners	10
Assistant Solicitors	4
Training contracts p.a.	1

J.R. JONES

56A The Mall Ealing W5 3TA
Tel: (0181) 566 2595 Fax: (0181) 579 4288
Contact: A. Chadha

Partners	2
Assistant Solicitors	6
Training contracts p.a.	2

KEELY BEEDHAM

28 Dam Street Lichfield WS13 6AA
Tel: (01543) 420000 Fax: (01543) 258469
Contact: Mr J.A.W. Parkes

Partners	9
Assistant Solicitors	3
Training contracts p.a.	2–3

KENNETH BUSH

Evershed House 23/25 King Street King's Lynn PE30 1DU
Tel: (01553) 692737 Fax: (01553) 691729
Contact: J.P. Eales

Partners	13
Assistant Solicitors	3
Training contracts p.a.	1

KENNETH ELLIOTT & ROWE

162-166 South Street Romford RM1 1SX
Tel: (01708) 757575 Fax: (01708) 766674
Contact: Mr Chris Dixon

Partners	11
Assistant Solicitors	8
Training contracts p.a.	3

KENT JONES AND DONE

Churchill House Regent Road Stoke-on-Trent ST1 3RQ
Tel: (01782) 20 20 20 Fax: (01782) 202040
Contact: Karen Duckworth

Partners	12
Assistant Solicitors	18
Training contracts p.a.	3

KIMBELL & CO

352 Silbury Court Silbury Boulevard
Milton Keynes MK9 2HJ
Tel: (01908) 668555 Fax: (01908) 674344
Contact: Richard Brown

Partners	6
Assistant Solicitors	11
Training contracts p.a.	1–2

KIRK JACKSON

97 Chorley Rd Swinton Manchester M27 2AB
Tel: (0161) 794 0431 Fax: (0161) 794 4957
Contact: Derek Sands

Partners	7
Assistant Solicitors	4
Training contracts p.a.	0–1

KNIGHT & SONS

The Brampton Newcastle-under-Lyme ST5 0QW
Tel: (01782) 619225 Fax: (01782) 717260
Contact: Ms Zoe Theofilopoulof

Partners	20
Assistant Solicitors	22
Training contracts p.a.	3

KNOWLES BENNING

2 George Street West Luton LU1 2BX
Tel: (01582) 736861 Fax: (01582) 457092
Contact: David Welch/Elaine Davis

Partners	10
Assistant Solicitors	15
Training contracts p.a.	1

KUIT STEINART LEVY

3 St. Mary's Parsonage Manchester M3 2RD
Tel: (0161) 832 3434 Fax: (0161) 832 6650
Contact: Mr Robert A. Levy

Partners	13
Assistant Solicitors	10
Training contracts p.a.	3

LAMPORT BASSITT

46 The Avenue Southampton SO17 1AX
Tel: (01703) 634931 Fax: (01703) 222346
Contact: John Newton

Partners	9
Assistant Solicitors	22
Training contracts p.a.	2

LANYON BOWDLER

23 Swanhill Shrewsbury SY 1 1NN
Tel: (01743) 236400 Fax: (01743) 354994
Contact: Mr A.G. Richards

Partners	14
Assistant Solicitors	11
Training contracts p.a.	2

LATIMER HINKS

5-8 Priestgate Darlington DL1 1NL	Partners	8
Tel: (01325) 341500 Fax: (01325) 381072	Assistant Solicitors	7
Contact: Mr D. Brown	Training contracts p.a.	1–2

LAWFORD & CO

Watchmaker Court 65 St. John's Street London EC1M 4HQ	Partners	11
Tel: (0171) 353 5099 Fax: (0171) 353 5355	Assistant Solicitors	25
Contact: Ms Lorainne Phillips	Training contracts p.a.	2

LAWSON COPPOCK & HART

18 Tib Lane Cross St Manchester M2 4JA	Partners	7
Tel: (0161) 832 5944 Fax: (0161) 834 4409	Assistant Solicitors	4
Contact: Mrs P.A. Powell	Training contracts p.a.	1

LEATHES PRIOR

74 The Close Norwich NR1 4DR	Partners	17
Tel: (01603) 610911 Fax: (01603) 610088	Assistant Solicitors	13
Contact: Martin Plowman	Training contracts p.a.	3

LEE CROWDER

39 Newhall Street Birmingham B3 3DY	Partners	14
Tel: (0121) 236 4477 Fax: (0121) 236 4710	Assistant Solicitors	27
Contact: Mr R. Whittingham	Training contracts p.a.	2

LEE & PEMBERTONS

45 Pont St London SW1X 0BX	Partners	22
Tel: (0171) 589 1114 Fax: (0171) 589 0807	Assistant Solicitors	17
Contact: Mrs Diana Graves	Training contracts p.a.	2

LEE & PRIESTLEY

12 Park Square Leeds LS1 2LF	Partners	15
Tel: (0113) 243 3751 Fax: (0113) 246 7357	Assistant Solicitors	9
Contact: Mrs J. Turner	Training contracts p.a.	3

LEIGH, DAY & CO

Priory House 25 St. John's Lane London EC1M 4LB

Tel: (0171) 650 1200 Fax: (0171) 253 4433

Contact: Mrs Frances Swaine

Partners	14
Assistant Solicitors	13
Training contracts p.a.	3

LEMON & CO

Chelsea House 1 Little London Court

Albert Street Swindon SN1 3HY

Tel: (01793) 496341 Fax: (01793) 511639

Contact: Stephen Moss

Partners	9
Assistant Solicitors	3
Training contracts p.a.	1

LEO ABSE & COHEN

40 Churchill Way Cardiff CF1 4SS

Tel: (01222) 383 252 Fax: (01222) 345572

Contact: Lesley Richard

Partners	12
Assistant Solicitors	40
Training contracts p.a.	2

LEONARD GRAY

72-74 Duke St Chelmsford CM1 1JY

Tel: (01245) 251411 Fax: (01245) 490728

Contact: Mrs Hutson

Partners	6
Assistant Solicitors	5
Training contracts p.a.	1

LESTER ALDRIDGE

Russell House Oxford Road Bournemouth BH8 8EX

Tel: (01202) 786161 Fax: (01202) 786110

Contact: Ms Juliet Milne

Partners	30
Assistant Solicitors	27
Training contracts p.a.	5

THE LEWINGTON PARTNERSHIP

Midland House 132 Hagley Road Edgbaston

Birmingham B16 9NN

Tel: (0121) 454 4000 Fax: (0121) 456 3631

Contact: Mrs Jog Hundle

Partners	14
Assistant Solicitors	21
Training contracts p.a.	2

LEWIS SILKIN

Windsor House 50 Victoria Street London SW1H 0NW

Tel: (0171) 227 8000 Fax: (0171) 222 4633

Contact: Mr Clive Greenwood

Partners	27
Assistant Solicitors	33
Training contracts p.a.	6

LINDER MYERS

Phoenix House 45 Cross Street Manchester M2 4JF
Tel: (0161) 832 6972 Fax: (0161) 834 0718
Contact: Mr Colin Davies

Partners	10
Assistant Solicitors	18
Training contracts p.a.	1

LLEWELYN ZIETMAN

Temple Bar House 23-28 Fleet Street London EC4Y 1AA
Tel: (0171) 842 5400 Fax: (0171) 842 5444
Contact: Ms Julie Evans

Partners	12
Assistant Solicitors	4
Training contracts p.a.	4

LLOYD COOPER

7A Grafton Street London W1X 3LA
Tel: (0171) 629 4699 Fax: (0171) 355 3796
Contact: P.L. Lloyd-Cooper

Partners	3
Assistant Solicitors	3
Training contracts p.a.	1

LOCKHARTS

Tavistock House South Tavistock Square
London WC1H 9LS
Tel: (0171) 383 7111 Fax: (0171) 383 7117
Contact: Miss Rosalind Parkin

Partners	3
Assistant Solicitors	2
Training contracts p.a.	0–1

LUPTON FAWCETT

Yorkshire Hse Greek St Leeds LS1 5SX
Tel: (0113) 280 2000 Fax: (0113) 245 6782
Contact: Suzanne Hopkins

Partners	15
Assistant Solicitors	13
Training contracts p.a.	3

LYONS DAVIDSON

Bridge House 48-52 Baldwin St Bristol BS1 1QD
Tel: (0117) 904 6000 Fax: (0117) 904 6001
Contact: Mrs J. Luscombe

Partners	18
Assistant Solicitors	40
Training contracts p.a.	7

MACDONALD OATES

Square House The Square Petersfield GU32 3HT
Tel: (01730) 268211 Fax: (01730) 261232
Contact: Mr S.R. Cox

Partners	7
Assistant Solicitors	6
Training contracts p.a.	1

MACE & JONES

Drury House 19 Water Street Liverpool L2 0RP	Partners	24
Tel: (0151) 236 8989 Fax: (0151) 227 5010	Assistant Solicitors	33
Contact: Craig Blakemore	Training contracts p.a.	4

MAGRATH & CO

52-54 Maddox Street London W1R 9PA	Partners	5
Tel: (0171) 495 3003 Fax: (0171) 409 1745	Assistant Solicitors	9
Contact: Mr Nick Goldstone	Training contracts p.a.	2

MALKINS

Inigo House 29 Bedford St Covent Garden		
London WC2E 9ED	Partners	12
Tel: (0171) 379 3385 Fax: (0171) 379 3137	Assistant Solicitors	3
Contact: Kevin Bichard	Training contracts p.a.	2

MANBY & STEWARD

Mander House Mander Centre Wolverhampton WV1 3NE	Partners	14
Tel: (01902) 578000 Fax: (01902) 424321/713564	Assistant Solicitors	16
Contact: Mrs J Burns	Training contracts p.a.	2

MANDER HADLEY & CO

1 The Quadrant Coventry CV1 2DW	Partners	12
Tel: (01203) 631212 Fax: (01203) 633131	Assistant Solicitors	2
Contact: Mr R. Pascall	Training contracts p.a.	1

MAPLES TEESDALE

21 Lincoln's Inn Fields London WC2A 3DU	Partners	10
Tel: (0171) 831 6501 Fax: (0171) 405 3867	Assistant Solicitors	5
Contact: Edward Bliss	Training contracts p.a.	1

MARTIN PROWEL, EDWARDS & DAVIES

Hallinans House 22 Newport Road Cardiff CF2 1TD	Partners	6
Tel: (01222) 496316 Fax: (01222) 498566	Assistant Solicitors	5
Contact: Mr Hywel Davies	Training contracts p.a.	1

MATTHEW ARNOLD & BALDWIN

PO Box No. 101 20 Station Rd Watford WD1 1HT	Partners	16
Tel: (01923) 202020 Fax: (01923) 215050	Assistant Solicitors	12
Contact: Trish Wallington	Training contracts p.a.	3

MAX BARFORD & CO

16 Mount Pleasant Road Tunbridge Wells TN1 1QU	Partners	6
Tel: (01892) 539379 Fax: (01892) 521874	Assistant Solicitors	5
Contact: Miss D. Evans	Training contracts p.a.	1

MAX GOLD & CO

Suffolk House 21 Silver Street Hull HU1 1JJ	Partners	1
Tel: (01482) 224900 Fax: (01482) 216068	Assistant Solicitors	10
Contact: Mr Wellock	Training contracts p.a.	1

MAXWELL ENTWISTLE & BYRNE

14 Castle Street Liverpool L2 0SG	Partners	10
Tel: (0151) 227 4545 Fax: (0151) 236 5067	Assistant Solicitors	10
Contact: Mrs Carol Head	Training contracts p.a.	1

MAY, MAY & MERRIMANS

12 South Square Gray's Inn London WC1R 5HH	Partners	11
Tel: (0171) 405 8932 Fax: (0171) 831 0011	Assistant Solicitors	5
Contact: Miss Alex Sarkis	Training contracts p.a.	1

MAYO & PERKINS

20 Gildredge Rd Eastbourne BN21 4RP	Partners	13
Tel: (01323) 730543 Fax: (01323) 737214	Assistant Solicitors	4
Contact: Mr C.J. Randall	Training contracts p.a.	2

MEMERY CRYSTAL

31 Southampton Row London WC1B 5HT	Partners	10
Tel: (0171) 242 5905 Fax: (0171) 242 2058	Assistant Solicitors	16
Contact: Mrs Elizabeth Grist	Training contracts p.a.	2

METCALFE COPEMAN & PETTEFAR

8 York Row Wisbech PE13 1EF	Partners 11
Tel: (01945) 464331 Fax: (01945) 476695	Assistant Solicitors 14
Contact: Jonathan Burton	Training contracts p.a. 1

METCALFES

46-48 Queen Square Bristol BS1 4LY	Partners 9
Tel: (0117) 929 0451 Fax: (0117) 929 9551	Assistant Solicitors 3
Contact: Mrs Judith Ellery	Training contracts p.a. 1

MIDDLETON POTTS

3 Cloth Street Barbican London EC1A 7LD	Partners 18
Tel: (0171) 600 2333 Fax: (0171) 600 0108	Assistant Solicitors 14
Contact: Ms Hazel Alton	Training contracts p.a. 3

MILBANK, TWEED, HADLEY & MCCLOY

Dashwood House 69 Old Broad Street London EC2M 1QS	Partners 5
Tel: (0171) 448 3000 Fax: (0171) 448 3029	Assistant Solicitors 12
Contact: Mr John Mc Hugh	Training contracts p.a. 2

MINCOFFS

Kensington House 4-6 Osborne Road	
Newcastle-upon-Tyne NE2 2AA	Partners 6
Tel: (0191) 281 6151 Fax: (0191) 281 8069	Assistant Solicitors 4
Contact: Mr Austen Science	Training contracts p.a. 1

MONIER-WILLIAMS & BOXALLS

71 Lincoln's Inn Fields London WC2A 3JF	Partners 9
Tel: (0171) 405 6195 Fax: (0171) 405 1453	Assistant Solicitors 4
Contact: Mr Peter McRoberts	Training contracts p.a. 0–1

MOORE & BLATCH

11 The Avenue Southampton SO17 1XF	Partners 13
Tel: (01703) 636311 Fax: (01703) 332205	Assistant Solicitors 30
Contact: Christine Chalk	Training contracts p.a. 1

MOWLL & MOWLL

34 & 36 Castle Street Dover CT16 1PN	Partners	8
Tel: (01304) 240250 Fax: (01304) 240040	Assistant Solicitors	3
Contact: Mr Lambert	Training contracts p.a.	1

MULLIS & PEAKE

Marshalls Chambers 80A South Street Romford RM1 1QS	Partners	8
Tel: (01708) 784000 Fax: (01708) 744099	Assistant Solicitors	6
Contact: Mr Peter Connell	Training contracts p.a.	1

NAPTHEN HOUGHTON CRAVEN

7 Winckley Square Preston PR1 3JD	Partners	10
Tel: (01772) 883883 Fax: (01772) 257805	Assistant Solicitors	5
Contact: John Woosnam	Training contracts p.a.	1

NASH & CO.

Beaumont House Beaumont Park Plymouth PL4 9BD	Partners	7
Tel: (01752) 664444 Fax: (01752) 667112	Assistant Solicitors	4
Contact: John Wyatt	Training contracts p.a.	1

NATHAN, SILMAN

Osprey House 78 Wigmore St London W1H 9DQ	Partners	4
Tel: (0171) 935 0898 Fax: (0171) 486 4803	Assistant Solicitors	2
Contact: Mr Stephen W. Lewis	Training contracts p.a.	1

NEEDHAM & JAMES

25 Meer Street Stratford upon Avon CV37 6QB	Partners	14
Tel: (01789) 414 444 Fax: (01789) 296 608	Assistant Solicitors	4
Contact: Roger Austin	Training contracts p.a.	1

NEIL F. JONES & CO

3 Broadway Broad Street Birmingham B15 1BQ	Partners	5
Tel: (0121) 643 1010 Fax: (0121) 643 1969	Assistant Solicitors	6
Contact: Simon Baylis	Training contracts p.a.	2

NELSON & CO

St. Andrew's House St. Andrew's Street Leeds LS3 1LF	Partners	8
Tel: (0113) 227 0100 Fax: (0113) 227 0113	Assistant Solicitors	9
Contact: Simon Bass	Training contracts p.a.	1

NEWSOME VAUGHAN

Greyfriars House Greyfriars Lane Coventry CV1 2GW	Partners	5
Tel: (01203) 633433 Fax: (01203) 256496	Assistant Solicitors	9
Contact: Mr Ian Grindal	Training contracts p.a.	1

OGLETHORPE STURTON & GILLIBRAND

16 Castle Park Lancaster LA1 1YG	Partners	8
Tel: (01524) 67171 Fax: (01524) 382247	Assistant Solicitors	5
Contact: Andrew Penny, Practice Manager	Training contracts p.a.	2

ORMEROD HEAP & MARSHALL

Green Dragon House 64-70 High Street Croydon CR0 9XN	Partners	12
Tel: (0181) 686 5000 Fax: (0181) 680 0972	Assistant Solicitors	8
Contact: Mr Graham Jones	Training contracts p.a.	2

OSBORNE MORRIS & MORGAN

Danbury House West Street Leighton Buzzard LU7 7DD	Partners	6
Tel: (01525) 378177 Fax: (01525) 851006	Assistant Solicitors	6
Contact: T.R. Osborne	Training contracts p.a.	1

OSBORNES

68 Parkway London NW1 7AH	Partners	6
Tel: (0171) 485 8811 Fax: (0171) 485 5660	Assistant Solicitors	12
Contact: Mr Angus Andrew	Training contracts p.a.	4

PALMER COWEN

16 Berkeley St London W1X 5AE	Partners	10
Tel: (0171) 491 7810 Fax: (0171) 491 0071	Assistant Solicitors	7
Contact: Mr Andrew Miller	Training contracts p.a.	2

PALSER GROSSMAN

Discovery House Scott Harbour Cardiff Bay CF1 5PJ
Tel: (01222) 452770 Fax: (01222) 452328
Contact: Christopher Nott

Partners	15
Assistant Solicitors	3
Training contracts p.a.	3–4

PARDOES

6-9 King Square Bridgwater TA6 3DG
Tel: (01278) 457891 Fax: (01278) 429249
Contact: Julie Mawfon

Partners	10
Assistant Solicitors	10
Training contracts p.a.	2

PARIS SMITH & RANDALL

Number 1 London Road Southampton SO15 2AE
Tel: (01703) 482482 Fax: (01703) 631835
Contact: Mr G.M. Day

Partners	13
Assistant Solicitors	17
Training contracts p.a.	2

PARK NELSON

1 Bell Yard London WC2A 2JP
Tel: (0171) 404 4191 Fax: (0171) 405 4266
Contact: Harvey Bell-Roberts

Partners	15
Assistant Solicitors	12
Training contracts p.a.	2

PARK WOODFINE

1 Lurke St Bedford MK40 3TN
Tel: (01234) 400000 Fax: (01234) 401111
Contact: Ms Elaine Clarke

Partners	10
Assistant Solicitors	7
Training contracts p.a.	2

PARROTT & COALES

14 Bourbon St Aylesbury HP20 2RS
Tel: (01296) 482244 Fax: (01296) 433723
Contact: Mr T.H. Dawe

Partners	8
Assistant Solicitors	5
Training contracts p.a.	1

O.H. PARSONS & PARTNERS

Sovereign Hse 212-224 Shaftesbury Avenue
London WC2H 8PR
Tel: (0171) 379 7277 Fax: (0171) 240 1577
Contact: Mr Matthew Cartledge

Partners	7
Assistant Solicitors	5
Training contracts p.a.	0–5

PERCY HUGHES & ROBERTS

19 Hamilton Square Birkenhead L41 6AY	Partners	6
Tel: (0151) 647 6081 Fax: (0151) 666 1080	Assistant Solicitors	5
Contact: Mrs Judith Smith	Training contracts p.a.	1

PETER CARTER-RUCK AND PARTNERS

International Press Centre 76 Shoe Lane London EC4A 3JB	Partners	9
Tel: (0171) 353 5005 Fax: (0171) 353 5553	Assistant Solicitors	5
Contact: Ruth Collard	Training contracts p.a.	2

PETER, PETER & WRIGHT

8 Fore Street Holsworthy EX22 6ED	Partners	12
Tel: (01409) 253262 Fax: (01409) 254091	Assistant Solicitors	15
Contact: James Rowland	Training contracts p.a.	1

PETERS & PETERS

2 Harewood Place Hanover Square London W1R 9HB	Partners	10
Tel: (0171) 629 7991 Fax: (0171) 499 6792	Assistant Solicitors	8
Contact: Ms Julia Balfour-Lynn	Training contracts p.a.	2

PETTMAN SMITH

79 Knightsbridge London SW1X 7RB	Partners	6
Tel: (0171) 235 1288 Fax: (0171) 235 2683	Assistant Solicitors	4
Contact: Mr Michael Pettman	Training contracts p.a.	2

PICKERING & BUTTERS

19 Greengate Street Stafford ST16 2LU	Partners	10
Tel: (01785) 603060 Fax: (01785) 607500	Assistant Solicitors	7
Contact: Mr C.C. Lee	Training contracts p.a.	2

PUNCH ROBSON

35 Albert Road Middlesbrough TS1 1NU	Partners	12
Tel: (01642) 230700 Fax: (01642) 218923	Assistant Solicitors	5
Contact: Mr Andrew Maisey	Training contracts p.a.	2

PYE-SMITHS

The Hall 4 New St Salisbury SP1 2QJ
Tel: (01722) 412345 Fax: (01722) 412321
Contact: Mrs Tatner

Partners	3
Assistant Solicitors	13
Training contracts p.a.	1

RATCLIFFE DUCE & GAMMER

49 & 51 London Street Reading RG1 4PS
Tel: (0118) 957 4291 Fax: (0118) 939 3143
Contact: Mr A. Chancellor-Weale

Partners	8
Assistant Solicitors	3
Training contracts p.a.	3

RAWLISON & BUTLER

Griffin House 135 High Street Crawley RH10 1DQ
Tel: (01293) 527744 Fax: (01293) 520202
Contact: Carl Burton

Partners	8
Assistant Solicitors	12
Training contracts p.a.	2

READ HIND STEWART

Trafalgar House 29 Park Place Leeds LS1 2SP
Tel: (0113) 246 8123 Fax: (0113) 244 2863
Contact: Mr Guy C. Jackson

Partners	14
Assistant Solicitors	8
Training contracts p.a.	2

REES PAGE

30-36 Lichfield Street Wolverhampton WV1 1DN
Tel: (01902) 577777 Fax: (01902) 577735
Contact: Mrs J.A. Tennant

Partners	15
Assistant Solicitors	12
Training contracts p.a.	4

RICHMONDS SOLICITORS

Richmond House White Rose Way Doncaster DN4 5JA
Tel: (01302) 762 900 Fax: (01302) 762 801
Contact: Stephen Shore

Partners	8
Assistant Solicitors	10
Training contracts p.a.	2

RICKERBY WATTERSON

Ellenborough House Wellington Street
Cheltenham GL50 1YD
Tel: (01242) 224422 Fax: (01242) 518428
Contact: Joanna Price

Partners	20
Assistant Solicitors	12
Training contracts p.a.	1

ROBERT MUCKLE

Noram House 12 New Bridge Street West
Newcastle-upon-Tyne NE1 8AS
Tel: (0191) 232 4402 Fax: (0191) 261 6954
Contact: Richard Lloyd

Partners	12
Assistant Solicitors	30
Training contracts p.a.	4

ROBINSONS

83 Friar Gate Derby DE1 1FL
Tel: (01332) 291431 Fax: (01332) 291461
Contact: Rob Styles

Partners	12
Assistant Solicitors	8
Training contracts p.a.	1

ROITER ZUCKER

5-7 Broadhurst Gardens Swiss Cottage London NW6 3QX
Tel: (0171) 328 9111 Fax: (0171) 644 8900
Contact: Mr Keith Maynard

Partners	7
Assistant Solicitors	3
Training contracts p.a.	1

ROLLIT FARRELL & BLADON

Wilberforce Court High Street Hull HU1 1YJ
Tel: (01482) 323239 Fax: (01482) 326239
Contact: Neil Franklin

Partners	28
Assistant Solicitors	15
Training contracts p.a.	2–3

ROOKS RIDER

Challoner House 19 Clerkenwell Close London EC1R 0RR
Tel: (0171) 689 7000 Fax: (0171) 689 7001
Contact: Ros Ehren

Partners	10
Assistant Solicitors	20
Training contracts p.a.	3

ROSENBLATT

9-13 St Andrew Street London EC4A 3AE
Tel: (0171) 955 0880 Fax: (0171) 955 0888
Contact: Miss Tania Baldwin

Partners	7
Assistant Solicitors	10
Training contracts p.a.	1–2

ROSLING KING

2-3 Hind Court Fleet St London EC4A 3DL
Tel: (0171) 353 2353 Fax: (0171) 583 2035
Contact: Mr Andrew Lyon

Partners	15
Assistant Solicitors	25
Training contracts p.a.	4

ROYTHORNE & CO

10 Pinchbeck Rd Spalding PE11 1PZ
Tel: (01775) 724141 Fax: (01775) 725736
Contact: Mr P.J. Brewster

Partners	16
Assistant Solicitors	15
Training contracts p.a.	2

SCHILLING & LOM AND PARTNERS

Royalty House 72-74 Dean St London W1V 6AE
Tel: (0171) 453 2500 Fax: (0171) 453 2600
Contact: Mr Jonathan Coad

Partners	6
Assistant Solicitors	13
Training contracts p.a.	2

SEDDONS

5 Portman Square London W1H 0NT
Tel: (0171) 486 9681 Fax: (0171) 935 5049
Contact: Harvey P. Ingram

Partners	14
Assistant Solicitors	6
Training contracts p.a.	2

SHARMAN & TRETHEWY

1 Harpur St Bedford MK40 1PF
Tel: (01234) 303030 Fax: (01234) 409040
Contact: Mr Neville Service

Partners	6
Assistant Solicitors	7
Training contracts p.a.	0–5

SHARPE PRITCHARD

Elizabeth House Fulwood Place London WC1V 6HG
Tel: (0171) 405 4600 Fax: (0171) 242 2210
Contact: Mr A. Badcock

Partners	11
Assistant Solicitors	8
Training contracts p.a.	4

SHULMANS

21 York Place Leeds LS1 2EX
Tel: (0113) 245 2833 Fax: (0113) 246 7326
Contact: Mr David Farrow

Partners	8
Assistant Solicitors	8
Training contracts p.a.	2

SILVERBECK RYMER

Heywoods Building 5 Brunswick Street Liverpool L2 0UU
Tel: (0151) 236 9594 Fax: (0151) 227 1035
Contact: Mr Pat Maher

Partners	10
Assistant Solicitors	61
Training contracts p.a.	3

THE SIMKINS PARTNERSHIP

45-51 Whitfield St London W1P 6AA
Tel: (0171) 631 1050 Fax: (0171) 436 2744
Contact: Howard Stacey

Partners	22
Assistant Solicitors	10
Training contracts p.a.	2

SIMONS MUIRHEAD & BURTON

50 Broadwick Street Soho London W1V 1FF
Tel: (0171) 734 4499 Fax: (0171) 734 3263
Contact: Angela Horne

Partners	9
Assistant Solicitors	6
Training contracts p.a.	1

SONNENSCHEIN

Royex House Aldermanbury Square London EC2V 7HR
Tel: (0171) 600 2222 Fax: (0171) 600 2221
Contact: Ms Sarah Balfour

Partners	5
Assistant Solicitors	5
Training contracts p.a.	2

SPEECHLY BIRCHAM

Bouverie House 154 Fleet St London EC4A 2HX
Tel: 0171 353 3290 Fax: (0171) 353 4825/4992
Contact: Fiona McLaren, Personnel Director

Partners	41
Assistant Solicitors	39
Training contracts p.a.	5

SQUIRE & CO

49-50 St. Johns Square London EC1V 4JL
Tel: (0171) 490 3444 Fax: (0171) 250 4087/4115
Contact: Mr Nicholas Squire

Partners	6
Assistant Solicitors	14
Training contracts p.a.	1

STANLEY TEE & COMPANY

High Street Bishop's Stortford CM23 2LU
Tel: (01279) 755200 Fax: (01279) 758400
Contact: Mr Govan Bramley

Partners	12
Assistant Solicitors	11
Training contracts p.a.	2

STEELE & CO

2 The Norwich Business Park Whiting Road
Norwich NR4 6DJ
Tel: (01603) 627107 Fax: (01603) 625890
Contact: Mrs Jane Nobbs

Partners	14
Assistant Solicitors	12
Training contracts p.a.	2

STEELE RAYMOND

Richmond Point 43 Richmond Hill Bournemouth BH2 6LR	Partners	12
Tel: (01202) 294566 Fax: (01202) 552285	Assistant Solicitors	7
Contact: Paul Longland	Training contracts p.a.	2

STEPHENS INNOCENT

21 New Fetter Lane London EC4A 1AP	Partners	7
Tel: (0171) 353 2000 Fax: (0171) 353 4443	Assistant Solicitors	15
Contact: Nicola Solomon	Training contracts p.a.	2

STEPHENS & SCOWN

25-28 Southernhay East Exeter 2603	Partners	33
Tel: (01392) 210 700 Fax: (01392) 274010	Assistant Solicitors	26
Contact: Brian Doyle	Training contracts p.a.	2

STEVENS & BOLTON

1 The Billings Walnut Tree Close Guildford GU1 4YD	Partners	15
Tel: (01483) 302264 Fax: (01483) 302254	Assistant Solicitors	17
Contact: Catherine Davey	Training contracts p.a.	2–3

STONES CANN & HALLETT

Northernhay Place Exeter EX4 3QQ	Partners	15
Tel: (01392) 666 777 Fax: (01392) 666 770	Assistant Solicitors	5
Contact: Mrs Bronwyn Courtenay-Stamp	Training contracts p.a.	2

SYDNEY MITCHELL

Cavendish House 39 Waterloo Street Birmingham B2 5PU	Partners	8
Tel: (0121) 698 2200 Fax: (0121) 200 1513	Assistant Solicitors	5
Contact: Tony Lewis	Training contracts p.a.	1

TAYLOR & EMMET

Norfolk Row Sheffield S1 1SL	Partners	12
Tel: (0114) 290 2200 Fax: (0114) 290 2290	Assistant Solicitors	12
Contact: Mr Jonathan Stittle	Training contracts p.a.	1

TAYLOR VINTERS

Merlin Place Milton Rd Cambridge CB4 4DP

Tel: (01223) 423444 Fax: (01223) 423486/425446

Contact: Michael Womack

Partners	22
Assistant Solicitors	21
Training contracts p.a.	4

TAYLOR WALTON

36-44 Alma Street Luton LU1 2PL

Tel: (01582) 731161 Fax: (01582) 457900

Contact: Mr J. Wriggleworth

Partners	18
Assistant Solicitors	30
Training contracts p.a.	2

THRINGS & LONG

Midland Bridge Bath BA1 2HQ

Tel: (01225) 448494 Fax: (01225) 319735

Contact: Mr Q.T.S. Elston

Partners	12
Assistant Solicitors	18
Training contracts p.a.	2

THURSFIELDS

14 & 27 Church Street Kidderminster DY10 2AJ

Tel: (01562) 820575 Fax: (01562) 66783

Contact: Mr A.W. Heaselgrave

Partners	13
Assistant Solicitors	6
Training contracts p.a.	2

TOWNLEYS

Dalby House 396-398 City Road London EC1V 2QA

Tel: (0171) 713 7000 Fax: (0171) 713 2999

Contact: Andy Korman

Partners	5
Assistant Solicitors	15
Training contracts p.a.	2

TOWNSENDS

42 Cricklade Street Swindon SN1 3HD

Tel: (01793) 410800 Fax: (01793) 616294

Contact: Lynn Ford

Partners	20
Assistant Solicitors	15
Training contracts p.a.	3

TOZERS

Broadwalk House Southernhay West Exeter EX1 1UA

Tel: (01392) 207020 Fax: (01392) 207019

Contact: Sue Allen

Partners	18
Assistant Solicitors	14
Training contracts p.a.	2

TRETHOWAN WOODFORD

New Street Salisbury SP1 2LY
Tel: (01722) 412512 Fax: (01722) 411300
Contact: Mr Andrew Mercer

Partners	17
Assistant Solicitors	12
Training contracts p.a.	2

TROBRIDGES

1 Ford Park Road Mutley Plain Plymouth PL4 6LY
Tel: (01752) 664022 Fax: (01752) 223761
Contact: C. Matthews

Partners	3
Assistant Solicitors	3
Training contracts p.a.	1–2

TRUMPS

P O Box 8000 One Redcliff Street Bristol BS99 2SD
Tel: (0117) 946 8200 Fax: (0117) 946 8201
Contact: Sheila Hirst

Partners	9
Assistant Solicitors	13
Training contracts p.a.	3

TUCKERS

39 Warren Street London W1P 5PD
Tel: (0171) 388 8333 Fax: (0171) 388 7333
Contact: Brian Craig

Partners	2
Assistant Solicitors	18
Training contracts p.a.	1

TURBERVILLES WITH NELSON CUFF

122 High Street Uxbridge UB8 1JT
Tel: (01895) 201700 Fax: (01895) 273519
Contact: Laura Haworth

Partners	10
Assistant Solicitors	13
Training contracts p.a.	2

TURNERS

1 Poole Rd Bournemouth BH2 5QQ
Tel: (01202) 291291 Fax: (01202) 553606
Contact: Mr Colin Wilson

Partners	15
Assistant Solicitors	4
Training contracts p.a.	0–5

TWITCHEN MUSTERS & KELLY

County Chambers 25-27 Weston Road
Southend-on-Sea SS1 1BB
Tel: (01702) 339222 Fax: (01702) 331563
Contact: Mr G.B. Mather

Partners	7
Assistant Solicitors	9
Training contracts p.a.	2

VEALE WASBROUGH

Orchard Court Orchard Lane Bristol BS1 5DS	Partners	25
Tel: (0117) 925 2020 Fax: (0117) 925 2025	Assistant Solicitors	34
Contact: Paul Cottam	Training contracts p.a.	5

VIZARDS

42 Bedford Row London WC1R 4JL	Partners	26
Tel: (0171) 405 6302 Fax: (0171) 405 6248	Assistant Solicitors	40
Contact: Mark R. Newman	Training contracts p.a.	5

WACKS CALLER

Steam Packet House 76 Cross Street Manchester M2 4JU	Partners	12
Tel: (0161) 957 8888 Fax: (0161) 957 8899	Assistant Solicitors	14
Contact: Mr A.T. Dempsey	Training contracts p.a.	0–2

WAKE SMITH

68 Clarkehouse Road Sheffield S10 2LJ	Partners	12
Tel: (0114) 266 6660 Fax: (0114) 267 1253	Assistant Solicitors	10
Contact: Mr Michael Tunbridge	Training contracts p.a.	1

WALKER SMITH & WAY

26 Nicholas Street Chester CH1 2PQ	Partners	24
Tel: (01244) 357 400 Fax: (01244) 357 444	Assistant Solicitors	31
Contact: Tony Britlin	Training contracts p.a.	5

WALLACE & PARTNERS

9 Great James St London WC1N 3DA	Partners	8
Tel: (0171) 404 4422 Fax: (0171) 831 6850	Assistant Solicitors	2
Contact: Richard Pike	Training contracts p.a.	2

WANSBROUGHS

Northgate House Devizes SN10 1JX	Partners	10
Tel: (01380) 723611 Fax: (01380) 728213	Assistant Solicitors	6
Contact: Richard Drury	Training contracts p.a.	1

WANSBROUGHS WILLEY HARGRAVE

103 Temple Street Bristol BS99 7UD	Partners	77
Tel: (0117) 926 8981 Fax: (0117) 918 2600	Assistant Solicitors	175
Contact: Carol Smith	Training contracts p.a.	15

WARD HADAWAY

Sandgate House 102 Quayside
Newcastle upon Tyne NE1 3DX
Tel: (0191) 204 4000 Fax: (0191) 204 4001
Contact: David R. Hesselberth

Partners	32
Assistant Solicitors	26
Training contracts p.a.	6

WARNER GOODMAN & STREAT

66 West Street Fareham PO16 0JR
Tel: (01329) 288121 Fax: (01329) 822714
Contact: Nigel Lewis

Partners	12
Assistant Solicitors	29
Training contracts p.a.	2

WARREN & ALLEN

24 Low Pavement Nottingham NG1 7ED
Tel: (0115) 955 2222 Fax: (0115) 948 4649
Contact: Mr Christophe Miller

Partners	10
Assistant Solicitors	13
Training contracts p.a.	2

WHISKERS

Gate House The High Harlow CM20 1LW
Tel: (01279) 441111 Fax: (01279) 444464
Contact: Mr Stephen Ray

Partners	6
Assistant Solicitors	7
Training contracts p.a.	2

WHITE & BOWKER

19 St. Peter St Winchester SO23 8BU
Tel: (01962) 844440 Fax: (01962) 842300
Contact: Anne Miller

Partners	15
Assistant Solicitors	12
Training contracts p.a.	2

WHITEHEAD MONCKTON

72 King St Maidstone ME14 1BL
Tel: (01622) 698000 Fax: (01622) 690050
Contact: Dawn Harrison

Partners	14
Assistant Solicitors	5
Training contracts p.a.	2

WHITTLES

Pearl Assurance House 23 Princess Street
Manchester M2 4ER
Tel: (0161) 228 2061 Fax: (0161) 236 1046
Contact: Mr D.M. Rogers

Partners	15
Assistant Solicitors	19
Training contracts p.a.	2–3

WILKIN CHAPMAN

PO Box 16 Town Hall Square Grimsby DN31 1HE
Tel: (01472) 358234 Fax: (01472) 360198
Contact: Mrs J. Whittaker

Partners	16
Assistant Solicitors	15
Training contracts p.a.	2

WILKINSON, WOODWARD & LUDLAM

11 Fountain St Halifax HX1 1LU
Tel: (01422) 340711 Fax: (01422) 330417
Contact: Robert Scott

Partners	9
Assistant Solicitors	1
Training contracts p.a.	1.5

WILLANS

28/29 Imperial Square Cheltenham GL50 1RH
Tel: (01242) 514707 Fax: (01242) 519079
Contact: David Glass

Partners	7
Assistant Solicitors	8
Training contracts p.a.	1

WILLCOX LANE CLUTTERBUCK WITH REES EDWARDS MADDOX

55 Charlotte Street Birmingham B3 1PX
Tel: (0121) 236 9441 Fax: (0121) 236 4733
Contact: Sue Stott

Partners	12
Assistant Solicitors	10
Training contracts p.a.	2

WILLIAM HATTON

Trinity House Trinity Road Dudley DY1 1JB
Tel: (01384) 211211 Fax: (01384) 456165
Contact: Mr A.T.R. Perry

Partners	7
Assistant Solicitors	3
Training contracts p.a.	1

WILLIAMSON & HORROCKS

17 Devonshire Square London EC2M 4SQ
Tel: (0171) 655 6500 Fax: (0171) 655 6501
Contact: Hugh Bryant

Partners	2
Assistant Solicitors	7
Training contracts p.a.	1

WILLIAM STURGES & CO

Alliance House 12 Caxton St London SW1H 0QY
Tel: (0171) 873 1000 Fax: (0171) 873 1010
Contact: Mr T. Tuthill

Partners	15
Assistant Solicitors	4
Training contracts p.a.	2–3

WILLMETT & CO

27 Sheet St Windsor SL4 1BX
Tel: (01753) 861381 Fax: (01753) 842172
Contact: Mrs A.R.A. Miller

Partners	10
Assistant Solicitors	6
Training contracts p.a.	1

WILSON BROWNE

PO Box No. 8 Meadow Road Kettering NN16 8TN
Tel: (01536) 410041 Fax: (01536) 410444
Contact: Mr James Wright

Partners	15
Assistant Solicitors	4
Training contracts p.a.	1

WILSON & CO

697 High Road London N17 8AD
Tel: (0181) 808 7535 Fax: (0181) 880 3393
Contact: Mr Michael Hanley

Partners	2
Assistant Solicitors	8
Training contracts p.a.	2

WILSONS SOLICITORS

Steynings House Fisherton St Salisbury SP2 7RJ
Tel: (01722) 412412 Fax: (01722) 411500
Contact: Carole Davidson

Partners	14
Assistant Solicitors	20
Training contracts p.a.	4

WINCKWORTH & PEMBERTON

35 Great Peter Street Westminster London SW1P 3LR
Tel: (0171) 593 5000 Fax: (0171) 593 5099
Contact: Mr R.H.A. MacDougald

Partners	17
Assistant Solicitors	19
Training contracts p.a.	3–4

WINSTANLEY-BURGESS

378 City Rd London EC1V 2QA
Tel: (0171) 278 7911 Fax: (0171) 833 2135
Contact: Joanna Toloczko

Partners	5
Assistant Solicitors	6
Training contracts p.a.	2

WINWARD FEARON

35 Bow St London WC2E 7AU
Tel: (0171) 420 2800 Fax: (0171) 420 2801
Contact: Edward Gore

Partners	10
Assistant Solicitors	17
Training contracts p.a.	2

WITHY KING

5 & 6 Northumberland Buildings Queen Square
Bath BA1 2JE
Tel: (01225) 425731 Fax: (01225) 315562
Contact: Mrs Lynn Clark

Partners	11
Assistant Solicitors	9
Training contracts p.a.	3–4

WOLFERSTANS

Deptford Chambers 60-64 North Hill Plymouth PL4 8EP
Tel: (01752) 663295 Fax: (01752) 672021
Contact: Neil Groves

Partners	26
Assistant Solicitors	16
Training contracts p.a.	2

WOOLLCOMBE BEER WATTS

Church House Queen Street Newton Abbot TQ12 2QP
Tel: (01626) 202404 Fax: (01626) 202420
Contact: Mrs Osborne

Partners	21
Assistant Solicitors	14
Training contracts p.a.	1–2

WRIGHT HASSALL & CO

9 Clarendon Place Leamington Spa CV32 5QP
Tel: (01926) 886688 Fax: (01926) 885588
Contact: Carol Matthews

Partners	19
Assistant Solicitors	10
Training contracts p.a.	2

A.E. WYETH & CO

Bridge House High Street Dartford DA1 1JR
Tel: (01322) 297000 Fax: (01322) 297001
Contact: Mrs Hilary Henderson

Partners	10
Assistant Solicitors	10
Training contracts p.a.	2

ZAIWALLA & CO

33 Chancery Lane London WC2A 1ZZ
Tel: (0171) 312 1000 Fax: (0171) 312 1100
Contact: Mr Terry Hodsdon

Partners	5
Assistant Solicitors	1
Training contracts p.a.	2

ZERMANSKY & PARTNERS

10 Butts Court Leeds LS1 5JS
Tel: (0113) 245 9766 Fax: (0113) 246 7465
Contact: Mrs Pamela Glynn

Partners	7
Assistant Solicitors	8
Training contracts p.a.	1

Training as a Barrister

Introduction
- *Timetable*
- *The Bar System*
- *Pupillage & Tenancy*

TIMETABLE FOR TRAINING AS A BARRISTER

Second Year Law Students and Third Year Non-Law Students

Autumn Term (Oct-Dec): Compile information about sets of Chambers. Obtain Chambers' literature. Attend law fairs on campus. Look into funding possibilities for the conversion course and/or the BVC.

Spring Term (Jan-March): Apply for mini-pupillages and other work experience. Apply for the conversion course before February closing date if necessary. Attend law fairs on campus.

Summer Term (April-July): Obtain application details for BVC from CACH (Centralised Applications Clearing House). Find out about pupillage application. Attend pupillage fairs.

Final Year Law Students and Students on the conversion course

Autumn Term: Apply for BVC. Sort out funding if possible. Research the Inns of Court and join one. Make further pupillage enquiries.

Spring and Summer Terms: Attend pupillage fair in London and pick up copy of Chambers Pupillages and Awards Handbook, complete with application disk. Make PACH (Pupillage Applications Clearing House) and non-PACH pupillage applications. Closing date for PACH is in July. Non-PACH Chambers all have their own application methods and closing dates.

BVC Students

Autumn Term: Attend pupillage interviews. In mid-November offers of pupillage are made through PACH. Applicants must accept or reject offers within seven days. The PACH pool system begins in December. Candidates will be informed of any remaining pupillage places.

THE BAR SYSTEM

About three quarters of barristers in England and Wales work in 'independent practice' and have tenancies at sets of chambers in London or one of the six circuits around the country. The remaining barristers work in 'employed practice' for organisations such as the Crown Prosecution Service (CPS), the Government Legal Service (GLS), local government, the armed forces, the Crown and a variety of commercial organisations. More information about these organisations can be obtained from the Bar Council. Here we deal mainly with independent practice.

Traditionally, solicitors instructed barristers to advise them on complex points of law and to present cases in court. While barristers still fulfil this dual role, the division between the two branches of the profession is becoming increasingly blurred. Many solicitors already have equal rights of audience in the courts, and with some organisations able to instruct counsel without solicitors – through Direct Professional Access, the role of barristers is changing.

Undoubtedly such changes will affect the bar, but it seems that apocalyptic predictions are premature and the bar will, for the time being, continue to provide the services it has for decades. Solicitors are grateful for specialist advice (on the rules of evidence, for example) from senior counsel; and junior counsel survive because, in certain cases, it is cheaper for solicitors to employ them than to handle the work themselves.

Barristers are also making efforts to rebrand themselves and their sets and are becoming more commercially aware. There is a trend towards larger sets of chambers offering a wider range of expertise and a tendency for barristers to move between chambers much more than they used to.

There has also been a shake-up in the education of barristers. Until September 1997, the Bar Vocational Course was only available at one institution: the Inns of Court Law School in London. Now there are seven other institutions around the country which are authorised to offer the vocational stage of training to would-be barristers. The Bar Council has also introduced continuing professional development (CPD) for barristers starting independent practice on or after 1 October 1997. The 'New Practitioners Programme' requires barristers to undertake 42 hours of education in areas such as ethics and advocacy in the first three years of practice. This is equivalent to the Law Society's CPD requirements for solicitors.

Obtaining pupillage and tenancy is highly competitive, and students should know what they are letting themselves in for if they decide to pursue a career at the bar. Of those who began the BVC in 1996 only half got pupillage, and of these only 60% have obtained a tenancy. Gary Eaton is a student at the Inns of Court School of Law. "The bar is not a profession which should be entered into lightly. Qualifying is extremely expensive, and elements of snobbery and nepotism still exist."

However, for those who do succeed, a career at the bar is generally a stimulating and rewarding one. While there may well be financial struggles early on, many barristers move on to enjoy considerable wealth, and being in independent practice provides more flexibility and freedom than many jobs. The bar remains a highly respected institution, and many barristers move on to other successful careers in business, academia or politics. Those who do not get tenancies should not despair. Their legal training will have provided them with a wealth of knowledge and skills which other employers will value. ▶

The Inns of Court

The bar of England and Wales is comprised of four Inns of Court – Inner Temple, Middle Temple, Lincoln's Inn and Gray's Inn. Anyone wishing to be "called to the bar" (ie. wishing to qualify as a barrister) must join an Inn. Only the Inns have the power to "call" new barristers.

You can join an Inn at any stage of your academic training, as long as you are a member by the end of June in the year that you begin the BVC. You can only apply to join one Inn, but being accepted should be no problem. Your choice of Inn does not dictate your choice of chambers for pupillage and tenancy or the area in which you wish to practise. Most people choose their Inn for practical or social reasons. They may prefer the location and facilities of one Inn above another, or they may have a friend or family connection with a particular Inn. All provide broadly the same services: a library, lunching and dining facilities, a collegiate support network, common rooms, social activities and beautiful gardens in the centre of London. They also offer a limited number of grants and scholarships and an opportunity to meet senior barristers in your favourite areas of practice.

Dining: the Inns and outs

In order to qualify as a barrister, students originally had to 'dine in hall' (ie. eat dinner in the dinng room of their Inn) a certain number of times. Now students must complete 12 qualifying units and 'dining' counts for some of them.

The other qualifying units include weekends at the Inn or at residential centres, and education days – primarily for students outside London. Dining is now divided into education dinners (with lectures or talks), domus dinners (when students and seniors dine together) and social dinners (such as Grand Night or nights when students can bring guests).

Many people ask why dining is needed at all. Originally the members would have had a much closer relationship with their Inn since the profession was much smaller. They would have been educated by their Inn, and many would have lived there. Anthea Tatton-Brown, the Deputy Under Treasurer for Students at Middle Temple, says: "the point of dining and the training weekends is to maintain the collegiate atmosphere of the Inn and to participate in a number of old traditions and customs. Dining gives students the chance to meet and talk with other students and with practitioners who are a few years ahead of them. The students can also meet judges and Masters of the Bench from the senior ranks of the profession."

Dinner itself only lasts an hour or so and is sometimes followed by entertainment such as music, mooting or talks. Dave Evans recently left Bar School, and has some advice for students who are a bit wary of dining. "You have to do it, so make the most of it. You get wine with the meal, and can make a good night of it if you sit with your friends."

PUPILLAGE & TENANCY

Pupillage Structure

Pupillage is the apprenticeship served by trainee barristers – 'pupils'. It is equivalent to the trainee solicitor's training contract, but where the training contract lasts two years, a pupillage normally takes one year. The pupillage is split into six-month periods, known as 'sixes'. The first and second six can be done at the same chambers or at two different sets of chambers. Neither route guarantees a tenancy (ie. a permanent place in chambers). In fact, third sixes are increasingly common for students who do not get tenancy at their first attempt.

Every pupil is assigned a pupil master or mistress. They are experienced barristers who organise the pupil's training, development and assessment within chambers. The first six months generally involve observing and assisting your pupil master/mistress and other barristers from chambers. You will be watching, listening, reading, researching and drafting. The second six involves building up your own case load. You will begin to have your own clients and appear in court on your own.

Applying for Pupillage

In 1996, the Bar Council launched PACH (Pupillage and Applications Clearing House). This system is intended to assist applicants by reducing the number of applications they make and ensuring that all chambers adhere to a common timetable for selection. By limiting the choice of sets to 12, it is intended that students will make more focused applications to sets which suit their interests and abilities.

The system is similar to the UCAS university application procedure and is monitored by the Bar Council. Students need to obtain from the Bar Council a copy of the Chambers Pupillages & Awards Handbook, together with the application form which is on disk. The handbook guides you through the somewhat lengthy and complex application process.

Not all chambers are members of PACH and most students will apply to non-PACH as well as PACH sets. You should apply individually to non-PACH chambers. It is possible to do a first six at a PACH set and a second six at a non-PACH set. For more details contact the Bar Council, PACH office, 2/3 Cursitor Street, London, EC4A 1NE, Tel: 0171 440 4014/4015.

Tenancy

Obtaining tenancy is the final and, arguably, most difficult hurdle in the long journey to becoming a barrister. As with pupillage, competition is intense and many excellent candidates struggle to get a tenancy. However, the really determined should not be discouraged and may have to accept that they need to do a third six or obtain work experience elsewhere before securing tenancy.

For successful candidates, there are a number of practical considerations involved in being self-employed at the independent bar. You will be entirely responsible for your own working environment and this includes your furniture, computer equipment and notebook PC to use in court. You must also purchase at least one dark three piece suit with tunic or court shirt, a wing or collar for court and a day collar for chambers. Your wig adds the finishing touch to the outfit and all this will set you back several hundred pounds. Despite the Equality Code for the Bar which aims to prevent discrimination of any kind, those students with a bit of extra money will certainly find the uphill battle to becoming a barrister a great deal easier.

Specialist Practice Areas

CHANCERY

Area of law

The chancery bar is something of a mystery to outsiders, but don't let this put you off applying for pupillage here. Half the work in the High Court is in the Chancery Division, and the chancery bar has a reputation for producing excellent lawyers and judges. Most chancery sets are based around Lincoln's Inn, although other sets will undertake some chancery work. Chancery sets tend to recruit fewer pupils than commercial or criminal law sets, but according to Jonathan Evans of Wilberforce Chambers, they offer tenancy to a higher proportion of their pupils.

Chancery has a reputation for being 'genteel' and slightly more formal than other areas of practice, with an emphasis on advisory work. This may have been the case in the past but the chancery bar is now becoming more modern and competitive. Some chambers are expanding and re-branding in order to compete with the commercial bar.

One senior silk we spoke to said "the prospect of higher overheads, greater competition and lower fees means that some sets will disappear and others will merge. It is happening now with the advent of a Premier League of chambers." However, small niche sets which specialise in certain areas of chancery such as trusts are likely to survive.

Type of work

There is no corresponding area of practice for solicitors, and the term chancery is quite difficult to define. The chancery bar undertakes a wide range of work, much of which is property-related, but company and financial matters play increasingly important roles in the life of a chancery barrister. Commercial litigation (including injunctions) is also handled by these sets.

Chancery sets can be roughly divided into traditional and commercial. Traditional chancery includes charities, joint ownership, mortgages, partnerships, pensions, probate, real property, revenue, trusts, settlements and wills. Commercial chancery involves banking, commercial contracts, companies, financial services, fraud, insolvency, IP, media, professional negligence and torts. The distinction is sometimes artificial because the chancery bar forms a continuous spectrum and cases often need a broad range of knowledge. Clients increasingly expect their counsel to deal with the whole case and not just limited aspects of it. It is a matter of emphasis whether a set is labelled traditional or commercial.

The general trend is for chancery chambers to do more and more commercial work, and they certainly market themselves as alternatives to commercial sets. "People are starting to redefine chancery," says Bernard Weatherill QC, chancery silk at 3 New Square. "A very large number of practitioners at the chancery bar have practices which are recognisably commercial." Other lawyers are predicting the emergence of a new 'Business Bar' which will be comprised of the most progressive commercial and chancery sets.

Work for a chancery pupil is likely to be intermittent. There is often a dearth of work during pupillage, but a steady supply in the early years of tenancy. Junior chancery barristers do a lot of residential landlord and tenant work as well as possession actions, 'winders' (winding up actions) in the Company Court, a small amount of insolvency, and a range of other general advice where the client cannot afford a more senior tenant. Advisory work takes the form of written opinions, telephone advice and conferences with solicitors and clients. A tenant of one year call told us "a high proportion of my work is advisory, much more so than my friends who do common law. I don't expect to be in court more than two or three times a week."

Skills needed

Chancery is for lawyers' lawyers. This is an area where an in-depth knowledge of the law, attention to detail, and diligence are paramount. Clients require a thorough analysis of their problems and expect counsel to arrive at the right answer on which they can depend. At a junior level there is more paperwork and less client contact and witness-handling than in other fields, and although there is scope for advocacy, flamboyance is not needed.

Jonathan Evans has been a tenant at Wilberforce Chambers since 1995, and he emphasises the need to mix intellectual ability with the art of persuasion. "Chancery practice requires an analytical mind, but this must be coupled with the ability to express difficult ideas logically and clearly. Unlike some other areas of work, the emphasis is on the law and not so much on the facts."

The Sets

The drive towards bigger sets offering a range of specialisms – a development seen throughout the Bar – has been particularly marked in the chancery field. The result has been a turbulent year for the Chancery sets. Some have been hit by defections, while one long-established set – 17 Old Buildings – has been subsumed into 10 Old Square after losing several tenants. Sets which have strengthened their positions include Serle Court Chambers, Wilberforce Chambers and 4 Stone Buildings.

The leading commercial sets include 13 Old Square, Serle Court Chambers and 4 Stone Buildings. High profile cases at Serle Court this year range from *Don King Productions* v *Warren* (rights on the termination of a boxing partnership) to *Bridge Trust Co* v *AG* of Cayman Islands (charitable trusts).

The top traditional sets are Wilberforce Chambers, 3 Stone Buildings, 3 New Square and 11 New Square. Wilberforce Chambers successfully straddle both traditional and commercial chancery work. Barristers have been involved in *IRC* v *McGuckian*, a leading House of Lords case on tax avoidance and *Don King* v *Warren* .

The main chancery set outside London is St Philip's Chambers in Birmingham. Others with chancery reputations include 40 King Street, Manchester and Guildhall Chambers in Bristol. ▶

Leading London Sets

	Traditional Chancery	Commercial Chancery	Pensions	Property	Tax
Barnards Inn Chambers (Bowles)				****	
4 Breams Bldgs (Lockhart-Mummery QC)				*****	
Enterprise Chambers (Mann QC)		****		****	
35 Essex Street (Inglis-Jones QC)			***		
Falcon Chambers (Gaunt/Lewison QC)				******	
8 Gray's Inn Square (Soares)					**
Gray's Inn Tax Chambers (Grundy)					*****
1 New Square (Hamilton QC)	****	****			
3 New Square (Goodhart QC)	****				
11 New Square (Crampin QC)	****				
11 New Square (Gardiner QC)					**
12 New Square (Mowbray QC)	***	***			
24 Old Buildings (Bretten QC)					***
24 Old Buildings (Brodie QC)		****			
9 Old Square (Reid QC)		*****		*****	
10 Old Square (Price QC)	***				
11 Old Square (Crawford/Simpkiss)	***				
13 Old Square (Lyndon-Stanford QC)	***	******		*****	
Pump Court Tax Chmbrs (Thornhill QC)					******
Serle Court Chambers (Sparrow QC)	***	******		****	
3/4 South Square (Crystal QC)		***			
3 Stone Buildings (Vos QC)	***	****	**		
4 Stone Buildings (Heslop QC)		******			
5 Stone Buildings (Harrod)	*****		***		
7 Stone Buildings (Aldous QC)		*****	**		
9 Stone Buildings (Ashe QC)	***				
11 Stone Buildings (Beckman QC)		***			
3 Temple Gardens (Braham QC)					**
Wilberforce Chambers (Nugee QC)	******	*****	******	****	

Sets and their star ratings are based on Chambers' Directory 1998–1999. Six stars represent a top-ranked set, five stars a second-ranked set, etc. See page 3 for further details.

COMMERCIAL

Area of law

All aspects of commercial law are handled at the commercial bar. From aviation to sports law – if there is a business dispute then commercial counsel will handle it. Some barristers go down a particular commercial route and develop a niche practice in construction or shipping or media work. Others focus more on company law (sometimes seen as a separate area of the bar) handling insolvency, financial services and partnership issues. Others still develop specialisms in obscure areas such as enforcing foreign judgements from certain African or South American countries. What they all have in common is a thorough knowledge of contract law and, increasingly, an understanding of international laws.

You will sometimes see commercial practice defined as work that goes to the Commercial Court or one of the County Court Business Courts. This is too narrow a definition, for a great deal of commercial work exists in the High Court and in arbitrations. Alternative Dispute Resolution is becoming more important at the bar, and barristers can expect a significant proportion of their commercial practice to involve ADR of some description.

The commercial bar is also likely to see increasing overlap with the chancery bar. The traditional divide between commercial and chancery work has been steadily eroded as commercial barristers become more willing to start cases in the Chancery division and chancery barristers to appear in the Commercial Court. "The artificial categories of work are disappearing," says Ric Martin, Chambers Director at leading commercial set Fountain Court. "Lawyers have been conditioned to compartmentalise the law, but clients seek a solution to their problem and are not interested in the distinctions between commercial and chancery work."

Type of work

Most work is contract-based, and there is often a significant international component, such as public international law, international trade law, conflict of laws and EU/competition law. Elements of tort, equity and restitution will also crop up. Regulatory work plays a significant part in the financial services and insurance-type work. If intent on a specific commercial route then industry knowledge will also be necessary. For example, John Blackburn QC of Atkin Chambers (a commercial set particularly known for its construction work) has developed detailed knowledge not only of the construction industry, but also of the computer and IT world, where he is recognised as one of the leading silks.

Michael Swainston is on the executive committee of Combar (the Commercial Bar Association). He has a background in shipping work, and now has a successful commercial practice at Brick Court Chambers. "In addition to my straightforward commercial practice, I have also developed what can be called ornaments to the conventional business cases. I was recently involved in a dispute between a Middle Eastern emir and his son who deposed him. There was a considerable element of public international law in the case, but it was basically commercial because of the amount of money involved. There are more opportunities to get diverse work at the commercial bar than many people think."

Instructing solicitors will usually be City firms or large regional commercial practices, with major companies as clients. In addition, the commercial bar is increasingly instructed directly by professional clients who do not have to go through solicitors and by in-house legal departments of major companies. Instructions from abroad are also on the increase.

In the early stages of practice, junior tenants will spend much time drafting pleadings and interlocutory applications. They will also give written and telephone opinions and advice in conference. They are unlikely to have trial work entirely of their own but will often act as a junior in large trials and arbitrations.

However they will get advocacy experience in interlocutory applications and through large commercial sets' efforts to deploy them in a range of tribunals.

Skills needed
Commercial nous is a prerequisite for this area of practice. Businesses are not only paying you for your knowledge of the law, but also for your awareness of the competitive environment in which they operate. For many companies, litigation is a means to an end, and is part of a wider corporate strategy that has little to do with legal niceties. You will have to advise clients on the best litigation strategy to achieve their aims.

A long attention span and a keen eye for detail are necessary. Cases can be heavy on paperwork, and you will have to sift through a great deal of material to find the real issues that need to be resolved. You will need to be extremely analytical, and able to express yourself clearly both on paper and in court. Teamwork is an integral part of life at the commercial bar. Most cases involve teams of instructing solicitors, several clients and more than one barrister. Being able to work together is essential.

Advocacy is more important to commercial practice than many students think. You will therefore need the temperament and mental agility to deal with a case in court. However advocacy in commercial cases is very different from advocacy before a jury. In general you will have much longer to prepare your case than a criminal barrister, (although interlocutory injunctions sometimes need dealing with at the drop of a hat). Careful preparation and planning and an intimate knowledge of the facts are more likely to impress the commercial court than the last minute theatrics of a criminal barrister who has only just seen his brief.

The Sets
In London the leading commercial sets are seen to be Brick Court Chambers, Essex Court Chambers, One Essex Court and Fountain Court. These sets field some of the best known, most expert and highly paid silks at the bar: Christopher Clarke QC, Gordon Pollock QC, Anthony Grabiner QC and Peter Scott QC. They handle major commercial disputes involving large sums of money for corporate clients, regulatory bodies and governments.

Other leading commercial sets are strong in particular areas. 3 Verulam Buildings have a reputation for their banking work; Blackstone Chambers for media and entertainment; 4 Essex Court for shipping; Erskine Chambers for insolvency and financial services; Atkin and Keating Chambers for construction and arbitration; 4 Field Court for shipping and Monckton Chambers for EU and competition law.

On the circuits, Guildhall Chambers and St Johns Chambers in Bristol lead in the west; St Philip's Chambers, 5 Fountain Court and 3 Fountain Court in Birmingham are strong in the Midlands; Enterprise Chambers in Leeds stands out in the north east and Byrom Street Chambers leads the field on the northern circuit. ▶

Leading London Sets

Arbitration

Atkin Chambers *(Blackburn QC)*	★★★★★	4 Essex Court *(Teare QC)*	★★★★
Brick Court Chambers *(Clarke QC)*	★★★★	20 Essex Street *(Johnson QC)*	★★★★★
Essex Court Chambers *(Pollock QC)*	★★★★★★	Fountain Court *(Scott QC)*	★★★
One Essex Court *(Grabiner QC)*	★★★★★	Keating Chambers *(Fernyhough QC)*	★★★★★

Aviation

Brick Court Chambers *(Clarke QC)*	★★★★★	20 Essex Street *(Johnson QC)*	★★★★
Essex Court Chambers *(Pollock QC)*	★★★★	Fountain Court *(Scott QC)*	★★★★★★
4 Essex Court *(Teare QC)*	★★★★	Monckton Chambers *(Fowler QC)*	★★★★

Banking

Brick Court Chambers *(Clarke QC)*	★★★★★★	Fountain Court *(Scott QC)*	★★★★★★
Erskine Chambers *(Sykes QC)*	★★★★★★	4–5 Gray's Inn Sq *(Appleby/Beloff QC)*	★★★★
Essex Court Chambers *(Pollock QC)*	★★★★★	3/4 South Square *(Crystal QC)*	★★★★★★
One Essex Court *(Grabiner QC)*	★★★★★★	3 Verulam Bldgs *(Neville Thomas QC)*	★★★★★★
20 Essex Street *(Johnson QC)*	★★★★★		

Company

Enterprise Chambers *(Mann QC)*	★★★★★	Serle Court Chambers *(Sparrow QC)*	★★★★★
Erskine Chambers *(Sykes QC)*	★★★★★★	3/4 South Square *(Crystal QC)*	★★★★★
One Essex Court *(Grabiner QC)*	★★★★★	4 Stone Buildings *(Heslop QC)*	★★★★★★
13 Old Square *(Lyndon-Stanford QC)*	★★★★★	7 Stone Buildings *(Aldous QC)*	★★★★★

Construction

Atkin Chambers *(Blackburn QC)*	★★★★★★	Monckton Chambers *(Fowler QC)*	★★★
2 Crown Office Row *(Powell QC)*	★★★★★	One Paper Buildings *(Slater QC)*	★★★
39 Essex Street *(Glasgow QC)*	★★★★	4 Pump Court *(Mauleverer QC)*	★★★★★
Keating Chambers *(Fernyhough QC)*	★★★★★★	3 Serjeants' Inn *(Naughton QC)*	★★★
12 King's Bench Walk *(Walker QC)*	★★★	2 Temple Gardens *(Phillips QC)*	★★★

Energy

Atkin Chambers *(Blackburn QC)*	★★★	Keating Chambers *(Fernyhough QC)*	★★★
Essex Court Chambers *(Pollock QC)*	★★★★★	7 King's Bench Walk *(Tomlinson QC)*	★★★★
One Essex Court *(Grabiner QC)*	★★★★★★	2 Mitre Court Buildings *(FitzGerald QC)*	★★★★★
Fountain Court *(Scott QC)*	★★★★★	1 Serjeants' Inn *(Read QC)*	★★★

European Union

Brick Court Chambers *(Clarke QC)*	★★★★★★	Monckton Chambers *(Fowler QC)*	★★★★★★

Financial Services

Blackstone Chmbrs *(Baxendale/Flint QC)*	★★★★★	3/4 South Square *(Crystal QC)*	★★★★★
Brick Court Chambers *(Clarke QC)*	★★★★★	4 Stone Buildings *(Heslop QC)*	★★★★★
Erskine Chambers *(Sykes QC)*	★★★★★★	3 Verulam Buildings *(Thomas QC)*	★★★★
One Essex Court *(Grabiner QC)*	★★★★		

Leading London Sets

General Commercial

Blackstone Chmbrs *(Baxendale/Flint QC)*	★★★	7 King's Bench Walk *(Tomlinson QC)*	★★★★
Brick Court Chambers *(Clarke QC)*	★★★★★★	11 King's Bch Wlk *(Tabachnik/Goudie QC)*	★★
Essex Court Chambers *(Pollock QC)*	★★★★★★	Littleton Chambers *(Burton QC)*	★★★★
One Essex Court *(Grabiner QC)*	★★★★★★	4 Pump Court *(Mauleverer QC)*	★★★
4 Essex Court *(Teare QC)*	★★	Serle Court Chambers *(Sparrow QC)*	★★★
Fountain Court *(Scott QC)*	★★★★★	3 Verulam Bldgs *(Neville Thomas QC)*	★★★★★
1 Hare Court *(Lord Neill/Southwell QC)*	★★★		

Insolvency

Enterprise Chambers *(Mann QC)*	★★★★	Serle Court Chambers *(Sparrow QC)*	★★★★
Erskine Chambers *(Sykes QC)*	★★★★★	3/4 South Square *(Crystal QC)*	★★★★★★
One Essex Court *(Grabiner QC)*	★★★★	4 Stone Buildings *(Heslop QC)*	★★★★★
1 New Square *(Hamilton QC)*	★★★★	11 Stone Buildings *(Beckman QC)*	★★★★
13 Old Square *(Lyndon-Stanford QC)*	★★★★★		

Insurance

Brick Court Chambers *(Clarke QC)*	★★★★★	Fountain Court *(Scott QC)*	★★★★
Essex Court Chambers *(Pollock QC)*	★★★★★★	7 King's Bench Walk *(Tomlinson QC)*	★★★★
One Essex Court *(Grabiner QC)*	★★★★	4 Pump Court *(Mauleverer QC)*	★★★
20 Essex Street *(Johnson QC)*	★★★	3 Verulam Bldgs *(Neville Thomas QC)*	★★★

IP/IT

One Essex Court *(Grabiner QC)*	★★★	19 Old Buildings *(Wilson QC)*	★★★
Three New Square *(Young QC)*	★★★★★★	One Raymond Buildings *(Morcom QC)*	★★★
8 New Square *(Fysh QC)*	★★★★★★	11 South Square *(Floyd QC)*	★★★★★★

Media

Blackstone Chmbrs *(Baxendale/Flint QC)*	★★★★★★	8 New Square *(Fysh QC)*	★★★★★★
Brick Court Chambers *(Clarke QC)*	★★★★★	5 Raymond Buildings *(Milmo QC)*	★★★★★
Doughty St Chambers *(Robertson QC)*	★★★★	11 South Square *(Floyd QC)*	★★★★
Essex Court Chambers *(Pollock QC)*	★★★★★	3 Stone Buildings *(Vos QC)*	★★★★
5 New Square *(Rayner/James QC)*	★★★★★	3 Verulam Bldgs *(Neville Thomas QC)*	★★★★

Shipping

Brick Court Chambers *(Clarke QC)*	★★★★★★	20 Essex Street *(Johnson QC)*	★★★★★★
Essex Court Chambers *(Pollock QC)*	★★★★★★	4 Field Court *(Brice QC)*	★★★★★★
4 Essex Court *(Teare QC)*	★★★★★★	7 King's Bench Walk *(Tomlinson QC)*	★★★★★★

Sports

Blackstone Chmbrs *(Baxendale/Flint QC)*	★★★★★★

Sets and their star ratings are based on Chambers' Directory 1998–1999. Six stars represent a top-ranked set, five stars a second-ranked set, etc. See page 3 for further details.

COMMON LAW

Area of law

The common law bar deals primarily with the law as it has developed in the common law courts by precedent (ie, case law) and the focus is on contract and tort claims. The work is mainly dealt with in the Queen's Bench Division of the High Court, with smaller claims in the County Court. However, the work handled by the common law bar is very broadly based and its edges blur into chancery and commercial law.

Legal aid cutbacks are expected to squeeze the junior end of the common law bar. Younger barristers who have no more skills than their solicitor counterparts will only survive if they provide a cheaper service than solicitors. 'No win no fee' may also have an important bearing on the the common law bar; perhaps increasing the volume of work but at the same time adding to the financial insecurity of juniors. The growth of alternative dispute resolution will also affect the way in which junior counsel have to deal with cases.

Despite these doubts about the future of the common law bar it is expanding rapidly. The way in which chambers operate is changing. Philip Naughton QC, Chairman of the Common Law and Commercial Bar Association, identifies one major shift in the bar recently. "In London there is a definite trend towards sets specialising in specific areas within common law, such as medical negligence."

Type of work

By far the largest source of work is personal injury claims and, to a lesser extent, professional negligence and other tort actions such as nuisance. In considering the variety of work undertaken at the common law bar, it is interesting to look at how some common law sets describe themselves and their work. 9 Gough Square, for example, says it is a "well-established common law set specialising in particular in personal injury, medical negligence, professional negligence, serious fraud

and family." 4 Kings Bench Walk write "Chambers provides expertise in almost every area of common law. Notable specialisms include contract, crime, employment, EU, family, immigration, personal injury, property, planning and professional negligence." In addition to these areas, many common law sets will handle some landlord and tenant work (which is strictly chancery) and statutory torts such as product liability. There is a tremendous variety of work at the common law bar.

The difference between the common law bar and the commercial bar is often more a matter of who you are working for than what type of cases you do. Big businesses tend to go to leading City law firms who will in turn instruct commercial chambers like Brick Court or Fountain Court. Smaller businesses and members of the public go to smaller firms who instruct common law sets of chambers such as Plowden Buildings or 7 Stone Buildings. If a junior barrister is acting for a small business in a contract action worth £20,000 it may be described as a common law matter, while a similar case for ICI worth £2 million would be dealt with by different chambers and called a commercial matter.

Skills needed

The variety of work at the common law bar means that early on you'll have to cope with any number of cases dealing with different areas of law. This will be tiring and demanding and you'll need stamina and mental agility to perform well. You'll have to be a quick learner and have a good short term memory for facts and the law. Perseverance is essential if you are to get to the stage where routine matters become familiar and straightforward and you can, perhaps, begin to specialise in a chosen area.

You'll probably be doing a mixture of written advice and presentation in court. There will be less client contact than in criminal law, but probably more than in commercial or chancery practice, so you'll need good people skills and an ability to adapt to a range of clients. As Philip Naughton QC points out, "this area involves many different types of litigant, so the demeanour of the barrister is very important."

A junior who has just entered her second year of tenancy said: "As a junior at the common law bar you are not being asked to do anything a competent solicitor cannot do. What they pay you for is your judgement, and your feel for how a case should be handled, which you get from dealing with so many cases. You have to develop the knack of being right."

The Sets

The leading personal injury sets in London are 39 Essex Street, 12 King's Bench Walk, Old Square Chambers and 2 Temple Gardens. The leading medical negligence sets include 3 Serjeants Inn, 1 Crown Office Row and 6 Pump Court. The leaders in professional negligence are 2 Crown Office Row.

The leading sets in employment law often describe themselves as common law/commercial sets and they include 11 Kings Bench Walk, Blackstone Chambers, Littleton Chambers and Old Square Chambers.

Some sets stand out for their niche practices in other common law areas. Gough Square Chambers is renowned for its consumer law expertise, while 2 Harcourt Buildings and One Paper Buildings specialise in product liability.

Other niche areas of common law such as defamation are dealt with by a small number of sets. The two clear leaders in this field are 1 Brick Court and 5 Raymond Buildings, while general common law set, New Court Chambers, is headed by famous libel silk, George Carman.

Outside London, there are fewer specialist chambers and many sets handle a range of common law, commercial and criminal work.

Leading London Sets

	Employment	Defamation	Product Liability	Consumer
Blackstone Chambers *(Baxendale/Flint QC)*	★★★★★			
1 Brick Court *(Hartley QC)*		★★★★★★		
Cloisters *(Cox QC)*	★★★			
Devereux Chambers *(Burke QC)*	★★★★★			
Doughty Street Chambers *(Robertson QC)*		★★★		
Essex Court Chambers *(Pollock QC)*	★★★			
Fountain Court *(Scott QC)*	★★★			
Gough Square Chambers *(Philpott)*				★★★★★★
4–5 Gray's Inn Sq *(Appleby/Beloff QC)*	★★★★★			
2 Harcourt Buildings *(Henderson QC)*			★★★★★★	
11 King's Bench Wlk *(Tabachnik/Goudie QC)*	★★★★★★			
Littleton Chambers *(Burton QC)*	★★★★★			
Old Square Chmbrs *(Melville Williams QC)*	★★★★★			
One Paper Buildings *(Slater QC)*			★★★★★★	
5 Raymond Buildings *(Milmo QC)*		★★★★★★		

Sets and their star ratings are based on Chambers' Directory 1998–1999. Six stars represent a top-ranked set, five stars a second-ranked set, etc. See page 3 for further details.

Leading London Sets (cont.)

	Personal Injury	Medical Negligence	Professional Negligence
9 Bedford Row *(Goldring QC)*	★★★	★★★	
29 Bedford Row Chambers *(Ralls QC)*	★★★		
Brick Court Chambers *(Clarke QC)*			★★★★
Cloisters *(Cox QC)*	★★★	★★★	
1 Crown Office Row *(Seabrook QC)*		★★★★★	
2 Crown Office Row *(Hamilton QC)*	★★★★★		★★★★★
2 Crown Office Row *(Powell QC)*			★★★★★★
Devereux Chambers *(Burke QC)*	★★★★		
Doughty Street Chambers *(Robertson QC)*		★★★★	
35 Essex Street *(Inglis-Jones QC)*	★★★	★★★	
39 Essex Street *(Glasgow QC)*	★★★★★★	★★★	★★★
Farrar's Building *(Elias QC)*	★★★★★		
Fountain Court *(Scott QC)*			★★★★
9 Gough Square *(Roberts QC)*	★★★★	★★★	
2 Harcourt Buildings *(Henderson QC)*	★★★		
Keating Chambers *(Fernyhough QC)*			★★★★
12 King's Bench Walk *(Walker QC)*	★★★★★★		
7 King's Bench Walk *(Tomlinson QC)*			★★★
Littleton Chambers *(Burton QC)*			★★★
Old Square Chambers *(Melville Williams QC)*	★★★★★★		
9 Old Square *(Reid QC)*			★★★
One Paper Buildings *(Slater QC)*	★★★		★★★★
4 Paper Buildings *(McGregor QC)*			★★★★★
Plowden Buildings *(Lowe QC)*	★★★★		
4 Pump Court *(Mauleverer QC)*			★★★★★
6 Pump Court *(Coonan QC)*		★★★★★	
3 Serjeants' Inn *(Naughton QC)*			
199 Strand *(Andrews QC)*	★★★	★★★	
1 Temple Gardens *(Carlisle QC)*	★★★		
2 Temple Gardens *(Phillips QC)*	★★★★★★		★★★★★

Sets and their star ratings are based on Chambers' Directory 1998–1999. Six stars represent a top-ranked set, five stars a second-ranked set, etc. See page 3 for further details.

CRIMINAL

Area of law

There is always a need for criminal lawyers. The criminal bar is still expanding, and the threat posed by solicitor-advocates has not been as damaging as once supposed. However, the long term future of the criminal bar remains in the balance. Crown Court prosecutions may be undertaken directly by the CPS in future, and some people are predicting an eventual fusion of the criminal bar with law firms.

Life at the junior bar is now hard, with intense competition for pupillage and tenancy, difficulty in obtaining funding, low fees for magistrates court work, delays in payment from the Legal Aid Board, long hours and poor job security. However, this does not put off many applicants. The financial rewards at the top are good, and the work can be exciting and rewarding.

Type of work

Work at the criminal bar can be anything from petty theft and motoring offences at the magistrates court to murder trials at the Old Bailey to serious fraud at the High Court. Obviously you will start off handling minor offences and, depending on your ability and a certain amount of luck, as the years progress so will the importance of your cases, in terms of both fact and law. For a few years though, unless you are very fortunate, you'll spend more time travelling to obscure courts than you will handling matters of any great worth.

"Pupillage at a criminal set can often be like work-shadowing, especially in the first six months," we were told by a pupil at a small regional set. 'First six' pupils will help pupil masters or mistresses research points of law, prepare skeleton arguments and watch them in court. When you progress into your second six, what you do will depend on your progress and the work available. You start to discuss your work with the clerks, but you can expect to be thrown into the deep end with very little notice.

As a second six months pupil or a junior you start to handle your own work which is usually quite straightforward. It is mainly bail applications and pleas in mitigation in the magistrates court, with the odd bit of advice on appeal. Within a year tenants will have their own trials in the magistrates court, and will appear in the Crown Court for sentencing and pre-trial reviews. Some members of the junior bar also advise on Criminal Injuries Compensation, and do voluntary work for legal advice centres or organisations such as Victim Support.

The supply of work for junior barristers at the criminal bar is unpredictable, and earnings can vary enormously between chambers and from week to week. One newly appointed tenant told us "last week I had a steady stream of work and appeared in court every day. You can be picking up a good living if you get that consistently, but you know it won't last. At the beginning of this week I had nothing to do and spent two days at home. My week was only saved by a more senior member of chambers falling ill, and his cases being passed to me. It's a bit nerve-wracking though, because in that situation you have to do cases which are much more difficult than you're used to. But I suppose that's the way you learn quickly."

Skills needed

Flexibility and resilience are particularly important. As a junior you may be asked to do unappealing work. It is common for pupils to have to travel a great deal with papers they have little time to prepare. It is also common for witnesses not to turn up and not that uncommon that the defendant doesn't either. Nightmare stories from junior practitioners are legion. A junior tenant told us that he was once asked to travel to Exeter to appear in a bail application, and the train fare cost £10 more than the brief fee. "It's very frustrating, but you can't refuse because you need the experience and the clerks take the work to keep loyal solicitors happy. You just have to grin and bear it."

A thick skin is another useful attribute. You'll be working in a demanding environment with little thanks. You'll have to deal with awkward (sometimes abusive) clients, and occasionally with abrupt judges and competitive colleagues. One junior tenant at a large criminal set of chambers in London described an incident in a Crown Court canteen: "I was prosecuting a criminal damage case, and left the papers on a table while I went to get another cup of tea. When I returned I found that someone had re-arranged the order of the file, and I later found out that it was defence counsel who had been sitting behind me. It took me half an hour to make sure all the papers were still there, during which he had time to prepare his submissions and I didn't. I was very annoyed."

You need to combine your thick skin with sensitivity. As well as dealing with clients who frighten you, you'll be helping many clients who are frightened themselves. Tact and patience are necessary to get the most out of them and also to give them confidence. You'll be dealing with a wide range of people and you'll need to consider how to adapt your approach to handle all of them. This includes your client, judges, opposition lawyers, instructing solicitors, witnesses, the police, and the Probation Service.

Pragmatism is essential – you need to be practical about the whole case, from your clients' plea to the suitability of different types of sentence. Running clever points of law in front of a magistrate is usually not as effective as making sure your client doesn't say anything rash or stupid.

Excellent oral presentation skills coupled with imagination are key to engaging the attention of tired juries or magistrates who have heard it all before. You'll have to think up new ways of making the same point.

Strong intellectual capabilities and a head for legal and factual intricacies go without saying.

The Sets

In London, the leading sets for general crime and fraud include 6 King's Bench Walk, Queen Elizabeth Building, 3 Raymond Buildings and 18 Red Lion Court.

There are many other sets with excellent reputations, brilliant individuals and impressive case lists. For example, members of Doughty Street Chambers have been involved in the Canary Wharf Bombing, the 'Essex Range Rover murders', the Bridgewater Four appeal and the Derek Bentley appeal. William Clegg of 3 Hare Court was involved in the Brent Walker fraud case and in *R* v *Stagg* (the murder of Rachel Nickell on Wimbledon Common). Head of chambers, Michael Mansfield QC of 14 Tooks Court, represented the family of Stephen Lawrence in the public inquiry into his murder.

Outside London, it is individuals who stand out rather than sets. However, there are several chambers with strong reputations. The best known are St John's Chambers in Bristol; Octagon House Chambers in Norwich; 30 Park Place in Cardiff; 3 Fountain Court in Birmingham; Exchange Chambers in Liverpool; 18 St John Street in Manchester and Park Court Chambers in Leeds.

Readers should note that our table of leading sets is limited in scope, and reflects the elite chambers. There are many sets at the bar which provide an excellent service and have very good criminal advocates, but it would be impossible to rank them all. ▶

Leading London Sets

Criminal	General	Fraud
9 Bedford Row *(Goldring QC)*	★★★★★	
36 Bedford Row *(Hunt QC)*	★★★	
9–12 Bell Yard *(Evans QC)*	★★	★★★
Cloisters *(Cox QC)*	★★★	
Crown Office Row *(Ferguson QC)*	★★★★	
Doughty Street Chambers *(Robertson QC)*	★★★★★	
23 Essex Street *(Lawson QC)*	★★	★★★★★
35 Essex Street *(Inglis-Jones QC)*		★★★
Farrar's Building *(Elias QC)*	★	
Furnival Chambers *(Mitchell QC)*	★★★★	
Two Garden Court *(Macdonald QC/Davies)*	★★★★★	
3 Gray's Inn Square *(Tansey QC)*	★★★★★	
2 Harcourt Buildings *(Mylne QC)*	★★★★	
1 Hare Court *(Kramer QC)*	★★★★★	
3 Hare Court *(Clegg QC)*	★★★★★	★★★★★
6 King's Bench Walk *(Worsley QC)*	★★★★★★	★★★★★
10 King's Bench Walk *(Thwaites QC)*	★	
1 Middle Temple Lane *(Dines/Trollope QC)*	★	★★★
5 Paper Buildings *(Mathew QC)*		★★★★
Queen Elizabeth Building *(Jeffreys/Whiteman QC)*	★★★★★★	★★★★★★
3 Raymond Buildings *(Nicholls QC)*	★★★★★★	★★★★★★
18 Red Lion Court *(Arlidge QC)*	★★★★★★	★★★★
3 Temple Gardens *(Goldberg QC)*	★★★★	
14 Tooks Court *(Mansfield QC)*	★	

Sets and their star ratings are based on Chambers' Directory 1998–1999. Six stars represent a top-ranked set, five stars a second-ranked set, etc. See page 3 for further details.

405

FAMILY

Area of law

Family law is one of the major areas of specialisation at the bar, and there are a number of specialist sets where the tenants devote themselves exclusively to this area of practice. Many general practitioners at common law sets also do a significant amount of family work, and most barristers will handle a family law issue at some point in their career.

Most family matters (such as divorce, separation, adoption, child residence and contact orders, financial provision and domestic violence) are dealt with in the County Court. The Family Division of the High Court handles larger or more complex cases, and there are also cases that only the High Court can deal with, such as child abduction. There are also family proceedings courts within magistrates courts, but these handle issues that are largely dealt with by solicitors.

The threats posed by solicitor advocates and the growth in mediation has not affected the family law bar as much as some have predicted. One senior practitioner said "the family law bar definitely has a future because there will always be family disputes, and people who want to go to court. There are surprisingly few specialist solicitors, and most solicitors don't have the time to take cases all the way to court. In the specialist family sets there is a lot of work at the moment, and I can't see it falling off in the future."

Type of work

As a junior the most common types of work handled are domestic violence injunctions, work relating to children and financial matters. Child work can be public law care cases or private disputes concerning residence or contact. Financial work covers ancillary relief, property disputes between non-married couples, pensions and inheritance disputes work.

As you progress, you will be dealing with much the same kind of issues, but they will become increasingly complex and important in terms of sums of money involved and points of law raised. There is a trend towards specialisation at the family bar as in other areas. Many barristers decide to take either the child care route or the matrimonial finance path, and after about six years it is not unusual to specialise exclusively in one or the other. However many of the current leading silks maintain excellent reputations in both areas. Timothy Scott QC of 29 Bedford Row Chambers for example, and Alison Ball QC of One Garden Court.

A major difference to other areas of law is the focus on mediation. There is an emphasis on negotiation, and the law requires an effort to be made to resolve disputes before they reach court. This means that cases are conducted differently to many other civil disputes, and the process is less adversarial. There will be more client contact, more talking, more listening and less paperwork and ploughing through documents than in other fields.

Skills needed

Nicola Fox, a tenant at One Garden Court Family Law Chambers, stresses that the key to being a good family law barrister is good client handling skills. "The most important qualities are tact and sensitivity. You are dealing with clients in difficult and emotional circumstances. You have to be able to get on with them and be approachable and down to earth. There is no room for the old-fashioned, aloof barrister."

Pragmatism and problem-solving ability are at a premium in family law, and workable solutions to apparently intractable problems have to be created. It is perhaps less law-intensive than areas like chancery, but a detailed knowledge of procedure, statute and case law is needed. You will also need a positive attitude: clients can be difficult and disputes can be traumatic. You must be able to motivate yourself because there is often a feeling with family breakdowns that everyone is losing.

The Sets

The leading sets in London include 29 Bedford Row Chambers, One Garden Court, One King's Bench Walk, 1 Mitre Court Buildings and Queen Elizabeth Building. Many other sets handle family work and some have made a name for themselves by handling high profile financial disputes and divorces. None more so than Robert Seabrook QC, head of chambers at 1 Crown Office Row, who acted for HRH The Prince of Wales in his 1996 divorce.

Chambers are increasingly organising themselves in a more business-like manner and taking an interest in branding and marketing. One Garden Court Family Law Chambers, for example, was established in 1989 and in 1997 became the largest set to specialise exclusively in family law. They have recently appointed a chief executive who is running the set along more corporate lines. It remains to be seen if other specialist sets will follow suit.

Outside London, there is a wealth of individual talent at the family law bar. It is difficult to pick out leading sets because the leading barristers are spread between a number of chambers. But some of the best known are East Anglian Chambers in Ipswich; Albion Chambers in Bristol; Southernhay Chambers in Exeter; 30 Park Place in Cardiff; 5 Fountain Court in Birmingham; 26 Paradise Square in Sheffield; Broad Chare Chambers in Newcastle and India Buildings in Liverpool.

Readers should note that our table of leading sets is limited in scope and reflects the elite chambers. There are many sets at the bar which provide an excellent service and have very good family advocates, but it would be impossible to rank them all.

Leading London Sets

Family

Set	Rating	Set	Rating
29 Bedford Row Chambers *(Ralls QC)*	★★★★★	14 Gray's Inn Square *(Dodson QC)*	★★★
4 Brick Court *(Medhurst)*	★★	One King's Bench Walk *(Townend QC)*	★★★★★
1 Grdn Crt Fam Law Chmbrs *(Platt/Ball QC)*	★★★★★	1 Mitre Court Buildings *(Blair QC)*	★★★★★
Gray's Inn Chambers *(Jubb)*	★★★	4 Paper Buildings *(Swift QC)*	★★★
1 Gray's Inn Square *(Scotland QC)*	★★	Queen Elizabeth Building *(Karsten QC)*	★★★★★

Sets and their star ratings are based on Chambers' Directory 1998–1999. Six stars represent a top-ranked set, five stars a second-ranked set, etc. See page 3 for further details.

PUBLIC LAW

Area of law

Public law is concerned with all decisions made by publicly accountable bodies, from central government through local government to local authorities, councils, development corporations, schools etc. Lawyers in this field will deal with the decisions of these public bodies and their effect on individuals, companies and the human race as a whole.

The new Human Rights Act has been described by a leading public law expert as "revolutionary," and according to several practitioners, it will have a profound effect on many areas of law. Lawyers predict an increasing amount of work over the next few years dealing with issues thrown up by the act.

This is a socially important and challenging area of law which directly or indirectly affects us all. One junior we spoke to told us: "if you come to the legal profession not to earn a lot of money, but to be involved in principles of justice and advancing and developing the law, then public law is the most exciting field."

Type of work

Cases will either appear in the context of judicial review, or in lesser tribunals such as the Immigration Appeals Tribunal, or Social Security or Education tribunals. There is also an increasing amount of work in official inquiries. These can take various forms, ranging from planning to child abuse inquiries, and some can be extremely high profile. Recent contrasting examples are the inquiry into the death of Stephen Lawrence and the BSE inquiry.

The most significant component of public law is immigration, with half the Crown Office List made up of immigration cases. These matters also tend to be among the most interesting and important in public law. Much of the rest of judicial review is concerned with the decisions of local authorities, and there is a great deal of work in the planning, environment and housing

sectors. Other areas of practice such as education, licensing, parliamentary and sports law will also feature in the work of a fully-rounded public lawyer's life.

It is highly unusual for a junior barrister to specialise exclusively in public law. You may be at a set which has a public law bias, but it is likely that you will also handle general common law and commercial work too. Public law practitioners frequently combine their practice with areas such as employment law. Indeed, the leading public law sets such as 4–5 Gray's Inn Square, Blackstone Chambers and 11 King's Bench Walk are also first-rate employment law sets. Conversely, many sets which do not sell themselves as public law sets will have some sort of judicial review experience.

Raza Husain is an immigration specialist at Two Garden Court, and has developed a respected junior practice in both immigration and judicial review. "I probably spend about 80% of my time on immigration, and 50% of my cases are judicial review. My practice is unusual in that I also do licensing work, but what you mix in your practice largely depends on which chambers you're at. For example, criminal barristers may have to deal with judicial review in the context of habeas corpus, extradition, or other general civil liberties cases."

Public law cases tend not to settle as often as commercial cases so you often end up in court. According to Rabinder Singh, secretary of the Administrative Bar Law Association and a leading junior at 4–5 Gray's Inn Square, this is because the cases are not usually about money, they are about things which can't be compromised – like personal liberty or having somewhere decent to live."

Skills needed

This sector is extremely law-intensive, so you will have to enjoy the law for its own sake.

There is an emphasis on statutory interpretation so a head for rules and regulations and an inquiring and analytical mind are essential. Case law is also important and an aptitude for learning cases is helpful.

There is some client contact, but less than in other areas of practice, so people skills are less important than in crime or family, for example. It is quite normal for the client not to turn up to the hearing at all. There is a relatively high turnover of cases and in general, hearings are short and the arguments very focused. You will have to be succinct and persuasive in court – there is no room for waffle or fancy jury skills.

"Probably the most important attribute to succeed in public law," commented one civil liberties solicitor, "is a real passion to understand and play a part in developing the fundamental rules by which we all live." You have to really care otherwise fighting your way through all the red tape will become too much.

On the legal side, a grounding in constitutional law, an understanding of the mechanics of central and local government and, increasingly, a knowledge of EU/competition and international law are essential.

The Sets

Sets which lead the field in administrative and public law include 4–5 Gray's Inn Square, Blackstone Chambers, 4 Breams Buildings and 11 Kings Bench Walk.

Other leading sets have niche specialisms in areas such as civil liberties. For example, Doughty Street Chambers, and 14 Tooks Court. Members of Doughty Street acted in the Myra Hindley sentencing judicial review and Michael Mansfield represented the Stephen Lawrence family. Two Garden Court are also strong in civil liberties and are the leading immigration set.

Many of the same sets lead the field in planning and local government. In addition, 2 Harcourt Buildings and 2 Mitre Court Buildings have strong reputations: members of both sets were involved in the Heathrow Terminal 5 inquiry.

Outside London, the only sets to have leading reputations are 5 Fountain Court, Birmingham, Iscoed Chambers, Swansea and 40 King Street, Manchester. ▶

Leading London Sets

	Administrative & public	Civil Liberties	Immigration	Planning
Blackstone Chmbrs (Baxendale/Flint QC)	*****	**	***	
4 Breams Bldgs (Lockhart-Mummery QC)	****			******
Cloisters (Cox QC)		***		
Doughty St Chambers (Robertson QC)	***	******	***	
Enfield Chambers (Hall)		*****		
39 Essex Street (Glasgow QC)	***		***	
Two Garden Crt (Macdonald QC/Davies)	***	*****	******	
2–3 Gray's Inn Square (Scrivener QC)	***			****
4–5 Gray's Inn Sq (Appleby/Beloff QC)	******			******
2 Harcourt Buildings (Ryan QC)				*****
6 King's Bench Walk (Kadri QC)		**	***	
11 King's Bnch Wlk (Tabachnik/Goudie QC)	****			****
2 Mitre Court Buildings (FitzGerald QC)				*****
Mitre House Chambers (Gilbert)		***		
Plowden Buildings (Lowe QC)			**	
1 Pump Court (Hoyal/Latham)		**		
1 Serjeants' Inn (Read QC)				*****
14 Tooks Court (Mansfield QC)		****	***	

Sets and their star ratings are based on Chambers' Directory 1998–1999. Six stars represent a top-ranked set, five stars a second-ranked set, etc. See page 3 for further details.

a-z of Barristers' Chambers

36 BEDFORD ROW (James Hunt QC)

36 Bedford Row London WC1R 4JH DX: LDE 360
Tel: (0171) 421 8000 Fax: (0171) 421 8080
Email: 36bedfordrow@link.org
Website: www.36bedfordrow.co.uk

No of Silks	10
No of Juniors	49
No of Pupils	3

Chambers Profile

36 Bedford Row is a London based Midland and Oxford
Circuit set with a reputation for high quality work, good management and a very professional yet friendly atmosphere. In
1996 Chambers moved from 1 King's Bench Walk to a large
well equipped, grade II listed building at 36 Bedford Row
equipped with E-mail, video-conferencing, access to CD-ROM
and legal on-line databases. 36 Bedford Row was the first
chambers to receive an ISO9002 quality accreditation based
upon the Bar Equality Code and Practice Management
Standard Compliance. Clear written policies are available
dealing with pupillage, tenancy, pupils not taken on, discipline
and grievance procedures. At the 1997 Minority Lawyers
Conference Chambers were awarded the Conference Award for
Commitment to Diversity and Equality in the Legal
Profession, and in 1998 chambers were named "Chambers of
the Year" by The Lawyer.

Type of Work Undertaken

Chambers operate within specialist teams covering Crime,
Family, Civil and Commercial work. Pupils see all areas of
chambers work during both the first and second six months of
pupillage. Junior tenants are encouraged to retain a broadly
based practice in the early years before specialising.
Chambers' practice is almost exclusively outside London.
Tenants and pupils regularly travel to courts including
Northampton, Lincoln, Grimsby, Peterborough, Leicester,
Luton and Aylesbury.

Pupillage

Junior tenants are recruited almost exclusively from our own
pupils and candidates for pupillage are considered on that
basis. In the last 5 years 80% of pupils have been offered a
tenancy. Chambers see pupils as their future junior tenants and
junior tenants as their future. Chambers aim to treat them both
accordingly.

Funding

Funding for each pupillage totals £18,000 consisting of an
award of £10,000 and guaranteed second six earnings of
£8,000. In the first two years of tenancy new members pay a
substantially reduced contribution to Chambers' expenses.

Contact
Pupillage Secretary

Method of Application
Applications for pupillage
should be made through
PACH.

Pupillages (p.a.)
12 months: 3

Income
1st 6 months: £18,000
 including award and
 guaranteed earnings

Annexes
There are annexes to
Chambers in Northampton
and Leicester; both are
equipped with video-
conferencing equipment and
are used by all members of
Chambers.

Formerly 1 King's Bench Walk

BLACKSTONE CHAMBERS (P Baxendale QC and C Flint QC)

Blackstone House Temple London EC4Y 9BW DX: 281

Tel: (0171) 583 1770 Fax: (0171) 822 7222

Email: clerks@blackstonechambers.com

Website: www.blackstonechambers.com

No of Silks	20
No of Juniors	34
No of Pupils	5

Chambers Profile
Established at its old site 2 Hare Court for many years, Blackstone Chambers recently moved to new purpose built fully networked premises in the Temple.

Type of Work Undertaken
Chambers' formidable strengths lie in three principal areas of practice of commercial, employment and public law. Commercial law including financial/business law, international trade, conflicts, media and entertainment, intellectual property and professional negligence. All aspects of Employment law, including discrimination, are covered by Chambers' extensive employment law practice. Public law incorporates judicial review, acting both for and against central and local government agencies and other regulatory authorities, human rights and other aspects of administrative law.

Pupil Profile
Chambers looks for articulate and intelligent applicants who are able to work well under pressure and demonstrate high intellectual ability. Successful candidates usually have at least a 2:1 honours degree, although not necessarily in law.

Pupillage
Chambers offers 5 or 6 12 month pupillages normally commencing in October each year. Pupillage is divided into 3 sections and every effort is made to ensure that pupils receive a broad training. The environment is a friendly one; pupils attend an induction week introducing them to the Chambers working environment. Chambers prefers to recruit new tenants from pupils wherever possible.

Mini Pupillages
Assessed mini-pupillages are available and are an important part of the application procedure. Applications for mini-pupillages and for pupillages must be made by 30th June; earlier applications are strongly advised and are preferred in the year before pupillage commences. Application forms for pupillages or mini-pupillage are available on request.

Funding
Awards of £23,000 per annum are available. The pupillage committee has a discretion to consider applications for up to £4,000 of the pupillage award to be advanced during the BVC year.

Contact
Ms Julia Hornor
Practice Manager

Method of Application
Chambers' own application form

Pupillages (p.a.)
12 months: 5 or 6
Required degree grade
Minimum 2.1 (law or non-law)

Income
Award: £23, 000
Earnings not included

Tenancies
Junior tenancies offered
in last 3 years 100%
No of tenants of 5 years
call or under 11

1 CROWN OFFICE ROW (Mark Strachan QC)

1 Crown Office Row (3rd Floor) Temple
London EC4Y 7HH DX: 212
Tel: (0171) 583 9292 Fax: (0171) 353 9292

No of Silks	4
No of Juniors	21
No of Pupils	4

Contact
James Dingemans
Michael Oliver
(Chambers Manager)

Method of Application
PACH

Pupillages (p.a.)
1st 6 months:	1
2nd 6 months:	1
12 months:	2

Tenancies
Junior tenancies offered in last 3 years	3
No of tenants of 5 years call or under	5

Chambers Profile

Whilst individual practices within Chambers differ significantly, most members of Chambers specialise in the field of commercial and business law. This includes everything from international arbitration to sale of goods and employment law. Members of Chambers frequently appear in the Privy Council undertaking constitutional, human rights cases and other appellate work. The work of Chambers also includes most areas of non-specialist civil litigation such as personal injury and landlord and tenant work. There is also work in the field of public and administrative law.

Pupil Profile

Chambers seeks to have 3 or 4 pupils at any time and offer 1st and 2nd six month pupillages and 12 month pupillages. Chambers are well aware that the aim of most pupils is to secure a tenancy and to this end seek to recruit one tenant of sufficient calibre every year. A 12 month pupil will be reviewed after 5 months and given an indication of whether that pupil has any prospect of becoming a tenant at the end of the year.

Mini Pupillages

Mini-pupillages and student visits are available. Application by letter and CV to Michael Oliver.

Funding

It is Chambers' policy to offer finance to two pupils in each six month period in excess of the minimum amounts specified by the Phillips Committee. There are two awards of £17,000, being £8,500 for the first six months and £8,500 from receipts and/or Chambers' funds in the second six months.

2 CROWN OFFICE ROW (John Powell QC)

2 Crown Office Row The Temple
London EC4Y 7HJ DX: 1041
Tel: (0171) 797 8000 Fax: (0171) 797 8001
Email: barristers@2cor.com

No of Silks	7
No of Juniors	33
No of Pupils	4

Chambers Profile

2 Crown Office Row is a friendly, medium-sized commercial and civil set, established in the Temple for over 50 years. In 2000 Chambers are moving to larger premises in Lincoln's Inn. Chambers aim to recruit an average of 2 tenants a year from their own pupils.

Type of Work Undertaken

2 Crown Office Row is particularly known for professional negligence work. In 1998 the set was rated as the top set for professional negligence in Chambers & Partners and other legal publications. Jackson & Powell on Professional Negligence is written and edited by members of chambers. Members act for and against a wide range of professions (including medical negligence) and have appeared in many leading and high profile cases. Other main areas of practice include employment, insurance, commercial, building and engineering contracts and product liability.

Pupil Profile

All pupils are seen as potential tenants. Chambers aim to recruit pupils of the highest ability. Successful applicants will usually have at least a good 2:1.

Pupillage

Chambers offer 4 12 month pupillages. They recruit through assessed mini-pupillage, having decided not to enter PACH, which is believed to be less suited to the interests of applicants and the set itself. Places are offered as and when suitable candidates are found (so that candidates usually have a pupillage arranged before beginning the BVC). One place is kept open until the summer of the year before pupillage. Early applications for mini-pupillage are encouraged and should be made by 19th February 1999 for Easter and 7th May 1999 for summer.

Funding

Each pupillage carries an award of £20,000, of which a third can be drawn down during the BVC.

Contact
Nicola Shaldon

Method of Application
Letter and CV, including full details of academic record, early applications are encouraged.

Pupillages (p.a.)
12 months: 4
Required degree grade
None, but usually candidates will have at least a good 2:1

Income
12 months: £20,000
Earnings not included
Junior tenants are guaranteed to receive £50,000 over the first 2 years of practice

Tenancies
10 most junior tenants were recruited exclusively from own pupils over the last 5 years

2 CROWN OFFICE ROW

BARRISTERS

The Chambers of John L. Powell Q.C.

ESSEX COURT CHAMBERS (Gordon Pollock QC)

24 Lincoln's Inn Fields London WC2A 3ED DX: 320
Tel: (0171) 813 8000 Fax: (0171) 813 8080
Email: clerksroom@essexcourt-chambers.co.uk
Website: http://www.essexcourt-chambers.co.uk

No of Silks	15
No of Juniors	42
No of Pupils	5

Chambers Profile
Essex Court Chambers is one of the leading commercial sets of Chambers.

Type of Work Undertaken
Barristers at Essex Court Chambers advise on international and domestic commercial law and appear as Counsel in litigation and commercial arbitration worldwide. Their principal fields of work are international trade and transport, banking and financial services, EC law, insurance and reinsurance and maritime law. Barristers here practise in other areas of law including administrative law, entertainment, human rights, industrial relations, employment, VAT and public international law. A detailed brochure and Notes for Prospective Applicants are available on request.

Pupil Profile
Chambers are seeking to attract the very best candidates. The work required of a pupil is intellectually demanding and Chambers generally require high academic achievements (high 2:1 degree or better).

Pupillage
Chambers offer up to 4 funded pupillages. These are for 6 months in the first instance. Pupils start in October. They provide in-house pupil training in their areas of specialisation and in advocacy skills. Tenancy decisions are taken at the end of the first 6 months of pupillage. Chambers support PACH and only accept applications for pupillage through PACH.

Mini Pupillages
A limited number of mini-pupillages are available to those who have already embarked on legal studies (degree or CPE). An allowance is paid for expenses. Application by letter and CV to the Pupillage Secretary.

Funding
Chambers' 4 pupillages are each worth £25,000 per annum, payable in 2 instalments (the second instalment being payable if your first six months is extended for a further 6 months). They will consider applications to advance part of their awards for the BVC year. In cases of hardship they will also make interest free loans available.

Contact
Pupillage Secretary

Method of Application
PACH (pupillage); Letter and CV (mini-pupillage)

Pupillages (p.a.)
1st 6 months: 4
2nd 6 months: 4 (renewable)
Required degree grade 2:1

Income
£25,000 p.a.

Tenancies
Junior tenancies offered in last 3 years 7

416

4 ESSEX COURT (Nigel Teare QC)

4 Essex Court Temple London EC4Y 9AJ
DX: 292 London (Chancery Lane)
Tel: (0171) 797 7970 Fax: (0171) 353 0998
Email: clerks@4essexcourt.law.co.uk

Chambers Profile
4, Essex Court is one of the foremost and longest-established sets of Chambers specialising in commercial law. Chambers has remained in Essex Court although it moved from No 2 to No 4 some 5 years ago. Chambers has kept abreast of the latest technological advances in Information and Computer Technology. 4, Essex Court offers a first class service at sensible fee rates and has a staff renowned for their openness and fairness.

Type of Work Undertaken
The challenging and rewarding work of Chambers encompasses the broad range of commercial disputes embracing Arbitration, Aviation, Banking, Shipping, International Trade, Insurance and Re-insurance, Professional Negligence, Entertainment and Media, Environmental and Construction Law. Over 70% of Chambers' work involves international clients.

Pupil Profile
4, Essex Court seeks high calibre pupils with good academic qualifications (at least a 2:1 degree) who exhibit good written and verbal skills.

Pupillage
Chambers offers a maximum of 4 funded pupillages of either 6 or 12 months duration. 12 months pupillages are reviewed after 6 months. Pupils are normally moved amongst several members of Chambers and will experience a wide range of high quality commercial work. Outstanding pupils are likely to be offered a tenancy at the end of their pupillage.

Mini Pupillages
Mini - pupillages are encouraged in order that potential pupils may experience the work of Chambers before committing themselves to an application for full pupillage.

Funding
Awards of up to £28,000 p.a. (£14,000 per 6 months) are available for each funded pupillage - part of which may be forwarded during the BVC, at the Pupillage Committee's discretion.

No of Silks	6
No of Juniors	27

Contact
Ms Ella Bowers
Secretary to Pupillage
Committee

Method of Application
PACH

Pupillages (p.a.)

1st 6 months:	4
2nd 6 months:	4
12 months:	
(reviewed at 6 months)	
Required degree grade	
	good 2.1+

Income

1st 6 months:	up to £14,000
2nd 6 months:	up to £14,000
Earnings not included	

Tenancies

Current tenants who served pupillage in chambers	18
Junior tenancies offered in last 3 years	8
No of tenants of 5 years call or under	4
Income (1st year):	c£40,000

20 ESSEX STREET (David Johnson QC)

20 Essex Street London WC2R 3AL DX: 0009 (Ch.Ln.)
Tel: (0171) 583 9294 Fax: (0171) 583 1341
Email: clerks@20essexst.com
Website: www.20essexst.com (opening soon)

No of Silks	12
No of Juniors	23
No of Pupils	3

Chambers Profile
20 Essex Street is the address of one of the country's longest established sets of commercial chambers. Chambers moved from its former address at 3 Essex Court to its current address in 1994.

Type of Work Undertaken
The practising members of 20 Essex Street specialise in Commercial and EC Law. Most members of Chambers specialise in Commercial Law, in particular shipping, international sales, carriage by land, sea and air, insurance and reinsurance, and every type of domestic and international commercial agreement, appearing in the High Court (principally the Commercial Court), Court of Appeal and House of Lords as well as in arbitrations. A part of Chambers' work comprises EC Law, with certain members of Chambers appearing before the European Court of Justice.

Pupil Profile
Chambers look for candidates with a good academic background who seek to practise at the commercial bar. Chambers usually insist on a First or a strong 2:1 honours degree, though not necessarily in law.

Pupillage
Pupillage begins in October and is for twelve months. Usually Chambers take between three and six pupils each October. All applications must be made though PACH, in accordance with the deadlines set by PACH.

Mini Pupillages
Write to Michael Coburn enclosing a CV and indicating the dates on which you would like to come. Write before Easter for summer mini-pupillages and before Christmas for Easter mini-pupillages.

Funding
Three funded pupillages with awards of £20,000 for twelve months are generally offered.

Contact:
Write to Andrew Baker about pupillage or Michael Coburn about mini-pupillage.
Other enquiries: write to Neil Palmer, Senior Clerk.

Method of Application
For pupillage, through PACH

Pupillages (p.a.)
12 months: 3–6

Income
Three pupillage awards of £20,000 p.a.

20 Essex Street

FALCON CHAMBERS (Jonathan Gaunt QC & Kim Lewison QC)

Falcon Court London EC4Y 1AA DX: 408
Tel: (0171) 353 2484 Fax: (0171) 353 1261
Website: www.falcon-chambers.co.uk

No of Silks	7
No of Juniors	19
No of Pupils	1
Pupillages (p.a.)	
1st 6 months:	3
2nd 6 months:	3
Required degree grade	2.1
Income	
1st 6 months:	£12,000
2nd 6 months:	£12,000

Chambers Profile
Falcon Chambers is regarded (and regularly described in reviews) as the leading set of chambers for property litigation and landlord and tenant law. Chambers work primarily in litigation, from the House of Lords down to county courts and valuation tribunals. Members are often briefed in arbitrations, and sometimes act as arbitrators, experts and legal assessors. Chambers also have substantial advisory and drafting practices, and have written most of the leading text books in our specialist fields of practice. Chambers is modern and friendly, but also demanding in the standards it sets, and successful.

Type of Work Undertaken
All Members of Chambers specialise in litigation in the real property and property-related fields, including some non-specialist commercial litigation. Apart from commercial and residential property work, Chambers has a strong speciality in agricultural, and agricultural tenancy law, and in general property law, including easements, restrictive covenants, mortgages and options. Chambers are regularly involved in solicitors and surveyors professional negligence cases, and in cases involving insolvency and more general chancery law.

Pupil Profile
Chambers looks for intelligent and enthusiastic pupils with a real interest in property law and the ability to become a good advocate. The minimum academic requirement is a 2:1 degree, not necessarily in law.

Pupillage
Up to three six-month pupillages are available each year. Chambers have a preference for pupils to spend their first six months at Falcon Chambers. Before starting pupillage with us, all pupils receive a one week intensive course in landlord and tenant law, taught in Chambers. Pupils have two pupilmasters, for three months each. All pupils sit in their pupilmaster's room, and accompany them to court. Pupils also have the opportunity to work with other Members of Chambers, and will go to court with the most junior tenants. It is Chambers' policy to seek to recruit annually. Mini pupillages are available, and prospective applicants for pupillage are encouraged to apply in writing enclosing a CV, to Emily Windsor in Chambers.

Funding
Each six month pupillage carries an award of £12,000. It is sometimes possible to receive part of this award in advance during the Bar Finals year.

FURNIVAL CHAMBERS (Andrew Mitchell)

32 Furnival Street London EC4A 1JQ DX: 72

Tel: (0171) 405 3232 Fax: (0171) 405 3322

Email: clerks@furnivallaw.co.uk

Website: www.furnivallaw.co.uk

No of Silks	3
No of Juniors	37
No of Pupils	4

Chambers Profile

Since its formation in 1985, Furnival Chambers has provided a comprehensive and specialist criminal law service. Chambers, with leading and junior counsel of considerable experience and ability, is experienced in dealing with cases of more serious and complicated nature. Following the occasion of our 10th Anniversary Chambers have moved from 171 Fleet Street to new accommodation at 32 Furnival Street. Chambers' new building is well suited to the traditions of the Bar, yet is able to offer those services which are essential in the 1990s including a communications system of the highest and latest specification, equipped to send and receive information through an integrated computer system.

Contact
Diane Hurtley
Pupillage Secretary

Method of Application
PACH

Pupillages (p.a.)

1st 6 months:	0
2nd 6 months:	0
12 months:	4
Award:	£4,000
Required degree grade	None

Type of Work Undertaken

The work of Chambers ranges from the most involved commercial fraud to the simplest road traffic matter. Expertise is therefore available in all areas of criminal law. Members specialise in cases of white collar fraud, drugs related offences, cases of a sexual nature including rape and child abuse, and crimes of violence including murder and terrorism. In addition, Furnival Chambers has a specialist team which deals with confiscation, asset forfeiture and money laundering. Members of the team have appeared in the vast majority of the leading cases in the High Court and Court of Appeal.

Tenancies

Current tenants who served pupillage in chambers	25
Junior tenancies offered in last 3 years	2
No of tenants of 5 years call or under	5

Pupil Profile

Chambers is an equal opportunity and multi-racial set. Chambers' aim is to ensure that all that is good in the traditional and independent Bar thrives in a modern environment.

Pupillage

Pupils will see a great deal of court work and undertake a certain amount of paperwork. Second six pupils will conduct a substantial amount of their own work whilst being monitored and assisted by their pupilmaster/mistress. Chambers offer excellent experience and run a continuing education programme for pupils including an in-house advocacy training course of approximately forty hours.

Mini Pupillages

Mini-pupillages and student visits are available.

Funding

The loan is interest free available during the second six months and is paid on a weekly basis against future earnings.

ONE HARE COURT (Lord Neill QC & Richard Southwell QC)

1 Hare Court Temple London EC4Y 7BE
DX: 0065 (Ch.Ln.)
Tel: (0171) 353 3171 Fax: (0171) 583 9127
Email: admin-oneharecourt@btinternet.com

No of Silks	5
No of Juniors	8
No of Pupils	2

Contact
Nicholas Lavender

Method of Application
Letter and cv by 28th
February 1999

Pupillages (p.a.)
1st 6 months:
2nd 6 months:
12 months: 2

Income
£20,000

Chambers Profile
A long-established set of chambers specialising in commercial, international and related fields of litigation, arbitration and legal advice. Former members of Chambers include Lord Slynn of Hadley, Sir Roger Parker (former Lord Justice of Appeal), Sir Mark Waller (Lord Justice of Appeal), Judge Raymond Jack QC (Judge of the Bristol Mercantile Court) and Sir Nicolas Bratza (Judge of the European Court of Human Rights).

Type of Work Undertaken
All aspects of commercial practice, with an emphasis on international work.

Pupil Profile
All candidates are considered strictly on merit. Successful applicants for pupillage will have demonstrated high intellectual ability, and will usually have at least an upper second class honours degree (not necessarily in law). Other (non-academic) interests and achievements are also taken into consideration.

Pupillage
Two twelve month pupillages commencing in October 2000. Pupils usually sit with a different pupil master every three months. The intention is to provide pupils with a broad experience of court and arbitration work and also of paperwork, in accordance with the pupillage checklist for general commercial chambers recommended by the Bar Council. This will include drafting of pleadings, opinions, grounds of appeal, etc., in both the High Court and the County Courts, and attendance at Court on a variety of matters.

Mini Pupillages
A small number of mini-pupillages are available for final year law students or CPE students. Application by letter and cv to Nicholas Lavender.

Funding
Awards of £20,000 per twelve month pupillage. Consideration is given in individual cases to advancing part of this award during the Bar Vocational Course.

LAMB CHAMBERS (Christopher Gardner QC)

Lamb Building Temple London EC4Y 7AS
DX: 418 London
Tel: (0171) 797 8300 Fax: (0171) 797 8308
Email: lambchambers@link.org

No of Silks	4
No of Juniors	27
No of Pupils	4

Chambers Profile

Lamb Chambers was created in 1958 and is a forward-looking set which offers an in-depth service in the three areas of commercial, property and personal injury/medical negligence work. It is based in the heart of the Temple and has a reputation for being a strong set with a number of leading practitioners in its three fields of expertise. It is friendly but businesslike in its approach and maintains state of the art IT in communications, research facilities and administration.

Type of Work Undertaken

Pupils will see heavy litigation in all three fields including High Court actions and commercial arbitrations. There will also be visits to Tribunal and County Court as well as a constant stream of paperwork and conferences. This is a very busy set and pupils are expected to be fully involved in the work.

Pupil Profile

Chambers choose our tenants from our pupils and they are looking for dedicated, intelligent and highly motivated applicants - preferably with a well-developed sense of humour and no sharp edges. Advocacy is one of their strong suits and pupils are expected to be keen to get on their feet - and confident that they will become good advocates. A good track record in debating and mooting is looked for. Chambers expect applicants to have achieved a 2:1 degree result unless their circumstances are exceptional.

Pupillage

You will spend your first six months with your designated pupil-master specialising in one of the three work areas. You will then move on to another specialist for the second six months. You sit with your pupil master and you are expected to take a full part in the life of Chambers. Pupillage begins in late September and the selection of tenants is announced by 31st July of the following year. Chambers take particular trouble to help those who are not successful in getting a place in Chambers.

Contact

Pupil contact: Jeremy Carcy
Senior Clerk: John Kelly

Method of Application

PACH/CV and letter to Chambers by 1.9.99

Pupillages (p.a.)

12 months:	4
Funding:	£8,250
Required degree grade	2.1

Income

2nd 6 months:	£3–4,000
Income (1st year):	£10,000

Tenancies

Current tenants who served pupillage in chambers	22
Junior tenancies offered in last 3 years	6
No of tenants of 5 years call or under	7

1 MITRE COURT BUILDINGS (Bruce Blair QC)

1 Mitre Court Buildings Temple London EC4Y 7BS
DX: LDE 342 Chancery Lane
Tel: (0171) 797 7070 Fax: (0171) 797 7435

No of Silks	7
No of Juniors	24
No of Pupils	4

Contact
Mr Martin Pointer QC
Pupillage and Tenancy
Committee

Method of Application
PACH

Pupillages (p.a.)
1st 6 months: 1
12 months: 3

Income
Fund of £30,000 and earnings

Chambers Profile
1 Mitre Court Buildings has been the family law set for decades. Chambers continues to be at the cutting edge of financial and child oriented work in a competitive and increasingly international field. Chambers offers advocacy, advisory and drafting work over the entire range of family and matrimonial law and undertakes work at all level of Court. Chambers' clients range from individuals (the legally aided and the multi-millionaire) to public bodies and the Official Solicitor.

Type of Work Undertaken
Chambers has leading practitioners in ancillary relief and international child abduction, and individual members of chambers are editors of some of the main family law text-books. Three of the current Family Division Judges and two Lord Justices of Appeal are former members of chambers.

Pupillage
The work is demanding, varied and of high quality. The environment of excellence in this busy, friendly set ensures a high standard of training. Twelve months' pupils are placed with three different pupil masters during the year. Six months' pupils have one pupil master. Pupils will also spend time with other members of chambers, at all levels, to ensure they see the broadest range of work possible. Chambers have a general policy of taking on a junior tenant annually and usually recruit from their pupils. They have a good record of placing pupils who have not been taken on by them.

Mini Pupillages
Mini pupillages and student visits are available. Application by letter and curriculum vitae to Judith Hughes QC.

Funding
Awards are made from a fund of £30,000. Additionally there is a limited amount of work available for pupils during their second six months.

OLD SQUARE CHAMBERS (Hon. John Melville Williams QC)

1 Verulam Buildings Gray's Inn London WC1R 5LQ
DX: 1046 Chancery Lane/London
Tel: (0171) 269 0300 Fax: (0171) 405 1387
Email: moor@oldsquarechambers.co.uk
Website: www.oldsquarechambers.co.uk

No of Silks	6
No of Juniors	32
No of Pupils	3–4

Contact
Sarah Moor

Method of Application
PACH

Pupillages (p.a.)
1st 6 months: 1
2nd 6 months: 0
12 months: 2–3

Tenancies
Junior tenancies offered
in last 3 years 4

For more information see our
Website or write to Sarah
Moor

Annexes
Hanover House
47 Corn Street
Bristol BS1 1HT
Tel: (0117) 927 7111
Fax: (0117) 927 3478

Chambers Profile
A highly specialised, forward thinking set committed to expansion.

Type of Work Undertaken
Employment, personal injury, product liability and environmental law, Public law and human rights issues are encompassed within these areas. There is some business and mercantile work and some medical negligence. There is much use of European jurisprudence. In employment law, members of chambers have been involved in many of the ground-breaking cases of the past 20 years. Our profile in personal injury law is excellent, particular strengths are disaster and multi-party litigation. Environmental law work is predominantly on large 'toxic tort' litigation - damage caused by pollution. Fields of practice are organised around Special Interest Groups in chambers enabling the sharing of information and effective marketing.

Pupil Profile
Chambers look for intelligent candidates who have the potential to be excellent advocates. You must be motivated to come to the bar and practise in at least one of Chambers' specialist fields. You must have ability to cope with hard work and deal with many different people. Chambers is committed to equal opportunities. Our recruitment methods are designed to prevent any discrimination on the grounds of race, gender, disability, sexuality or religion.

Pupillage
Chambers offer high quality training, generously funded. Pupils spend 3 months with each pupil supervisor. Preferences for fields of work will be considered. There is the opportunity to undertake work for silks on complex and sometimes high profile work.

Mini Pupillages
Mini pupillages are available but in demand. Preference is given to final year students. Send William Birtles your CV and a letter explaining your interest in chambers.

Funding
1999 grant: between £16,000 and £20,000 for 12 months in London, £14,000 in Bristol. 2nd six pupils undertake work on their own account, fees are retained without any deduction.

OLD SQUARE CHAMBERS

10 OLD SQUARE (Leolin Price CBE QC)

10 Old Square Lincoln's Inn London WC2A 3SU DX: 306
Tel: (0171) 405 0758 Fax: (0171) 831 8237

No of Silks	2
No of Juniors	25
No of Pupils	4

Chambers Profile
10 Old Square is a specialist Chancery set of chambers with 28 full-time tenants and a number of eminent academic members. The Head of Chambers, Leolin Price CBE QC, is a renowned Chancery silk and the set is well known for its high-quality trust and probate specialists.

Contact
Mr Nicholas Harries
Pupillage Secretary

Method of Application
PACH

Type of Work Undertaken
Chambers undertake the entire range of work which falls within the commercial and traditional Chancery fields. Their brochure, which is available upon request, provides further information.

Pupillages (p.a.)

1st 6 months:	2
2nd 6 months:	2
12 months:	0
Required degree grade	2:1 or higher

Pupil Profile
Chambers seek to recruit pupils with excellent academic records; in the absence of exceptional circumstances, applicants should have attained a degree at class 2:1 or higher. Candidates should also have a proven ability to formulate complex arguments and to express them clearly, both orally and in writing.

Income
Awards up to 2 funded pupillages each carrying up to £8,000.

Pupillage
Pupils are usually assigned to two pupil masters during the course of a six month pupillage, spending 3 months with each. In addition, pupils are encouraged to undertake occasional work for other tenants. Chambers aim to provide pupils with a thorough grounding for practice at the Chancery bar.

Mini Pupillages
Mini pupilllages are available. Successful applicants will usually have completed at least one year of a law degree course, or will be in the process of completing their CPE. Applications (by handwritten covering letter with a CV enclosed) should be made to Robert Arnfield.

Funding
Up to two funded six month pupillages are available every year; each carries an award of £8,000. In addition Chambers may offer up to two unfunded six month pupillages.

10 OLD SQUARE

425

12 OLD SQUARE (Charlotte Boaitey)

12 Old Square Lincoln's Inn London WC2A 3TX
Tel: (0171) 404 0875 Fax: (0171) 404 8377

No of Silks	1
No of Juniors	25
No of Pupils	1

Chambers Profile
Chambers of Mrs Charlotte Boaitey has been operating for 30 years. It aims to promote a professional but friendly approach to its client. The senior clerk adopts a flexible approach in the setting of fees.

Contact
Steven Russell
Senior Clerk

Type of Work Undertaken
In the area of criminal law, Chambers have more than 10 counsel providing a full range of predominantly defence work. Chambers have 15 counsel specialising in nationality, immigration and human rights, attending all levels of hearing up to the Court of Appeal. The Chambers also does Family, Landlord & Tenant, Housing, Civil Law including actions against the police, Education and Employment.

Method of Application
CV and handwritten letter to Chambers

Tenancies

Current tenants who served pupillage in chambers	6
Junior tenancies offered in last 3 years	8
No of tenants of 5 years call or under	9

Pupil Profile
Chambers looks for intelligent and ambitious pupils with excellent powers of oral and written critical reasoning. The minimum academic requirement is a 2:1 degree or unless a candidate can display other outstanding achievements.

Pupillage
Chambers offer two pupillage per annum. The work is Chambers is varied and demanding. New tenants are usually recruited from pupils and the set is keen to expand.

Mini Pupillages
Mini-pupillages and student visits are available. Preference is given to final year students. Application by handwritten letter and CV to Steven Russell.

4 PAPER BUILDINGS (Lionel Swift QC)

4 Paper Buildings Temple London EC4Y 7EX DX: 1035
Tel: (0171) 583 0816 Fax: (0171) 353 4979
Email: clerks@4paperbuildings.co.uk

No of Silks	4
No of Juniors	30
No of Pupils	2

Chambers Profile

4 Paper Buildings has a reputation as one of the friendliest sets in which to do your pupillage. An informal atmosphere is combined with high-profile work of the highest calibre in both civil law (especially professional negligence and employment) and all aspects of family law.

Type of Work Undertaken

Family law: Adoption care proceedings (for local authorities, families and guardians ad litem), child abduction, Children Act cases, cohabitees, divorce, inheritance and family provision, judicial review, matrimonial finance and wardship. Civil: Arbitration, banking and securities, construction, contract (commercial and general), employment and industrial tribunals, judicial review, landlord and tenant, personal injury, professional negligence, sale of goods and consumer credit.

Pupil Profile

4 Paper Buildings follows the Equality Code for the Bar and aims to select the best, irrespective of race, ethnic origin, sex, sexual orientation, marital status, disability, religion, political persuasion or age. The chances of tenancy following pupillage are high, and pupils who do not obtain tenancy with Chambers have, in the last five years, invariably been offered tenancies elsewhere.

Pupillage

If your application is successful, you will enjoy effective training with 3 or 4 different pupil masters and mistresses and will be encouraged to go to court with every member of Chambers. Current trends indicate that you will be extremely busy during your second 6 months, and will be in court most days.

Mini Pupillages

Please write to Alexander Schofield at 4 Paper Buildings or e-mail him at clerks@paperbuildings.co.uk.

Funding

Both awards are for £12,000 per annum, payable quarterly in advance. You will keep all your earnings, save for a small clerking percentage, in addition to your award.

Contact
Mr Michael Reeves
Senior Clerk

Method of Application
Via PACH

Pupillages (p.a.)
12 months: 2

Income
1st 6 months: £6,000
2nd 6 months: £6,000
Earnings not included
Income (1st year): £20,000

Tenancies
Current tenants who served
pupillage in chambers 21
Junior tenancies offered
in last 3 years 4
No of tenants of 5 years
call or under 5

4
PAPER
BUILDINGS

5 PAPER BUILDINGS (John Mathew QC)

5 Paper Buildings Temple London EC4Y 7HB DX: 365
Tel: (0171) 583 6117 Fax: (0171) 353 0075
Email: clerks@5-paperbuildings.law.co.uk

No of Silks	9
No of Juniors	22

Chambers Profile

5 Paper Buildings are a leading, well established set of
Chambers specialising in all areas of criminal law. Members
undertake a broad range of work with an emphasis on commercial fraud. Members of Chambers have appeared in some
of the largest fraud cases in recent years: Guinness, BCCI,
Maxwell etc. Other tenants undertake civil and commercial litigation including contempt, restraint of trade, civil actions
against the police.

Contact
Robert O'Sullivan
Pupillage Committee

Method of Application
12 months and 2nd six
months via PACH. 3rd six
months by application form
only available from Chambers

Pupillage

When Chambers recruit pupils they look for candidates who
have the abilities to become successful advocates. When interviewing, Chambers are looking at applicants as potential tenants. Chambers offer 12 month pupillages, as well as 2nd and
3rd six pupillages. Pupils can look forward to a variety of
work in and around London. Chambers also offer an education
programme for all pupils.

Pupillages (p.a.)
1. Chambers offer 3 pupillages
a year through PACH:
a combination of 2nd six and
12 months pupillages.
2. In addition, Chambers offer
3 3rd six pupillages in October

Mini Pupillages

Mini pupillages are available - contact Senior Clerk, Stuart
Bryant. Student visits are not available.

Tenancies
Junior tenancies offered
in last 3 years 5
No of tenants of 5 years
call or under 5

Funding

Twelve month pupils will receive an award of approximately
£5,000 in their first 6 months and with 2nd six pupils are
guaranteed earnings of £7,500. On successful completion of
Bar Finals, up to £1,000 may be claimed in advance, for guaranteed earnings.

PARK COURT CHAMBERS (Smith QC and Stewart QC)

40 Park Cross Street Leeds LS1 2QH DX: 26401
Tel: (0113) 243 3277 Fax: (0113) 242 1285

No of Silks	11
No of Juniors	29

Method of Application
PACH

Pupillages (p.a.)
12 months: 1

Chambers Profile
Park Court Chambers is a mixed common law set with 11
silks and 29 juniors. By the time that this guide is in print the
set will have moved to larger premises which have been fully
prepared for the 21st century. Chambers is happy and relaxed
internally and relationships with law and professional users
are marked by a client-friendly approach.

Type of Work Undertaken
Chambers works throughout the North Eastern circuit and
beyond. There are large criminal, civil and family teams,
although pigeonholing practitioners into formal departments
is resisted. Criminal work encompasses fraud (including
Revenue fraud). Civil work includes professional and medical
negligence, landlord and tenant and Mercantile Court practice
as well as personal injury work. Family work deals with both
children and financial resolution.

Pupil Profile
Chambers looks to recruit one pupil per year, although the
policy is not to pass up any outstanding candidate. Intellectual
ability is a major consideration but an overall view of a candidate's ability is sought. Interviews are deliberately challenging
and Chambers looks for candidates who can think through a
problem and argue on their feet.

Mini Pupillages
Mini-pupillages are available. Applications should be made to
Simon Myerson at Chambers or by e-mail - simon.myer-
son@netserv.net. Giving a variety of available dates assists.

Funding
Pupillages are funded in the sum of £6,000 of which £3,000 is
allocated to the first six months and £3,000 represents guaranteed earning in the second six months.

33 PARK PLACE (Wyn Williams QC)

33 Park Place Cardiff CF1 3BA DX: 50755
Tel: (01222) 233313 Fax: (01222) 228294

No of Silks	3
No of Juniors	34
Door Tenants	3 silks
	4 juniors

Chambers Profile
33 Park Place is a well known set of Chambers with an established reputation. It has a wide ranging area of practice, both geographically and in subject matter. Accommodation is in a recently refurbished building occupying a prominent and convenient location with a full range of up to day facilities. Informal but business like the approach is forward looking whilst building upon past strengths.

Contact
Graham Walters
(Head of Pupillage)

Method of Application
PACH

Type of Work Undertaken
A broad based common law Chambers, there is a flexible division into criminal, civil and family practitioner groups. In addition to extensive criminal, family and personal injury work, there is particular experience in specialist areas including chancery, planning, licensing, commercial, employment, professional negligence and local government law.

Pupillages (p.a.)
12 months: 2
Required degree grade
2:1 degree strongly preferred

Income
£6,000

Pupil Profile
Chambers is looking for pupils who are committed to success and able to take advantage of the significant opportunities for rapid progress that circuit work offers. Academic and all round ability will be recognised and rewarded.

Tenancies
Junior tenancies offered
in last 3 years 6
No of tenants of 5 years
call or under 12

Pupillage
Twelve month pupillage, ordinarily providing experience in each of the specialist practitioner areas of law, it is nevertheless responsive to individual preferences. All members of Chambers welcome the oportunity to train and help pupils.

Mini Pupillages
Application by letter with CV to the Clerk to Chambers, Graham Barrett.

Funding
£6,000 p.a.

18 RED LION COURT (Anthony Arlidge QC)

18 Red Lion Court London EC4A 3EB DX: 478 LDE
Tel: (0171) 520 6000 Fax: (0171) 520 6248/9

Chambers Profile
Chambers operate from a spacious listed building off Fleet Street near the Temple. Comprising 18 silks and 39 juniors, we offer one of the most comprehensive cross-sections of expertise in the field of criminal law.

Type of Work Undertaken
18 Red Lion Court covers the whole range of crime, defending and prosecuting at all levels. Particular strengths are commercial fraud, Inland Revenue and VAT offences, money laundering, corruption, drugs and drug trafficking and sex cases, including child abuse and obscene publications. Individual members are involved in international human rights cases from Rwanda to Santa Monica. Others have written well respected practitioners texts on a wide range of topics. Chambers' work is centred primarily on the South Eastern circuit with an emphasis on London and East Anglia. Much of the East Anglian work is serviced by our annexe in Chelmsford. A few practitioners undertake civil and administrative law work.

Pupil Profile
Chambers look for pupils with potential to develop into first class advocates. Pupils are selected for a combination of marked intellectual ability, together with good judgement and independent personalities.

Pupillage
Chambers offer 4 funded twelve months pupillages and two unfunded first six months. Funded pupils receive £10,000, made up of £5,000 award and £5,000 guaranteed earnings. Our pupils receive excellent training. In addition to experiencing a broad range of work, all pupils participate in our in-house advocacy programme. Nearly all of our pupils get tenancies with us or elsewhere. Pupillage applications should be made through PACH. Chambers do not offer 2nd or 3rd six pupillages. Sponsored pupils are accepted.

Mini Pupillages
Applications should be made to Tom Forster.

No of Silks	18
No of Juniors	39
No of Pupils	6

Contact
Elizabeth Webster
Pupillage Secretary

Method of Application
Through PACH

Pupillages (p.a.)
1st 6 months:	2
12 months:	4

Income
1st 6 months:	unfunded
12 months:	£10,000
Earnings	

Tenancies
Junior tenancies offered
in last 3 years   5

Annexes
Chelmsford

3 VERULAM BUILDINGS (R. Neville Thomas QC)

3 Verulam Buildings Gray's Inn London WC1R 5NT

DX: LDE 331

Tel: (0171) 831 8441 Fax: (0171) 831 8479

Email: clerks@3verulam.co.uk

Website: www.3verulam.co.uk

No of Silks	12
No of Juniors	36
No of Pupils	6

Chambers Profile

3 Verulam Buildings is a large commercial set with a history of expansion by recruitment of tenants from amongst pupils. Over the past ten years at least two of its pupils have become tenants every year. Chambers occupies recently refurbished, spacious offices overlooking Gray's Inn Walks with all modern IT and library facilities. Chambers prides itself on a pleasant, friendly and relaxed atmosphere.

Type of Work Undertaken

A wide range of commercial work, in particular banking and financial services, insurance and reinsurance, commercial fraud, professional negligence, company law, entertainment, insolvency, public international law, EU law, arbitration/ADR, environmental law, building and construction as well as other general commercial work. Members of Chambers regularly appear in high profile cases and a substantial amount of Chambers' work is international.

Pupil Profile

Chambers looks for intelligent and ambitious candidates with strong powers of analysis and reasoning, who are self confident and get on well with others. Candidates should normally have at least a 2.1 grade in an honours subject which need not be law.

Pupillage

Chambers takes 3–5 funded twelve months pupils every year through PACH. Each pupil spends three months with four different members of Chambers to gain experience of different types of work. Chambers also offers unfunded pupillages to pupils who do not intend to apply for a tenancy in Chambers.

Mini Pupillages

Mini pupillages are available for one week at a time for university, CPE or Bar students who are interested in finding out more about Chambers' work. Applications are accepted throughout the year and should be addressed to Natalie Baylis.

Funding

In the year 1999–2000 the annual award will be £20,000 payable monthly.

Contact
Ms Natalie Baylis
Pupillage Committee

Method of Application
PACH/CV and handwritten letter to Chambers.

Pupillages (p.a.)
1st 6 months: 2
12 months: 4
Required degree grade 2.1

Income
£20,000 per annum.
Earning not included

Tenancies
Current tenants who served pupillage in chambers 35
Junior tenancies offered in last 3 years 7
No of tenants of 5 years call or under 11

Funding

FUNDING

TRAINEE SOLICITORS

Most trainee solicitors find their training contracts as challenging as they are rewarding, and the last thing they need are distracting financial worries. Research commissioned by the Law Society and published in 1997 shows that 73% of LPC graduates are in debt, with the average amount owing per student totalling £5,000. Fortunately, the higher-than-average trainee salaries mean that most major banks are happy lending money to trainees, and on good terms too. Loan benefits generally include low interest rates, no arrangement fees, and repayments deferred until after the training contract.

Not all banks or their branches offer the same service, however, so it is worth considering others than your own. If you find a better offer elsewhere, do not hesitate to change – it is far easier to do this now than during your training contract. Aside from financial considerations, other factors to consider include whether the bank is conveniently located and the level of personalised service on offer.

"Finding an account manager you can build up a relationship with and get straight through to on the phone is crucial when choosing a bank," advises a second-year trainee at City firm Stephenson Harwood. She is now changing her bank for another whose account manager has been specifically recommended by a work colleague.

Prospective trainees should not underestimate their future living costs, either. "I thought I would be working so hard, I'd have no time for spending money. But training as a solicitor can be expensive especially if, like me, four years' study at university and law college have left you with substantial debts," she says, adding that she has borrowed £6,000.

Even buying appropriate work clothes cost her an initial £700. Then there was the deposit for a shared house and first month's rent, which cost another £1,000. "Going out is expensive too,"

she says. "Life at most law firms is a social whirl for everyone who works there. Training at a firm includes getting to know your work colleagues, and this tends to take place in expensive wine bars and restaurants."

With so much hard work and fun ahead, choosing a bank can seem rather a mundane chore. But get it wrong, and what should be some of the most challenging and satisfying years of your life could be overshadowed by financial worries which, with a little forethought, could have been avoided. For details of sponsorship and awards from individual firms see pages 206 to 334.

TRAINEE BARRISTERS

The issue of funding for junior barristers is controversial. State funding is virtually non-existent and other sources are limited and unpredictable. While many law firms offer some form of financial assistance to trainee solicitors during the CPE and LPC, most pupils receive nothing from their chambers during the CPE and BVC. Similarly, most trainee solicitors are paid a good salary during their training contract, while remuneration for pupil barristers is variable and in some instances, pupillages are unfunded. It is worth remembering that the average cost of completing the vocational stage of training (ie. CPE and/or BVC) is estimated at over £15,000, including living expenses.

The Inns of Court

Each Inn of Court distributes over £400,000 a year to students taking the CPE, BVC, and pupillage. Some awards are based on merit; others are based on a mixture of merit and need. Students can only apply to their own Inn for funding, so it is worth checking out the best deals before choosing an Inn.

Chambers

In 1997-98, 500 of the 750 pupillages available were funded to some degree. In the second six months, you can expect some income from your own work and in some sets, you can be paid by more senior members to work on their cases for them - this is known as "devilling". Very few sets provide funding for CPE and BVC.

Work

The Council for Legal Education (CLE) discourages students from getting a job while studying the BVC full-time, but some students do manage it. The BVC is supposed to provide the workload a junior lawyer would undertake, so if you think you can do this while working part-time, then good luck.

Benefits

You will not be able to claim benefits during the CPE as it is a full time course of higher education. The CLE issues certificates which state that the BVC is not "designated" as a full time course, so if you are actively seeking work during the BVC and ready to begin work immediately, you should be entitled to sign on. However, this cannot be relied upon because each local authority will have its own policy.

Loans

Student Loans are not available for postgraduate work, but the banks have been quick to provide facilities for trainee barristers. They will advance up to £10,000, and delay repayment of the loan until pupillage finishes.

Bar Council

The Bar Scholarship Trust provides a small number of loans of up to £4000 for pupillage.

Stages in Brussels

Six-month secondments with the European Commission count towards pupillage. Each candidate receives £5000.

Other sources

There are numerous local charities and educational foundations which provide small amounts of funding for students. Check in your local library.

Useful Names and Addresses

Local Education Authority – contact them for this publication:
Student Grants and Loans: A Brief Guide 1998/1999

Career Development Loans, Freepost, Newcastle-upon-Tyne, NE85 1BR
Tel: 0800 585 505

The Inns of Court – contact each Inn for details of grants and scholarships:
Lincoln's Inn – Tel: 0171 405 0138
Inner Temple – Tel: 0171 797 8208
Middle Temple – Tel: 0171 427 4800
Gray's Inn – Tel: 0171 404 8649

Barclays Bank, Chancery Lane & Goslings, 147 High Holborn, London, EC1N 2NU
Tel: 0171 441 5821

Lloyds TSB, Law Courts, 222 The Strand, London, WC2R 1BB
Tel: 0345 30 00 04

Midland, Chancery Lane & Fleet St Branch, 123 Chancery Lane, London WC2A 1QH
Tel: 0171 599 6752

NatWest, Law Courts, Temple Bar Legal Centre, PO Box 11052, 217 Strand, London, WC2R 1AR.
Tel: 0171 664 9113

Universities and Law Schools

BOURNEMOUTH UNIVERSITY

School of Finance and Law Dorset House Fern Barrow Poole BH12 5BB
Tel: (01202) 595 187 Fax: (01202) 595 261
Email: fandl@bournemouth.ac.uk
Website: www.prospectus@bournemouth.ac.uk

College Profile

Bournemouth University currently enjoys first place in the graduate employment league tables with 79.3% out of 1996 graduates being in full time employment within six months of graduating. The School of Finance and Law has an excellent reputation for both employment and post-graduate study among its graduates. Established in 1983, the School of Finance and Law is accredited by the Law Society for both its undergraduate and postgraduate legal studies. Most recently the School has established the first qualifying LLB Tax Law in the UK and is currently developing an innovative range of post-graduate programmes in areas including intellectual property management, international business law and media and practice.

Undergraduate Courses

The School of Finance and Law offers qualifying Law degrees in Business Law and Tax Law. Both courses are four years long with Year 3 spent on placement. The learning and teaching ethos of the School is evident in the high practical content of both programmes.

Postgraduate / Professional Courses

The School of Finance and Law is also accredited to deliver the Legal Practice Course (in association with The Nottingham Law School) as well as offering the MA/PG Dip Law (CPE) conversion course. Both these courses are offered on a full time basis. For details of Scholarships and special discounts for taking both courses you should contact Deborah Smith, Course Administrator. Telephone: 01202-595543.

Research Degrees

The School also offers places for Research Degrees, details are available from Philippa Crosse, School Administrator. Telephone: 01202-595543

BPP LAW SCHOOL

Rochdale House 128 Theobalds Road London WC1X 8RL

Tel: (0171) 430 2304 Fax: (0171) 404 1389

College Profile

BPP Law School is based in London and offers postgraduate law courses for students intending to become barristers or solicitors. As part of the BPP Professional Education Group, the Law School is extremely well-resourced and is amongst those with the best teaching facilities in the country. The teaching team comprises practitioners and academics and the school has a reputation for being professional and friendly, providing well-taught and well-organised courses.

LPC full-time or part-time

Designed for those intending to practise as solicitors, emphasis is on the application of legal knowledge in practice. As well as the core subjects of Business, Litigation and Conveyancing, a wide range of city, commercial and private client options is on offer. The Law Society has awarded a "Good" rating to this course since October 1995.

BVC full-time only

This course is designed both for those who intend to practise at the Bar and for those who intend to pursue a career in commerce and industry or the Civil Service. The course is skills-based and practical, demanding a high level of commitment and work from the student. Instruction is given by an experienced team, the majority of whom remain in practice or have had recent experience at the Bar.

Postgraduate Diploma in Law full-time or part-time

The Diploma is intended to provide a stimulating course in itself as well as a positive foundation for the final professional courses and practice thereafter. All foundation subjects required by the CPE Board are included and, unlike the old-style CPE, the Diploma presents the substance in an integrated form, designed specifically for graduate students as a postgraduate qualification.

Contact Name
Christine Taylor

Address for application and course information:

BVC:
Central Applications Clearing House (CACH),
General Council of the Bar,
2/3 Cursitor Sreet,
London EC4A 1NE

LPC & PGDL
(full-time courses):
Central Applications Board,
PO Box 84, Guildford,
Surrey GU13 1YX

LPC & PGDL
(part-time courses):
Course Registrar,
Administration Department,
BPP Law School, Rochdale House, 128 Theobolds Road,
London WC1X 8RL

440

CARDIFF LAW SCHOOL

Centre For Professional Legal Studies PO Box 294 Cardiff CF1 3UX

Tel: (01222) 874964 Fax: (01222) 874984

Email: Selley@Cardiff.ac.uk

Website: http://www.cf.ac.uk/uwc/claws/pls

College Profile

Contact Name
Ms Zoe Selley

Cardiff Law School is long established, well-resourced and enjoys an international reputation for its teaching and research. In the most recent assessment of research quality conducted by the Higher Education Funding Council, Cardiff achieved a grade 5 rating, placing it in the top dozen law schools in the country. Cardiff offers opportunities for students to pursue post-graduate study by research leading to the degrees of M.Phil and Ph.D. In addition, taught Masters degrees in the areas of canon, commercial and medical law are offered in full and part-time mode.

The Law School is housed in its own building at the heart of the university campus, itself located in one of the finest civic centres in Britain and only a short walk from the main shopping area. Recent redevelopments within the Law School include extensive IT provision together with dedicated facilities for the vocational courses which house a practitioner library and spacious classrooms designed for successful teaching and learn-ing. In addition, the main law library contains a substantial collection of primary and secondary material.

Within the Law School, the Centre for Professional Legal Studies is validated to offer both the Legal Practice Course and, for the first time outside London, the Bar Vocational Course. Students are taught by experienced solicitors and barristers who have been specifically recruited for this purpose. All students pursuing the vocational courses are guaranteed placements with solicitors' firms or sets of chambers, while students studying the Bar Vocational Course additionally enjoy a one week place-ment with a Circuit Judge. Cardiff's Legal Practice Course has been rated "Excellent" by the Law Society; one of only four of the 30 providers of this course to achieve the top ranking.

CITY UNIVERSITY

The Law Department Northampton Square London EC1V 0HB
Tel: (0171) 477 8301 Fax: (0171) 477 8578

College Profile

City University was granted a Royal Charter in 1966. The University is located close to the legal centre of London, within walking distance of the Law Society, the major City firms of solicitors, the Bar Council, the Inns of Court, the Royal Courts of Justice and the Central Criminal Court. Almost half the students studying at the University are studying for a postgraduate qualification. The Law Department has close ties with the professions and the Inns of Court School of Law is affiliated to the University. City Law Department graduates currently have a guaranteed Legal Practice Course place available to them at the College of Law.

Diploma in Law / Common Professional Examination (Full-time (one year) or two years part-time)

The original CPE, City's Diploma in Law is the largest University Diploma/CPE course and benefits from specialist staff with unrivalled experience. Visiting academics come from Oxford, Cambridge and other established Universities and some have taught on the course since its inception in 1977. Unashamedly academic in the way it is taught, the City Diploma can be converted into an LLB by completing additional course units on a part-time basis and may be converted into an MA by thesis. The course may be attended on a full-time or part-time basis (day only) and all students benefit from the University's facilities and extra curricular activities. There is also an annual mooting competition sponsored by the Inns of Court and a departmentally organised Careers Fair attended by City solicitors.

Graduate-entry LLB Honours degree

City's graduate-entry LLB is a programme designed for non-law graduates who want a broader two-year course leading to a qualifying law degree. The course is designed to provide both a general knowledge of the central areas of the law and to allow special interests to be developed. In addition to completing the seven foundation subjects students choose two additional subjects from a range of options. The academic work and examinations are of first degree standard and the course is taught jointly with the Department of Law's three year undergraduate LLB degree. Separate tutors and tutorials give this course its own special identity within the Department.

Contact Name
Diploma in Law/CPE
Applications for the full-time course should be made to the Central Applications Board by 6 February 1999. Part-time applications direct to City University by 30 April.

Course Director (Admissions):
Katherine Reece Thomas
Tel: (0171) 477 8301
Fax: (0171) 477 8578
E-mail: CPE@city.ac.uk

Graduate-entry LLB
Applications should be made to City University preferably by 30 April 1999.

Course Director:
Dr Yvonne Jacobs
Tel: (0171) 477 8301
Fax: (0171) 477 8578
E-mail: Y.JACOBS@city.ac.uk

CITY University

Northampton Square
LONDON EC1V 0HB

THE COLLEGE OF LAW

Braboeuf Manor Portsmouth Road Guildford GU3 1HA
Tel: (0800) 3280153 Fax: (01483) 460460
Email: info@lawcol.co.uk
Website: http://www.lawcol.org.uk

College Profile

The College of Law, the largest legal training establishment in
Europe, has branches in Guildford, London, Chester and York.
The College has an excellent reputation with law firms and
chambers and its teaching staff are professionally qualified as
solicitors or barristers. The College's specialist knowledge and
extensive contacts are coupled with its careers advisory service,
specifically geared towards law students, to help students gain
training contracts and pupillages. It offers the following courses:

Contact Name
Admissions Department

Common Professional Examination / Diploma in Law (Full-time, Part-time or Distance Learning)

The CPE is the law conversion course for graduates of disciplines other than law who wish to become solicitors or barristers. Students will receive in-depth tuition in seven foundation
subjects from tutors with a proven track record in providing
legal education. Successful students receive a Diploma in Law
and are guaranteed a place on the College's Legal Practice
Course.

Legal Practice Course (Full-time or Part-time)

The LPC is the vocational stage of training for prospective
solicitors. The College's LPC has been developed in consultation with both City and provincial firms to address the real
needs of today's legal profession, and ensure the course meets
the demands of life in practice.

Bar Vocational Course (Full-time)

The BVC is the vocational stage of training for prospective
barristers and is available at the College's new site in Chancery
Lane, London. It has been developed in conjunction with practising barristers to prepare students for life in their early years
at the Bar. Practitioners from highly respected sets of chambers
also contribute to the delivery of the course. For further information about courses at any of the College's branches please
contact Admissions.

DE MONTFORT UNIVERSITY

Department of Professional Legal Studies The Gateway Leicester LE1 9BH

Tel: (0116) 257 7177 Fax: (0116) 257 7186

Website: http://www.dmu.ac.uk

Department Profile

The department was formed in 1989 specifically to deliver professional legal courses. It has established a strong reputation for both the CPE/PGDL and the LPC. It is also a major provider of CPD courses for the profession and has recently launched an LLM in advanced legal practice for practitioners.

Contact Name
Please apply to Admissions, quoting the relevant course.

Legal Practice Course (Full-time or Part-time)

Vocational training course for those intending to practice as solicitors. The course is offered on three sites including Leicester, at the University of Birmingham, and in Bristol in association with the University of Bristol. As a very large provider the department is able to offer over eleven electives, including specialist city electives and those suitable for a solicitor specialising in private client work. The part time programme is by open learning mode and is ideal for those wishing to combine work with part time study.

Common Professional Examination (Postgraduate Diploma in Law) (Full-time or Distance Learning)

The academic stage of training for non-law graduates wishing to become a solicitor or barrister. The programme includes lectures supported by small group workshops. Revenue Law is offered as an option subject. The Distance Learning Programme is designed for those wishing to combine full-time work with part-time study.

LLM in Advanced Legal Practice.

This two year programme is offered in association with Central Law Training Ltd and is accredited for CPD requirements. Practitioners are able to select from one of ten specialist subject areas relevant to their own working practice. The programme comprises a series of short CPD courses combined with a research dissertation in the relevant specialist area.

UNIVERSITY OF GLAMORGAN

Law School Pontypridd CF31 1DL
Tel: (01443) 483007 Fax: (01443) 483008
Website: http://www.glam.ac.uk

College Profile

Professional Law courses have been offered at the University
of Glamorgan for over twenty years and in the recognition of
continued success of these and undergraduate law courses, a
new Law School was created in 1995.

The Law School is housed in new 'corporate style' premises - a
short walk from the main facilities on campus including the
student accommodation blocks, Learning Resources Centre,
Recreation Centre and the Students' Union.

After the official opening of the Law School by the Right
Honourable Lord Justice Pill, one of the guests (the chairman
of one of the largest solicitors firms in Wales) said of the Law
School's new facilities: "...nowhere have I seen anything more
superior."

Following a £2 million investment, the Law School now
provides students with an independent law library with associated study facilities, open access computer laboratories, video
conferencing equipment, exclusive postgraduate research
rooms and student dining and recreational areas. There is parking for staff and students and the train station is just 10 minutes
walk away.

Professional Legal Studies is a thriving and forward-looking
division of the School and boasts a portfolio of programmes
including the Postgraduate Diploma in Law (Common
Professional Examination) and Legal Practice Course in both
full and part time modes, as well as continuing professional
development programmes for the legal profession.

Contact Name
Mrs Pat Brand

445

ILEX TUTORIAL COLLEGE

College House Kempston Manor Kempston Bedford MK42 7AB
Tel: (01234) 841010 Fax: (01234) 841373
Email: itslaw@ilex-tutorial.ac.uk
Website: http://www.ilex-tutorial.ac.uk

College Profile

ILEX Tutorial College (ITC) specialises in distance-learning courses including solicitors' vocational courses (run in association with De Montfort University) and courses in over 30 subjects for examinations set by the Institute of Legal Executives (ILEX). Over 4,000 students undertake ITC's courses annually.

Contact Name
Lorraine Richardson
(Solicitors' Vocational Courses)
Elaine Nixon
(ILEX Courses)

Distance-Learning Post-Graduate Diploma in Law (formerly the CPE)

A 2-year course for non-law graduates or Fellows of ILEX leading to entry on to the LPC or BVC. Primarily distance-learning with some face-to-face tuition at De Montfort University.

Distance-Learning Legal Practice Course (LPC)

The only distance-learning LPC validated by the Law Society. Face-to-face sessions take place at De Montfort University over 3 full weeks and 14 study weekends spread over the course of the 2-year period.

Fast-track Professional Skills Course (PSC)

ITC in association with De Montfort University offers a 20-day fast-track PSC.

Distance-Learning LLM/Post-Graduate Diploma in Business Law

An extremely versatile course run in association with De Montfort University leading to either a post-graduate diploma after 1 year or a Masters degree after 2 years. Students can select areas of business law of specific interest to them from the course options available including EU Competition Law, Consumer Law, Intellectual Property Law, Company Law, Individual Labour Law and others. Relevant for students wishing to develop their career within the legal profession or in industry and commerce.

Distance-Learning ILEX Courses

Distance-learning courses for examinations set by ILEX. Law graduates who wish to qualify as Members of ILEX are usually exempt from all heads of law and have to sit only three practice exams. Further information from the Institute of Legal Executives on 01234 841000.

KINGSTON UNIVERSITY LAW SCHOOL

Kingston Hill Kingston-upon-Thames Surrey KT2 7LB
Tel: (0181) 547 2000 x.5376 Fax: (0181) 547 7038
Email: t.follows@kingston.ac.uk or alan.clark@kingston.ac.uk
Website: http://www.kingston.ac.uk

College Profile

Kingston University Law School is situated on the Kingston
Hill Campus of the University adjacent to Richmond Park and
Wimbledon Common. It is very close to the A3 and is easily
accessible by car from London and the M25. Nearby railway
mainline stations are situated in Surbiton, Norbiton and
Kingston and the University runs a free student bus service
linking the University sites, Surbiton, Kingston and Norbiton
stations. The Law School offers an LLM in Business Law, an
LLM in Dispute Resolution, a general LLM and an MA in
Legal Studies. There are excellent IT, library and catering facilities. The Law School is part of the Faculty of Business and
Law which offers numerous postgraduate courses in accounting, human resources, business administration and so on.

The LLM programmes

These are open to law graduates and persons with a legal
professional qualification, whether from the UK or overseas.
They each consist of 10 taught modules, assessed by course-
work, and a 12–15,000 word supervised Dissertation. The LLM
in Business Law and the LLM in Dispute Resolution each
contain 5 compulsory and 5 optional taught modules. The
general LLM requires the student to complete any 10 taught
modules from those offered on the LLM in Business Law and
the LLM in Dispute Resolution.

The MA in Legal Studies

The MA is open to students who have successfully completed
the Postgraduate Diploma in Law (CPE), or the Legal Practice
Course (or Law Society Final), or the Bar Vocational Course
(or Bar Finals) and requires the student to submit a satisfactory
12–15,000 word supervised Dissertation which can be in any
area of law of the student's choice, but subject to the ability of
the School to provide satisfactory supervision.

Contact Name
Please apply to: Alan Clark,
Course Administrator or Terry
Follows, Course Director

MANCHESTER METROPOLITAN UNIVERSITY

School of Law Elizabeth Gaskell Campus Hathersage Road Manchester M13 OJA
Tel: (0161) 247 3050 Fax: (0161) 247 6309

College Profile

The School of Law is one of the largest providers of legal education in the UK, and enjoys an excellent reputation for the quality and range of its courses. The School's courses are well designed and taught, combining rigorous academic standards with practical application. Giving you the best possible start for your career.

Contact Name
Contact the Admissions Tutor for the appropriate course.

Bar Vocational Course (Full-time)

This course provides the vocational stage of training for intending practising barristers. Adopting a Syndicate Group approach, the BVC is activity based and interactive. Extensive IT and audio visual facilities combine with dedicated, well equipped premises to provide an enjoyable and stimulating experience. Excellent student support is provided including mentoring by practising barristers and an Additional Professional Programme which is designed to bridge the gap between student and professional life.

Legal Practice Course (Full-time or Part-time)

This course is for those wishing to qualify as a solicitor. Offering a full range of commercial and private client electives the Legal Practice Course prepares you for everyday practice, taught by professionally qualified staff. There is a dedicated Resource Centre and an excellent pastoral care programme for LPC students. Consistently recognised by the Law Society for its high quality.

Postgraduate Diploma in Law/CPE (Full-time or Part-time)

An increasing number of graduates enter the legal profession this way, with employers attracted by the applicant's maturity and transferable skills. The course places emphasis on the acquisition of legal research and other relevant legal skills. The School guarantees a place on the LPC or BVC subject to interview and satisfactory performance on the PGDL/CPE.

the
MANCHESTER
METROPOLITAN
UNIVERSITY

MIDDLESEX UNIVERSITY

Middlesex University Business School The Burroughs Hendon London NW4 4BT

Tel: (0181) 362 5000 Fax: (0181) 202 1539

Email: C.Chang@mdx.ac.uk

Website: http://www.mdx.ac.uk

College Profile

Middlesex University is a dynamic University that places a strong emphasis on research, publications and consultancy. It has a record of achievement in twenty-six years, which gives it a distinct, mature character. The Law Group is part of the Middlesex University Business School and has twenty-one full time staff who are committed to creating a caring and supportive teaching environment. The Law Group hosts the Centre for Research in Industrial and Commercial Law (CRICL) which has a strong research programme particularly in employment law.

Undergraduates studying law at the University either take the LLB, which has been running since 1974, or the Joint Honours Qualifying Law Degree where they combine their law studies with another subject such as accountancy, languages or criminology. The School also runs the Postgraduate Diploma in Law/Common Professional Examination (CPE) which enables non-law graduates to enter the legal profession through the Legal Practice Course or the Bar Vocational Course. It is recognised for that purpose by the Law Society and the General Council of the Bar. The CPE is run on a full-time (one year) and distance learning (two years) mode. The distance learning mode is run in conjunction with Semple Piggot Rochez Limited (trading as Wolsey Hall Law). Students completing the CPE can use it in part to count towards an MA in Legal Studies. The Business School also runs an LLM course in Employment Law, part-time over two years.

Contact Name
Mr Chris Chang

For details of the distance learning CPE course contact:
Ms Jane O'Hare
Semple Piggot Rochez Limited
Tel: (01869) 277 805
Email: j.ohare@spr-law.co.uk

**MIDDLESEX
UNIVERSITY**

UNIVERSITY OF NORTHUMBRIA AT NEWCASTLE

School of Law University of Northumbria

Sutherland Building Newcastle-upon-Tyne NE1 8ST

Tel: (0191) 227 4494

Fax: (0191) 227 4557

Email: david.stabler@unn.ac.uk

Website: http://www.unn.ac.uk

College Profile

The School of Law at the University of Northumbria is known for its excellence in the provision of academic and professional legal education. Situated in central Newcastle the School has over 50 teaching staff and is one of the largest departments in the University. Full-time, part-time and distance learning modes of study are available. In addition to the Legal Practice course and the Common Professional Examination course the School is also validated to provide the Bar Vocational Course. It also offers the Professional Skills Course and a wide choice of LLM programmes including two new distance learning programmes, the LLM in Mental Health Law and the LLM in Commercial Law. The Law School has dedicated lecture and workshop accommodation together with its own Law Skills Centre which includes a large practitioner library, court room and offices with full CCTV facilities plus open access IT equipment.

Contact Name
Mr D Stabler

LPC (full-time or part-time)

- the vocational training course for students who wish to qualify as solicitors
- a wide range of corporate and private client electives
- practical workshops

BVC (full-time)

- the vocational training course for students who wish to qualify as barristers
- practical skills training in dedicated accommodation
- strong practitioner participation

CPE

- the academic stage of training for non-law graduates who wish to qualify as solicitors or barristers
- structured study materials
- opportunity to obtain a law degree with an additional study programme
- guaranteed places on our Legal Practice Course or Bar Vocational Course for successful students

UNIVERSITY of NORTHUMBRIA at NEWCASTLE
Promoting Excellence in Higher Education

NOTTINGHAM LAW SCHOOL

Nottingham Law School The Nottingham Trent University
Belgrave Centre Nottingham NG1 5LP
Tel: (0115) 948 6871 Fax: (0115) 948 6878

College Profile
The Bar Vocational Course (BVC): Nottingham Law School has
designed their BVC to develop to a high standard a range of
core practical skills, and to equip students to succeed in the
fast-changing environment of practice at the Bar. Particular
emphasis is placed on the skill of advocacy, utilising the Law
School's expertise as a leading provider of advocacy training.
The BVC is taught entirely by recently practising barristers, and
utilises the same integrated and interactive teaching methods as
all of the school's other professional courses. Essentially,
students learn by doing and Nottingham Law School provides a
risk-free environment in which students are encouraged to
realise, through practice and feedback, their full potential.

Legal Practice Course
The LPC is offered by full-time and part-time block study. This
course has been designed to be challenging and stimulating for
students and responsive to the needs of firms, varying from
large commercial to smaller high street practices.

Nottingham Law School's LPC features: integration of the
transactions and skills, so that each advances the other, whilst
ensuring the transferability of skills between different subject
areas. Carefully structured inter-active group work which will
develop an ability to handle skills and legal transactions effectively, and in an integrated way. A rigorous assessment process
that nevertheless avoids 'assessment overload', to maintain a
teaching and learning emphasis to the course. A professionally
qualified team, retaining substantial links with practice. A top
rating from The Law Society's Assessment Panel in every year
of its operation.

The Postgraduate Diploma in Law (full-time):
The Nottingham Law School PGDL is a one year conversion
course designed for any non-law graduate who intends to
become a solicitor or barrister in the UK. The intensive course
effectively covers the seven core subjects of an undergraduate
law degree in one go. It is the stepping stone to the LPC or the
BVC at Nottingham Law School, and a legal career thereafter. It
is a postgraduate Diploma (Dip Law) in its own right, which can
be presented to employers. It operates on a similar basis to the
LPC (see above), though inevitably it has a more academic bias.

Contact Name
Nottingham Law School
Belgrave Centre, Chaucer
Street, Nottingham, NG1 5LP.

451

SEMPLE PIGGOT ROCHEZ

66 Banbury Road Oxford OX2 6PR

Tel: (01865) 310 310 Fax:

Website: www.wolseyhall-law.co.uk www.spr-law.co.uk

College Profile

Semple Piggot Rochez acquired Wolsey Hall Law in March 1998. Working with their partner, The Law Group at Middlesex University, Semple Piggot Rochez delivers a two year part-time Distance Learning Postgraduate Diploma in Law (CPE) accredited by the CPE Board and recognised by The Law Society and General Council of the Bar.

Supported online on the internet

While it is not necessary to have internet access to do the course - as the course is self contained - those with access to the net will be able to access our specially designed course web site. Students joining the programme will be given free access to LAWTEL and be provided with their own Virtual Workstation online. The Virtual Workstation will enable students to access all course materials online, email other students (and tutors), post messages to an academic conference bulletin board, engage in real time text based discussion with other students over the internet and use Consilio, an electronic library of course specific links to resources on the net. Consilio, Semple Piggot Rochez's Group research wing, also publishes a weekly legal newsletter linking to legal news providers on the net and resourcing articles and analyses written by practitioners and academics involved with our legal education and professional development programmes.

Part of a Group of legal training firms

Semple Piggot Rochez is part of a training group. They are the first in the world to provide a law degree delivered entirely over the internet (The University of London LLB Degree (External programme)). The LLB course is run by Semple Piggot Norrie Aquino (www.sppa.co.uk). They also own their own internet bookshop for lawyers, Lawbooks Online, the first specialist bookshop for law students and lawyers in the UK (www. lawnbooks-online.com), and their Continuing Professional Development wing, The Norrie Semple Piggot Partnership, will be the first to be accredited by The Law Society to deliver CPD courses over the internet to practitioners (www.nsp-partnership.co.uk). Having been involved in the founding of BPP Law School (Mike Semple Piggot was a co-founder and first CEO), Semple Piggot Rochez has a great deal of experience of delivering well resourced high level courses. This experience, together with extensive links with the profession and an involvement at the cutting edge of technology, ensures that they can offer you a truly unique experience on their course.

Contact
Jane O'Hare
Course Director
01869 277 805
Ann White Registrar
01865 310 310

Prospectus
Online:
www.wolseyhall-law.co.uk
www.spr-law.co.uk
Printed:
Semple Piggot Rochez
66 Banbury Road
Oxford OX2 6PR

SEMPLE PIGGOT ROCHEZ

UNIVERSITY OF WESTMINSTER

School of Law 4 Little Titchfield Street London W1P
Tel: 0171 911 5088 Fax:
Email: regent@wmin.ac.uk
Website: www.wmin.ac.uk

College Profile

The University of Westminster's School of Law has an exceptional location in the centre of London. It is characterised by its strong links with the legal profession and commitment to quality and flexibility. Newly refurbished, our Law School building provides modern, purpose designed teaching accommodation with an extensive law library and state of the art facilities.
There is an annual mooting competition judged by a member of the High Court Bench, a client counselling competition and regular seminars from outside speakers form both sides of the profession.

Law Fairs attended: UCL
3/12/98 and Kings 26/1/99
LPC Open Day: 10th February
1999, 24th March 1999

Legal Practice Course (full or part-time)

The LPC has been taught at the University of Westminster since its introduction and is rated "good" by the Law Society. The course, which is delivered by a professionally qualified teaching team, is housed on a dedicated floor of the Law School with its own resources room, skills suite and teaching rooms. With places limited to 120 on the full-time and 50 on the part-time course, the hallmark of our approach is small interactive group work with an emphasis on the use of IT. The course offers a broad range of electives, many sponsored by specialist firms and provides training for students preparing to enter commercial or high street practice.

Common Professional Examination (full-time)

The academic stage of training for non-law graduates wishing to become solicitors or barristers. The University has over twenty years' experience of teaching this course and our CPE graduates regularly take places in the top 100 of the Bar Vocational Examination or gain distinctions on the LPC. Many of our professionally qualified staff teach on other academic programmes and are therefore able to offer a breadth of view unequalled by many vocational training providers.

UNIVERSITY OF WESTMINSTER

453

UNIVERSITY OF WOLVERHAMPTON

School of Law Molineux Street Wolverhampton WV1 1SB
Tel: (01902) 321000 Fax: (01902) 321570

College Profile

Based in Wolverhampton and offers courses for students
intending to become solicitors. The law school has been offering these courses for nearly 20 years. Their LPC programme
has had consistently good ratings. The lecturers are drawn from
ex-solicitors, barristers, academics and individuals from business and industry. There are excellent IT facilities, a well-
stocked library and a sports centre.

Legal Practice Course (full/part-time)

The vocational training course for those intending to practise as
solicitors. The core subjects of Business, Litigation and
Conveyancing are taught, together with a range of commercial
and private client options. Professional skills courses, practical
workshops and seminars are all part of the training. Close links
with local practitioners, mentoring, and CV distribution.

Common Professional Examination (full/part-time)

The academic stage of training for non-law graduates wishing
to become solicitors or barristers. A full programme of lectures
and tutorials is offered on this demanding course. Students are
taught by ex-solicitors and barristers. Places on the LPC and
BVC are guaranteed for successful students. Flexible studying
choices are under review.

Contact Name
Lynn Layton-Johnstone
Head of Marketing
(01902) 321 999

ANGLIA POLYTECHNIC UNIVERSITY

The Admissions Office Victoria Road South Chelmsford CM1 1LL
Tel: (01245) 493131 Fax: (01245) 490835
Email: admissions@anglia.ac.uk
Website: www.anglia.ac.uk
Contact: Law Admissions Officer
Course Information: CPE (full-time); LPC (full-time); LLM (Cambridge campus only) in International and European Business Law; LLM - MA International Sports Law; LLB (2 year Graduate Entry).

UNIVERSITY OF BIRMINGHAM

The Faculty of Law Edgbaston Birmingham B15 2TT
Tel: (0121) 414 6290 Fax: (0121) 414 3585
Contact: Mr David Salter
Course Information: CPE full-time (contact Mrs D Lees); LPC (through De Montford University); taught LLM full-time (contact Bernadette Lynch); LLM by research; MJur by research; PhD by research full or part-time (contact Sally Lloyd-Bostock)

UNIVERSITY OF BRISTOL

Department of Professional Legal Studies Wills Memorial Building
Queens Road Bristol BS8 1HR
Tel: (0117) 928 8646 Fax: (0117) 925 6717
Contact: Mr Maurice Cook
Course Information: PhD; LLM (both taught and by research 2 years); MA in Legal Studies (2 years); LPC (1 year); Diploma in Intellectual Property Law and Practice (part-time for recently qualified solicitors); weekend certificate courses

UNIVERSITY OF CENTRAL ENGLAND

Faculty of Law & Social Sciences Franchise Street Perry Barr Birmingham B42 2SU
Tel: (0121) 331 6614 Fax: (0121) 331 6622
Contact: Mike Spencer or Ms Isabelle Clarke (asst)
Course Information: CPE (full and part-time: Liz Ragosa (0121) 331 6646); LPC (full-time: Kay Jones (0121) 331 6629); LPC (part-time: Judy Darlington (0121) 331 6629); MA Legal Practice (Judy Darlington (0121) 331 6629)

UNIVERSITY OF CENTRAL LANCASHIRE
Department of Legal Studies Preston PR1 2HE
Tel: (01772) 893060 Fax: (01772) 892792
Email: h.doupe@uclan.ac.uk
Contact: Department of Legal Studies
Course Information: CPE (full and part-time); LPC (part-time); LLM Employment Law
(full and part-time); LLM Environmental Law (full and part-time); MA International
Business Law (full-time); MPhil/PhD

UNIVERSITY OF DURHAM
The Law Department 50 North Bailey Durham DH1 3ET
Tel: (0191) 374 2000 Fax: (0191) 374 2044
Website: http://www.dur.ac.uk.law
Contact: The Law Department
Course Information: LLM International and European Legal Studies; MA International
Boundaries; research degrees: PhD and MJur

UNIVERSITY OF EAST ANGLIA
The Norwich Law School Norwich NR4 7TG
Tel: (01603) 592 520 Fax: (01603) 250 245
Email: law@uea.ac.uk
Website: www.uea.ac.uk/law
Contact: Ms Kerry Berry
Course Information: LLM Family Law and Family Policy; LLM Family Justice Studies;
LLM International, Commercial and Business Law; Post Graduate Diploma in Legal
Studies; Post Graduate Degrees by research LLM/MPhil and PhD

UNIVERSITY OF ESSEX
The Department of Law Wivenhoe Park Colchester CO4 3SQ
Tel: (01206) 872585 Fax: (01206) 873428
Email: alcam@essex.ac.uk
Contact: The Graduate Secretary
Course Information: LLM International Human Rights; LLM European Community Law;
LLM International Trade; LLM Public Law; LLM Law in Transition in the New Europe;
Doctoral programme in Legal Theory; PhD and MPhil research programmes.

UNIVERSITY OF EXETER

The Centre for Legal Practice Amory Building Rennes Drive Exeter EX4 4RJ
Tel: (01392) 263157 Fax: (01392) 263196
Email: Jenny.L.Cook@exeter.ac.uk
Contact: Professor Vivienne Shrubsall
Course Information: PG Dip Law 45 places; LPC 120 places

UNIVERSITY OF HERTFORDSHIRE

Central Admissions Hatfield Campus College Lane Hatfield Herts AL1 9AB
Tel: (01707) 285 197 Fax: (01707) 286 205
Email: m.temple@herts.ac.uk
Website: http://www.herts.ac.uk/business/division/law/pages
Contact: Mrs Margaret Temple
Course Information: PG Dip LPC (P/T), LLM (various subjects), LPC, CPD Short Courses
for Barristers, Research degrees in various subjects

UNIVERSITY OF HOLBORN

Registry 200 Greyhound Road London W14 9RY
Tel: (0171) 385 3377 Fax: (0171) 381 3377
Email: HLT@holborncollege.ac.uk
Website: http://www.holborncollege.ac.uk
Contact: Mr Paul Little
Course Information: LLM in conjunction with the University of Wolverhampton; Bar
course (Full time) for non U.K. Practitioners; New York Bar course; LDip/CPE

UNIVERSITY OF HUDDERSFIELD

The Department of Law Queensgate Huddersfield HD1 3DH
Tel: (01484) 472192 Fax: (01484) 472279
Contact: The Secretary at the Department of Law
Course Information: PgDip in Law (CPE) (full and part-time, open and distance learning);
LPC (full and part-time); LLM (distance learning); LLM European Business Law

INNS OF COURT SCHOOL OF LAW

4 Gray's Inn Place Gray's Inn London WC1R 5DX
Tel: (0171) 404 5787 Fax: (0171) 831 4188
Email: bvc@icsl.ac.uk/llm@icsl.ac.uk
Website: http://www.icsl.ac.uk
Contact: Admissions Section
Course Information: BVC; LLM Criminal Litigation

KEELE UNIVERSITY

Law Department Keele ST5 5BG
Tel: (01782) 583229 Fax: (01782) 583228
Website: www.keele.ac.uk
Contact: Mrs Jackie Greatbatch
Course Information: LLM Child Law; LLM General Legal Studies and Research; MPhil
and PhD by research; Diploma Legal Studies; CPE; MA Childcare Law

LEEDS METROPOLITAN UNIVERSITY

The School of Law Cavendish Hall Beckett Park Campus Leeds LS6 3QS
Tel: (0113) 283 2600 Fax: (0113) 283 3206
Contact: Mrs Pauline Joyce
Course Information: PG Dip Law (full and part-time); PG Dip Legal Practice (full and
part-time)

UNIVERSITY OF LEICESTER

The Faculty of Law University Road Leicester LE1 7RH
Tel: (0116) 252 2753. Fax: (0116) 252 5023
Email: jmg16@le.ac.uk
Contact: Mrs J Goacher
Course Information: LLM or MA Criminal Law and Justice; LLM European and
International Trade Law; LLM European Higher Legal Studies; LLM or MA Human Rights
and Civil Liberties; LLM or MA Legal Studies; LLM or MA Welfare Law

LIVERPOOL JOHN MOORES UNIVERSITY

School of Law and Applied Social Studies Josephine Butler House 1 Mertle Street
Liverpool L7 4DN
Tel: (0151) 231 3907 Fax: (0151) 231 3908
Email: lswdmage@livjm.ac.uk
Contact: Deborah Magee
Course Information: LLM in European Business Studies (part-time); LPC (part-time)

LONDON GUILDHALL UNIVERSITY

Department of Law 84 Moorgate London EC2M 6SQ
Tel: (0171) 320 1616 Fax: (0171) 320 1163
Email: enqs@lgu.ac.uk
Website: www.lgu.ac.uk
Contact: Course Enquiry Unit
Course Information: LLM International and Comparative Business Law; Legal Practice
Course; CPE

UNIVERSITY OF NEWCASTLE-UPON-TYNE

Newcastle Law School Newcastle-upon-Tyne NE1 7RU
Tel: (0191) 222 7558 Fax: (0191) 212 0064
Email: newcastle.law-school@ncl.ac.uk
Contact: Ms I. Cheyne
Course Information: LLM International Legal Studies; LLM International Trade; LLM
Environmental Legal Studies; MPhil or PhD by research; MA Environmental Law and Policy

UNIVERSITY OF NORTH LONDON

School of Law Ladbroke House 62-66 Highbury Grove London N5 2AD
Tel: (0171) 607 2789 Fax: (0171) 753 5403
Course Information: CPE (full-time 1 year; part-time 2 years) - contact Janet Loveless;
LPC (part-time 2 years) - contact Helen Carr

OXFORD BROOKES UNIVERSITY

School of Social Sciences and Law Gipsy Lane Headington Oxford OX3 OBP

Tel: (01865) 484901 Fax: (01865) 484930

Email: sebannister@brookes.ac.uk

Website: http://www.brookes.ac.uk/school/social/law

Contact: Ms Samantha Bannister

Course Information: Advanced Diploma in Law; LLM in Criminal Justice

OXFORD INSTITUTE OF LEGAL PRACTICE

King Charles House Park End Street Oxford OX1 1JD

Tel: (01865) 722 619 Fax: (01865) 722 408

Email: oilp@brookes.ac.uk

Website: http://www.161.112.26/oilp/default.htm

Contact: Mr Nick Johnson

Course Information: Legal Practice Course

QUEEN MARY AND WESTFIELD COLLEGE UNIVERSITY OF LONDON

Centre for Commercial Law Studies London E1 4NS

Tel: (0171) 975 5127 Fax: (0181) 980 1079

Email: admissions-ccls@qmw.ac.uk

Contact: The LLM Administrator

Course Information: LLM Commercial Law (wide range of modules available) full and part-time; MSc Management of Intellectual Property; Diplomas in Advanced Commercial Law; Certificate in Intellectual Property Law; research degrees: MPhil and PhD

UNIVERSITY OF SHEFFIELD

The Law Department Crookesmoor Building Conduit Road Sheffield S10 1FL

Tel: (0114) 222 6752 Fax: (0114) 222 6832

Email: lpc@sheffield.ac.uk

Contact: The Central Applications Board

Course Information: LPC (full-time) plus others. Information on application.

SOUTH BANK UNIVERSITY

Post Graduate Admissions 103 Borough Road London SE1 0AA
Tel: (0171) 815 8218 Fax: (0171) 815 8250
Email: enrol@sbu.ac.uk
Website: www.sbu.ac.uk
Contact: Mr Mike Morland
Course Information: LLM Law; PG Dip Legal Studies (CPE); PG Dip Legal Practice
(LPC); Certificate in applied advice work

STAFFORDSHIRE UNIVERSITY

Staffordshire University Law School Leek Road Stoke on Trent ST4 2DF
Tel: (01782) 294550 Fax: (01782) 294335
Contact: Ms Pat Hopkins
Course Information: LLM (27 modules available); CPE; LPC; LLM in Legal Practice; MA
Legal Studies; Postgraduate MPhil by dissertation; MA in Child Care. MA Legal Studies.
Places available: LPC - 100 full-time, 25 part-time; CPE - 30 full-time, 30 part-time

UNIVERSITY OF STRATHCLYDE

Centre for Professional Legal Studies The Law School 141 St. James' Road
Glasgow G4 0LT
Tel: (0141) 548 2745 Fax: (0141) 552 4264
Email: linda@law.strath.ac.uk
Contact: Mrs Linda Iron
Course Information: Pg Dip Legal Practice (full-time); Postgraduate Diploma/LLM in
Construction Law and in Information Technology Law (full and part-time); Masters
Programme Information Technology (distance learning); research degrees (variety of sub-
jects); LLM Commercial Law

UNIVERSITY OF SUSSEX

Centre for Legal Studies Art Block E Falmer Brighton BN1 9SN
Tel: (01273) 678 562 Fax: (01273) 678 466
Email: L.O-Meara@sussex.ac.uk
Website: www.susx.ac.uk
Contact: Ms Lynn O'Meara
Course Information: LLM International Criminal Law; LLM International Commercial
Law; LLM; CPE

THAMES VALLEY UNIVERSITY

Thames Valley University St Mary's Road Ealing London W5 5RF
Tel: (0181) 231 2592 Fax: (0181) 231 2553
Email: LPC@tvu.ac.uk
Website: http://www.tvu.ac.uk
Contact: Central Applications Board
Course Information: CPE F/T and P/T(eves), LPC F/T and P/T(subject to validity), MA
Legal Practice (subject to validity)

UNIVERSITY OF THE WEST OF ENGLAND

Faculty of Law Frenchay Campus Frenchay Bristol BS16 1QY
Tel: (0117) 976 2171 Fax: (0117) 976 3841
Email: law@uwe.ac.uk
Contact: Ms Louise Barks
Course Information: CPE full-time and open learning; LPC full-time and open learning;
BVC; PSC full and part-time; modular MA/LLM

WORCESTER COLLEGE OF TECHNOLOGY

Deansway Worcester WR1 2JF
Tel: (01905) 725 582 Fax: (01905) 289 06
Email: mps@wortech.ac.uk
Contact: John Duddington
Course Information: PG Dip Legal Studies (CPE) MA Legal Studies

NOTES